INTRODUCTORY

INSECT
PHYSIOLOGY

ROBERT L. PATTON

PROFESSOR OF INSECT PHYSIOLOGY
CORNELL UNIVERSITY

W. B. SAUNDERS COMPANY
PHILADELPHIA AND LONDON 1963

PREFACE

Insect physiology is a field attractive to entomologists, because it offers a means of acquiring fundamental information applicable to the solution of practical problems and because it offers a bridge between the natural and the exact approach to the study of insects. The subject matter that is presented can be assimilated best by students who are well grounded in the various disciplines of biology and who have a strong background in physical science.

This is a textbook. As such, it is intended to serve as a basis from which both students and instructors can expand the subjects that are discussed in the chapters. Each chapter could be expanded into a book length treatise. The material that is presented represents a bare summary of existing knowledge with a minimum of discussion of exceptions and possible deviations.

In writing this introductory textbook, the author has tried to provide a background of subject matter sufficient to satisfy the inquiring entomology student, to guide instructors not specifically trained in the field, and to inspire at least a few of the readers to specialize in the field of insect physiology.

Cornell University   Robert L. Patton

Contents

XI

XII

AN INTRODUCTION
TO SOME PRINCIPLES
OF PHYSIOLOGY

Physiology is the branch of biological science that has as its subject matter the fundamental mechanics of animals and plants. It is a science of organic function closely associated with, but distinct from, anatomy and morphology on one hand and biochemistry and biophysics on the other. It is the study of the processes that make it possible for an animal to live—a sort of biological mechanics of the things that give organisms the property called *life*. This is the author's definition. Others, defining the same term, describe physiology as the analysis of function in living organisms[1] or as the study of the fundamental activities of organisms (specifically cells).[2] Another way of describing the science is that it is a synthetic science that applies physical and chemical methods to biology.[1] None of these definitions may seem concise; this is because of the broad scope of subject matter that can be included legitimately in a physiological study. Specialization has necessitated limitations, and in this context the material treated lies between morphology and biochemistry with frequent encroachments in both directions.

HISTORY OF PHYSIOLOGY

Physiology came into being through the curiosity of the scientists of the Renaissance. The early history is confused with medicine and alchemy, and the hypotheses proposed to explain animal functions were often fantastic. Interest in the field grew because of its importance to medicine, and as knowledge increased, specialization developed. Now physiologists may specialize in the physiology of humans, mammals, invertebrates, insects, plants, and cells. With advances in knowledge through improved technology, the degree of specialization has become even greater. Considering this factor, along with the realization that numerically about nine tenths of the animals in the world are insects, it is not surprising that the field of insect physiology evolved or that distinct disciplines exist within this field.

History of Insect Physiology

Pseudophysiological observations of insects occur in the writing of some of the early biologists. Gesner included observations on insects in his *Historia Animalium* published in 1551. Aldrovandi worked with insects, and Charles Butler wrote a treatise on honeybees in 1609. Many of the Seventeenth Century biologists studied insects, and an active interest was continued through the Nineteenth Century.

With the approach of the Twentieth Century came the relatively new concepts of insect control, but except for the contributions of a small group in Europe, little work of significance appeared. The efforts of many of these men have been virtually forgotten, and it is not unusual to find their work repeated in the current literature. A good review of this period is found in Paul Marchal's *Physiologie des Insectes*, a fairly comprehensive treatise rarely cited in bibliographies.

In the United States, physiological work with insects was so completely eclipsed by economic problems that interest was lacking and contributions were sporadic. This situation ended in 1934 when Wigglesworth from England published his monograph, titled simply *Insect Physiology*, followed by his textbook in 1939. At the same time, converted physiologists, entomologists, and biochemists began to appear on the staffs of major universities as professional insect physiologists.

Insect physiology really came of age with the introduction of DDT. Accompanying the introduction of DDT came a flood of new synthetic insecticides and the problems of resistance, specificity, and mammalian toxicity. These problems took the study of insect physiology out of the luxury class and made it a distinct necessity. In recent years the field has grown by leaps and bounds, and there have been both significant breakthrough contributions and disappointing reversals. Technological developments in the field have been overshadowed by the enthusiasm of the investigators so that the status of much of the available information is still rather fluid. Reversals of opinion and factual information appear often, and this situation will continue as improvements in analytical technology and instrumentation enable critical analyses to be made on progressively smaller quantities. Technology is still one of the most important obstacles to progress in insect physiology. As new developments appear, changes in concepts are bound to come, and the serious student is warned to read all work critically and be prepared to accept changes. It is entirely appropriate to preface many of our supposedly "established" facts with the phrase *subject to change without notice*.

THE LITERATURE OF INSECT PHYSIOLOGY

Entomologists and insect physiologists are not the only contributors to the literature pertaining to insect physiology. Important articles are widely distributed throughout the scientific publications of the world, and the volume of this literature is second only to that of mammalian physiology. This extensive literature and the high degree of specialization developing make it difficult to conceive that one individual might be considered competent as a general insect physiologist. Just as taxonomists become specialists in a relatively small group of insects, physiologists are known for specialties such as nutrition and neuromuscular physiology. It is possible—in fact essential—that a serious student cover the literature in detail as it pertains to his specialty; but it is unreasonable for him to try to cover the literature of the entire field. Fortunately, various of the specialized disciplines are reviewed and summarized at regular intervals, and it is therefore possible to keep up with progress.

THE POTENTIAL OF INSECT PHYSIOLOGY

Students often argue about a superficial division between fundamental and applied research. Fundamental research is loosely defined as work designed to fulfill a basic inquisitiveness and to further general knowledge; applied research is defined as the application of basic principles to the solution of practical problems. There is really no conflict between the two because almost all basic information has an application in practice; there is such a wealth of undiscovered information on the physiology of insects that the field offers broad horizons for either approach. Regardless of the approach or the specialty within the broad field of entomology, knowledge of the basic concepts of physiology has become an absolute necessity.

The use of insects has many advantages over that of other animals for experimental study. They are inexpensive to rear, have a very high biotic potential, have a short life cycle, and offer a somewhat less complicated structure than mammals, even though they have several million years' advantage in evolutionary adaptation. The only disadvantage is their small size, a factor that has deterred many people and driven others to the study of the marine invertebrates, which remotely resemble large insects in appearance, but not necessarily in physiology. As the science of instrumentation develops, this obstacle will become progressively less important.

THE REQUISITES OF AN INSECT PHYSIOLOGIST

There are very few beginners in this field, and most of the practicing personnel have moved into the study of insect physiology from biochemistry, physiology, or entomology, with an interest born of necessity. Physiology is a bridge between the natural and the exact sciences. The growth and development of quantitative biology places the physiologist in an admirable position.

The technology of insect physiology is largely adapted from that of biochemistry and biophysics, but the object of investigation remains a living organism, with all of the intricacies and variations best understood by a biologist. Failure to recognize the problems of both the natural and exact sciences will surely lead to mistakes, and many of the anomalies recorded in the literature can be traced to this source. For research in the field of insect

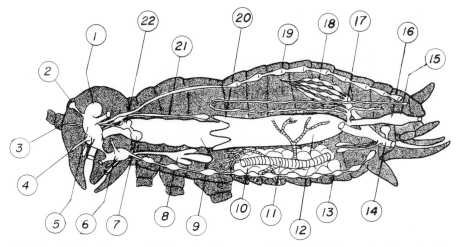

FIG. 1-1. Sectional diagram of the functional anatomy of a hypothetical insect (drawing adapted from DuPorte).

1. Brain (protocerebrum)—modulation.
2. Ocellar pedicel—sensory.
3. Antennal nerve—sensory.
4. Labral nerve—sensory.
5. Brain (deutocerebrum)—modulation.
6. Subesophageal ganglion—excitation of locomotion, neurosecretions.
7. Corpus allatum—hormone secretion.
8. Salivary gland—enzyme secretion.
9. Foregut, crop, stomodeum—digestive tract.
10. Fat body—storage, intermediary metabolism.
11. Tracheal trunk—respiration.
12. Midgut, ventriculus.—digestion and assimilation.
13. Ganglion of the central nerve cord—central nervous system.
14. Oviduct and accessory glands—reproduction.
15. Rectum—reabsorption.
16. Hind gut, proctodeum.
17. Malpighian tube—excretion.
18. Ovarioles—reproduction.
19. Dorsal vessel, heart—circulation.
20. Gastric ceca—digestive function, not entirely known.
21. Median recurrent nerve—stomodeal system, secretion, or hormones.
22. Corpus cardiacum—hormone secretion.

physiology, the ideal situation is a closely coordinated team of specialists. When this is not feasible, the necessary background of knowledge must be acquired by a single person, either through formal training or by extensive reading and practice.

For the discussions that follow, it is assumed that the reader has a reasonable background in exact science and a thorough grounding in entomology. One of the important requisites is that the reader have complete familiarity with the internal morphology and anatomy of living insects, particularly the species with which he is working. Unfortunately, most entomologists are taught external morphology primarily for purposes of taxonomy and have limited experience in dissection of preserved specimens. Such a background is inadequate for physiological research, and one of the first and most important steps is the correction of this deficiency.

Figure 1–1 shows a longitudinal section of a hypothetical insect. The location and probable function of the principal organ systems are indicated. This can serve as a starting point in the location of specific systems in living insects. Speed and skill are necessary in the ultramicrosurgery required of physiological experimentation; and because of the very high biochemical activity of some of the tissues, great care must be exercised to assure uniformity when sampling by biopsy.

VITAL PROCESSES COMMON TO ALL ANIMALS

All animals depend upon certain functions to maintain their coordinated existence. These functions are carried out by the simultaneous activity of groups of specialized cells which comprise the tissues that are the component parts of the organ systems. In order to study the vital processes, it is necessary to consider the individual functions of the various parts; however, it is important to recognize that the function of the whole animal is not the simple sum of the functions of the parts but a highly complex interrelationship of these.

For the animal to maintain itself, it must be supplied with food that it is able to digest and assimilate. The assimilated fractions have to be transported to the organs and tissues, where they are metabolized to produce energy. For this, the animal must have a source of oxygen, obtained through respiration; and the excesses and waste products must be removed by the regulatory function of excretion. To find food and a mate, the animal must be able to move about and to recognize these when found. This is a function of the neuromuscular system. For the species to continue to exist, it must reproduce. All these functions are coordinated by the secretory activity of the endocrine system; and the whole animal is held together by a supporting structure—the skeleton.

From the standpoint of the individual, the most important function is the production of usable energy, and all other functions are related to or dependent upon it. The general scheme is the same for all animals. The ultimate source of energy is the sun, and this is captured by the photosynthetic process of plants. The plant products, principally carbohydrates, are eaten and metabolized by the animal to release the stored energy. The medium of exchange in this reaction is a high energy chemical bond, usually the terminal phosphate of adenosine triphosphate (ATP). Nature has been lavish in providing multiple pathways by which this may be accomplished; but in the final analysis, this is the energy that is available to the organism, to be used to drive synthetic processes, to force materials across membranes against gradients, and to produce heat and motion.

Somewhere in the energy production process there is an oxidation reaction that ultimately involves atmospheric oxygen. The atmosphere is the original source in all cases, but gaseous oxygen does not cross the living membranes so that the proximate source to the tissues is an aqueous solution of atmospheric gas. This oxygen is relatively inert, and it is never the aggressor in the oxidation of the substrate. Instead, the oxygen is combined with active hydrogen that is split off from the substrate by an enzyme system. A direct combination is rarely achieved. The union is more likely to be made through a series of compounds called *carriers*, which are readily oxidized and reduced when activated by the appropriate enzymes.

All the reactions in the metabolic processes are controlled by enzymes. These are specialized proteins, sometimes called *biological catalysts*, that exist in very large but undetermined numbers in all animals. If their chemistry is disrupted, part of a chemical process will fail, and if the disturbance is severe, the animal will die. Most enzyme reactions are reversible, and a large proportion of the reactions take place as a cyclical chain of chemical events.

These broad concepts have few exceptions. If they are fully understood, it will be easier to comprehend further discussions. In each section that follows, it is of utmost importance for the student to fully understand both the true and the connotative meaning of each term. Every discipline has its own vocabulary, which may approach a jargon. Lack of understanding of the meanings of descriptive words peculiar to a science poses a serious hazard in the communication of information.

SUMMARY

Physiology is the study of function, and insect physiology is the study of the physical and chemical mechanisms that make it possible for the various insect species to live. All animals have certain vital functions, and from the standpoint of the individual animal these all lead to the production of energy.

Physiology became a defined field of biology by necessity, and for the same reason insect physiology has become a distinct field of specialization. Most of the interest and many of the advances have come about since 1930, but the work of the earlier investigators, particularly those of the Nineteenth Century, should not be ignored.

The study of insects offers both a challenge and a potential for the development of animal research. The use of insects for study has many advantages over that of other animals, but insects also have the disadvantage of small size. This can be overcome by advanced technology, but the use of this advanced technology makes it necessary for insect physiologists to be thoroughly grounded in physical as well as biological sciences.

LITERATURE CITED

1. Prosser, C. L., and Brown, F. A. 1961. Comparative Animal Physiology. 2nd Ed. W. B Saunders, Philadelphia.
2. Giese, A. C. 1962. Cell Physiology. 2nd Ed. W. B. Saunders, Philadelphia.

GENERAL REFERENCES

1. Chauvin, R. 1956. Physiologie de l'Insecte. 2nd Ed. W. Junk, The Hague.
2. Heilbrunn, L. V. 1952. An Outline of General Physiology. 3rd Ed. W. B. Saunders, Philadelphia.
3. Marchal, Paul. 1911. Physiologie de Insectes. Ancienne Librairie Germer Baillière, Paris.
4. Pflugfelder, O. 1958. Entwicklungsphysiologie der Insekten. Geest and Portig, Leipzig.
5. de Reaumur, R. A. F. Mémoires pour servir à l'Histoire des Insectes. Paris. De l'Imprimerie Royal. Seven volumes from 1734.
6. Roeder, K. D. 1953. Insect Physiology. John Wiley, New York.
7. Seifriz, W. E. 1936. Protoplasm. McGraw-Hill, New York.
8. Wigglesworth, V. B. 1934. Insect Physiology. Methuen., London.
9. Wigglesworth, V. B. 1956. The Principles of Insect Physiology. Wiley, New York.

2

INSECT NUTRITION

Nutrition is the study of the food requirements of organisms, in this case, insects. These studies may include the constituents of the normal diet, or the studies may be expanded to include substances that produce energy in the most efficient way.

In the basic terminology of the nutritionist, food constituents are classified as *essential* or *nonessential*. The first term designates those components that must be included in the diet because they cannot be synthesized by either the metabolic system of the animal or the normal compliment of symbionts. The second term indicates food materials that may have to be consumed to produce energy and that can be converted into a form in which they can be utilized through metabolic processes. Vitamins, amino acids, and certain mineral salts are common examples of essentials. Although carbohydrates, proteins, and fats are individually nonessential, the animal must eat at least one of these "nonessentials" to maintain life. Many animals have the ability, which may be born of necessity or may be the result of evolutionary development, to convert one type of food to another through metabolic processes.

The nutritionist directs his investigations in various ways, depending upon the type of animal he studies. Human nutritionists work on the diets that bring the best possible health to humans and study the effects of deficiencies and their correction. The classic example of this work was the introduction of vitamin C to prevent and cure scurvy in the British navy by feeding the sailors lime juice. Animal husbandrymen who study nutrition emphasize the importance of the ability of animals to utilize foods efficiently to increase fecundity and develop larger animals. The conversion of carbohydrate to protein and the processes that control this conversion are of great economic importance.

Insect nutritionists have worked in at least three directions. The first is the study of the natural food of insects. In a group so highly diverse as insects, it is expected (and experienced) that for almost everything comestible there is an insect that will eat it. Brues[8] has discussed this in his *Insect Dietary*.

The second direction is the study and search for food combinations that can maintain normal populations for laboratory study or produce large numbers of insects for sale as bird food, fish food, or fish bait. These food combinations include growing plants, dehydrated or extracted plant tissue, commercial feeds such as dog food, and combinations of ingredients that can be described by specific chemical analysis. A large part of the research in insect nutrition falls into this category.

The third direction is the study of essential food components with diets derived from chemically defined ingredients, often in bacteriologically sterile formulation, and with insects reared from externally sterilized eggs. This study is an approach to the determination of essential food components, particularly if the contributions of symbiotic fauna-flora and food reserves that pass through the egg are taken into account.

An extensive literature on the subject of insect nutrition has accumulated, but it is widely scattered. Fortunately, the entire subject, as well as special aspects, has been reviewed frequently by specialists in the field. These reviews furnish a running summary of progress and complete bibliographies.

The classic review of insect nutrition was published by Uvarov in 1928 as a by-product of a nutritional study of the natives of Kenya.[31] More recent summaries have been prepared by Trager,[30] Lipke and Fraenkel,[22] Friend,[12] House,[19,20] and Gordon.[15] A summary of principles and a statement of the goal toward which nutritionists should work was presented by Dougherty.[10]

THE IMPORTANCE OF INSECT NUTRITION

The table of contents of Uvarov's monograph could serve well as a guide for nutritional research, and his introduction clearly states the importance of the field. Uvarov began his treatise as follows:

It is well known that the enormous losses regularly caused by insect pests to cultivated plants, domestic animals, and human life are directly or indirectly connected with their feeding habits. On the other hand, the products of a few useful insects, like the honey bee, silkworm, lac insect, etc., are, from the physiological point of view, substances of definite importance in the metabolism of insects and their quality and output depends on the character of the food taken.

It would seem, therefore, that the problem of the nutrition and the metabolism of insects should be regarded as a key both to the successful control of injurious insects and to the progress of the industries dependent upon the products of useful insects. It would be natural to expect that the attention of entomologists always has been and still is concentrated on its solution. If this were so, we might possess a thorough theoretical knowledge of the nutritional physiology of, at least, all the most important insects, and be in a position to apply it to practical purposes.

Regarding his compilation of data, Uvarov continues:

The first glance at the summary, and, particularly, at the voluminous bibliography, including nearly six hundred titles, may give the impression that a very large amount of work has been done on the problems of insect nutrition and metabolism, but when all the data available on each particular subject are put together it becomes clear that very few points have been touched and that the results achieved are but a drop compared with the ocean of unknown phenomena.

Thus, to begin with, existing knowledge of the food of various insects from the chemical point of view is extremely meagre. It is, of course, known that many insects feed on green plants, but the question which substances are utilized by phytophagous insects and which are not, is doubtful and has been very little studied. The problem has, however, an enormous practical importance, since the immunity of certain varieties, or species, of plants against particular insects must be closely connected with it. With regard to another group of insects of great economic importance, viz., those boring in timber, destroying forests and buildings, only one fact has so far been established that either they feed not on wood, but on fungi in the burrows, or that the assimilation of their food depends on the presence of special micro organisms in their bodies;

thus the whole problem of their nutrition is highly peculiar and still unstudied from a physiological point of view. In the case also of the blood sucking insects which cause enormous losses in human and animal life in the tropics and elsewhere, there is practically no information on the chemical side of their nutrition, although there is a voluminous literature on the anatomy of the digestive apparatus, on the mechanics of its action, on the selection of hosts for feeding purposes, etc. . . . it is, perhaps, worth while pointing out that there is still no information available regarding the actual food of the larvae of the commonest insect, viz. the housefly; it is known that the larvae breed in various decomposing substances and that some bacteria seem to be necessary for their development, but what the larvae actually feed on has never been properly investigated. As a matter of fact, there are very few insects on the food of which there is a reasonable amount of information. Curiously enough, the insect best studied in this respect is the banana fly (*Drosophila*) which is largely used in experiments on genetics and is therefore bred in numbers in laboratories all over the world; unfortunately, the data obtained on this insect are of very little practical value. Another well studied insect is the cockroach, again a common laboratory species, and again one presenting but little interest to the general entomologist. The same may be said with regard to flesh flies also very favored in physiological laboratories where the objects for the study are naturally enough chosen as a rule without regard to their interest for entomologists. It is the duty of all entomologists to draw the attention of physiologists and biochemists to the existence of many other insects which can be raised in the laboratory with equal ease, and which are equally interesting from physiological and chemical points of view, but are at the same time very important from other points of view.

The ideas expressed by Uvarov will remain worthy of serious consideration for many years. The possibility is worth considering that nutrition may have an effect upon resistance, either by improving the general physiological status of insect populations or by providing a particular factor in natural food that imparts the resistance characteristic. Actually, all experimental studies should begin with a thorough understanding of the nutrition of laboratory species and, in some instances, the laboratory strain. This understanding will become possible only after more careful work has been completed in the study of insect nutrition.

SOME GENERAL PRINCIPLES OF INSECT NUTRITION

House[20] has summarized the progress that has been made in the study of the nutrition of insects as follows:

The present understanding is based upon research that ranges from investigations of the natural foods to the studies, most of which have been conducted during the last 10 years, of the effects of single components of chemically defined diets. Thus far, the data are limited almost entirely to the needs of insects during part of the development of one generation, and in only a few cases more than one. Most data have been derived from the study of a few representatives of the orders Coleoptera, Diptera, Lepidoptera, and Orthoptera.

The factor of symbiosis which occurs particularly in species that feed on plant juice, blood—and stored products, and also includes cockroaches and some other omniverous forms—has made it difficult to reach finite conclusions. Other factors that must be considered include: the nutrient reserves that are passed along in the egg or accumulate in the immature stages to be used in later stages of development, the possibility of the inclusion of small quantities of harmful substances that may stimulate a metabolic system and result in improved nutrition, and the effects of the presence or absence of phagostimulants that can render an otherwise suitable diet unsatisfactory.

Nutritional requirements of young insects may vary with sex and developmental state, and may depend on the nutritional state of the parent; also data indicate that nutritional deficiencies may have the greatest effect on the smallest individuals. The requirements for specific factors (e.g., amino acids) tend to be more or less uniform during larval life but may vary widely in adults. This variation may be especially true in adult females, which require changes in nutrition during egg formation and maturation. Some adult forms do not feed but rely entirely on nutrients carried over from the immature stage. Others feed on carbohydrates, etc.

Despite these variables, the accumulated research indicates that insects require, or can utilize, carbohydrate, protein, mineral salts, sterol, and most water-soluble (vitamin B) vitamins. Fats are utilized by many insects, but relatively few species have been shown to have a definite requirement.

The fat-soluble vitamins (A, D, K, and E) are considered unnecessary. Insects grow readily on vitamin A-free diets, and vitamin A has not been detected in extracts of large numbers of insects.[6] However, no data are available to prove or disprove that a deficiency of vitamin A affects visual acuity in insects. There is a visual pigment in insects that responds to light in a manner similar to that of vertebrates, but this pigment probably is not chemically derived from pigment vitamin A.[28] The insect exoskeleton does not have the calcium-phosphorus complex found in vertebrate bone, which may explain why vitamins A and D are not essential. Vitamin K is required for normal blood coagulation in vertebrates, but blood coagulation in insects is accomplished by another means. The case of vitamin E, sometimes called the fecundity vitamin, seems to be more difficult to rationalize, but its essentiality is doubtful.

Vitamin C (ascorbic acid) apparently is synthesized by many insects in sufficient quantity, but this is not so in the migratory locust (*Schistocerca gregaria*), which requires ascorbic acid.[9]

PROCEDURES IN THE STUDY OF INSECT NUTRITION

The production of normal insects for laboratory experimentation in other phases of physiology is an important application of the study of nutrition. Commercial animal feeds have been recommended for many of the omniverous species, and some of these feeds are satisfactory. It is important that the diet used for a laboratory colony is nutritionally sufficient in all respects. The presence of deficient insects in a colony very likely alters the results of other experimental work. So far, no single diet has been developed that can be used for all insect species, although the requirements of insects are qualitatively similar and basically the same as for vertebrates, with the exception of vitamins. With the diverse feeding habits of the different insect groups, quantitative differences in diet are important, and the factor of phagostimulation can be decisive.

Commercial dog food, nonmedicated chick mash, fish food, and rabbit food supply all the essentials for many insects; colonies can flourish for generations on any of these. The necessary nutritional and chemical constituents are present in all of these prepared diets, but the physical properties may require some adjustment.

The problem of determining essentials for insect growth and development has lead to a considerably more complicated experimental process, and through necessity, a specialized terminology. The development of this specialized terminology is an attempt to define both procedures and diets in terms that have absolute meanings and are free of connotative meanings, which can lead to confusion. The practice of implying connotative meanings, which the author calls "willful misunderstanding," is a real hazard in the communication of ideas. Such is the case with the terminology that has been used in nutrition; to correct these semantic difficulties, new words derived from classical languages have been introduced.[10]

In this vein, the word *defined* (or *chemically defined*) has not always been applied to components that are characterized with chemical precision (e.g., a diet containing dextrin, agar, or a racemic amino acid would not be defined). The new word that indicates a medium composed of components that have a precisely known chemical structure before compounding is *holidic*. This definition ignores the possible changes through interaction during compounding or by association with the organism, but these possibilities must be considered in actual practice. A diet with a holidic base, to which is added at least one substance of unknown structure or uncertain purity, is described as *meridic;* a diet comprised of crude organic material (e.g., dog food) is *oligidic*.

In the description of colonies or cultures of organisms, a similar situation exists. Those who object to the word *pure*, as it applies to a culture, on the basis that purity is relative, prefer to describe a culture that contains just one species as *axenic*. When the species present in the culture are known, the system is *gnotobiotic*. An axenic culture has a single known species growing gnotobiotically. If more than one species is present and if they are positively identified, the culture is *synxenic*. The opposite of a gnotobiotic culture is an *agnotobiotic* or *xenic* system, in which the number of species (or their identification) is not certain. This is the case with insects reared in association with their normal complement of symbionts (either inter- or intracellular) or in a normally infected or infested environment. These terms are being adopted by most writers in insect nutrition. The practical impossibility of satisfying some of the more rigid definitions will undoubtedly lead to the use of comparative terms, which will negate the value of the definitions.

Criteria of a Satisfactory Diet

The most popular method for assaying nutritional factors is growth. This method may be described in terms of the increase in size or weight of individuals, or of whole colonies. Much of the data has been drawn from observations on one generation, or even on one or two stages of development. Gordon suggested a series of improvements that might be added to experimental procedure.[14]

The first improvement concerns weight as a criterion and relates this to the duration of culture under the conditions of the experiment. As an illustration of this method, House[18] indicated that arginine is essential for the first generation growth of the German roach, because arginine-free diets produced individuals that grew at a rate that was 80 per cent that of the control insects. These results might also be interpreted as indicating that while arginine accelerates growth, it must be present in the reserves carried over in the egg or synthesized by the insect, in which case it would not be essential. To avoid such uncertainty, the term *essential nutrient* should be reserved for substances that must be present in the diet to maintain growth and reproduction *indefinitely*.

The second improvement suggested by Gordon is the elimination of all nonessential elements to attain a minimal diet. Conventional experimental procedure begins with a basic diet, and the obvious procedure is to compound each new diet as the basic, minus one component. This assumes that nutrients are not interconvertible, which is not necessarily true.

The third improvement suggests the investigation of alternate nutrients whenever possible. These alternate substances fall into three classes—precursors that have no activity of their own but are converted into chemically active substances in the animal, comprising nutrients that have chemical activity but that are not readily formed from or converted to other nutrient materials, and precursor nutrients that exhibit chemical activity but are also convertible into other nutrients. The last category can be further subdivided, depending upon the extent to which conversion takes place and the degree of activity of the converted nutrient.

The problems of assaying nutrients for essentiality are complex, and strict adherence to definitions proposed by Dougherty[10] is at the present stage impossible. Adherence to these definitions must be considered a desirable goal toward which to work, with the realization that they may be approached but not attained.

That essential nutrients must be considered both qualitatively and quantitatively makes the number of possible combinations of nutrients almost infinite. The number of assays necessary may be limited by the use of an advanced statistical design in the experiments, and some of the initial problems can be resolved by interpreting the data for essentiality as a distinctly positive or negative reaction. In any case some compromises are necessary, and Gordon[14] made several good suggestions, based on his extensive study of the nutrition of the German roach, reared in colonies under xenic conditions on a meridic diet. His criteria are expressed numerically.

The first criterion is the survival fraction, defined as the ratio of the final number of adults to the initial number of nymphs. This cannot be used if adults are not produced. The second criterion is the growth index. This index is defined as the ratio of the product of the average length times the number of nymphs at the end of the nymphal growth period divided by the product of the average length times the number of nymphs at the beginning of the experiment (zero days). The third criterion is the maturation period—the interval in days between the appearance of the first and the last adult. The maturation period is a rough indicator of growth rate but not necessarily a criterion of adequacy. The fourth criterion is the reproduction index—the number of nymphs produced per egg capsule (as in the German roach) in the first hatch divided by the number of days from the start of the experiment. This has significance not only in that it proves that reproduction has occurred, but also because it gives a record of the duration of the life cycle.

Development of a Nutritional Medium

A diet must contain a source of energy, usually in the form of a carbohydrate; a source of amino nitrogen, a protein; a source of sterol, often supplied as a minor component of a fat or oil; vitamins, particularly the B series; and mineral salts. In addition, the physical and chemical properties of the diet must make it acceptable to the species to be fed. An inert carrier is often necessary to provide bulk and texture for synthetic diets.

Carbohydrates.   Plant starch is the principal source of carbohydrate, but various types of sugar may be ingested in the normal diet from plant sap, nectar, and tissue. The utilization of the carbohydrate depends upon the ability of the insect species to convert the complex polysaccharides and oligosaccharides into assimilable simple sugars. The carbohydrates in the order of utilization by insects generally include: dextrin, fructose, glucose, lactose, maltose, mannitol, raffinose, sorbitol, starch, sucrose, and trehalose.[19] Glucose and fructose are usually utilized well; sorbose and galactose not so well; and in general, pentoses are not used at all.[20]

Results from the study of the requirements of *Schistocerca gregaria* indicate the quantitative requirements for carbohydrate.[9] These insects grew poorly and failed to complete development when no digestible carbohydrate was incorporated into the diet. Normal growth was obtained when glucose and sucrose formed 13 per cent of the diet, but the rate of development was not maintained beyond the third instar. Satisfactory growth and development occurred with 26 per cent carbohydrate, and 39 per cent gave normal development but poor growth. That a quantitative optimum for carbohydrate in the diet exists is indicated by the statement of Lipke and Fraenkel[22] that carbohydrates may be nutritionally inert; may be satisfactory, but unacceptable from a physical or chemical standpoint; or may be toxic.

Proteins and Amino Acids.   Proteins are complex nitrogenous compounds composed of chains of α-amino acids. They are the principal component of animal tissue. From a nutritional standpoint, the requirement for protein is a requirement for the individual amino acids that comprise them.

Twenty-one amino acids make up the list currently accepted as occurring in nature. This means that these 21 amino acids are present in natural plant or animal proteins. These amino acids with their formulas are listed in Table 2-1. It should be immediately apparent that asymmetric carbons are present in all but glycine, and that isoleucine and threonine have more than one asymmetric carbon each. This configuration suggests special isomerism, which does exist and is indicated by "D" or "L" used as a prefix (*d* and *l* in the older literature). In addition to the D and L forms, isoleucine and threonine have an *allo* form. It is a generality that only the L amino acids are utilized by animals, and there is always the possibility that the allo amino acids are physiologically different. At least one D amino

TABLE 2-1. The Naturally Occurring Amino Acids

Amino Acid	Chemical Name*	Formula*
Alanine	2-Amino proprionic acid	$CH_3CH(NH_2)COOH$
Arginine	1-Amino-4-guanidovaleric acid	$HN{=}C(H_2N){-}NHCH_2CH_2CH_2CH(NH_2)COOH$
Aspartic acid	Amino succinic acid	$HOOCCH_2CH(NH_2)COOH$
Cystine	3,3'-Dithiobis(2-amino-propanoic acid)	$CH_2{-}S{-}S{-}CH_2$ $H_2N{-}CH \quad\quad CH{-}NH_2$ $\;\;\;\;COOH \quad\quad COOH$
Glutamic acid	2-Aminopentanedioic acid	$HO_2CCH_2CH_2CH(NH_2)COOH$
Glycine	Aminoacetic acid	NH_2CH_2COOH
Histidine	α Amino-4 (or 5)-imid-azoleproprionic acid	(imidazole ring)$CH_2CH(NH_2)COOH$
Hydroxyproline	4-Hydroxy-2-pyrrolidine carboxylic acid	(pyrrolidine ring)
Iodogorgoic acid	3,5-Diiodotyrosine	$HO{-}(C_6H_2I_2){-}CH_2CH(NH_2)COOH$
Isoleucine	α Amino-β-methylvaleric acid	$CH_3CH_2CH(CH_3)CH(NH_2)COOH$
Leucine	Aminoisocaproic acid	$(CH_3)_2CHCH_2CH(NH_2)COOH$
Lysine	α,ϵ-Diaminocaproic acid	$NH_2(CH_2)_4CH(NH_2)COOH$
Methionine	α-Amino-γ-methylmercapto-butyric acid	$CH_3SCH_2CH_2CH(NH_2)COOH$
Phenylalanine	α-Amino-β-phenylproprionic acid	$C_6H_5CH_2CH(NH_2)COOH$

*Chemical names and formulas from *The Merck Index*, 7th Edition, 1960.

TABLE 2-1. (continued)

Amino Acid	Chemical Name*	Formula*
Proline	2-Pyrrolidinecarboxylic acid	
Serine	2-Amino-3-hydroxypropanoic acid	$HOCH_2CH(NH_2)COOH$
Threonine	α-Amino-β-hydroxybutyric acid	$CH_3CH(OH)CH(NH_2)COOH$
Thyroxine	β- [(3,5-Diiodo-4-hydroxy-phenoxy)-3,5-diiodo-phenyl] -alanine	
Tryptophan	1-α-Amino-3-indolepropionic acid	
Tyrosine	β-(p-Hydroxyphenyl)alanine	
Valine	α-Aminoisovaleric acid	

*Chemical names and formulas from *The Merck Index,* 7th Edition, 1960.

acid (D-alanine) was found in the blood of the milkweed bug (*Oncopeltus fasciatus*), and it is apparently synthesized by the insect.[2]

Amino acids incorporated into diets may come from proteins, from protein hydrolysates, or from purified compounds isolated from hydrolysates. Some synthetic preparations are also all present. The most common proteins available in a reasonably pure state include albumin, casein, gelatin, and zein. As ingredients in commercial feeds these proteins come from meat scrap, grass and leaves (e.g., alfalfa meal), yeast, whole wheat flour, and bran. The calculated amino acid content of each of these proteins is shown in Tables 2-2 and 2-3. The values from these tables should be accepted with some caution because of probable losses of amino acid during hydrolysis.[5] The tabular figures are percentages calculated on the basis of

TABLE 2-2. The Amino Acid Composition of Common Proteins*

Amino Acid	Protein (per cent amino acid on the basis of 16 grams of nitrogen)			
	Casein	Gelatin	Zein	Albumin (Egg)
Arginine	4.2	8.2	1.8	6.1
Histidine	3.2	0.9	1.7	2.4
Lysine	8.5	5.0	0.0	6.5
Tyrosine	6.4	0.5	5.2	4.2
Tryptophan	1.3	0.0	0.1	1.5
Phenylalanine	6.3	2.3	6.4	7.5
Cystine	0.4	0.1	1.0	2.4
Methionine	3.5	0.8	2.3	5.5
Serine	6.8	3.5	7.7	8.5
Threonine	4.5	1.9	3.0	4.2
Leucine	10.0	3.5	23.7	9.4
Isoleucine	7.5	1.7	7.3	7.5
Valine	7.7	2.8	3.0	6.4
Glutamic acid	23.0	11.0	26.6	16.0
Aspartic acid	7.0	6.2	5.6	9.0
Glycine	2.1	23.6	.0.0	3.6
Alanine	3.3	8.2	11.4	7.4
Proline	13.1	15.3	10.4	8.1
Hydroxyproline	0.0	13.0	—	—

*Values assembled from tabular material by Block and Bolling. [5]

TABLE 2-3. The Amino Acid Composition of Crude Feed Components*

Amino Acid	Protein (per cent amino acid on the basis of 16 grams of nitrogen)				
	Meat Scrap	Grass and Leaves	Yeasts	Whole Wheat	Bran
Arginine	7.0	7.0	4.0 - 5.0	4.3	7.5
Histidine	3.5	2.0	3.0	2.1	1.7
Lysine	5.6	5.5	7.0 - 8.0	2.7	3.9
Tyrosine	3.2	5.0	3.6	4.0	—
Tryptophan	0.7	2.2	1.3	1.2	1.3
Phenylalanine	5.1	5.0 - 6.0	4.5	5.1	3.0
Cystine	1.2	2.0	1.1	1.8	1.5
Methionine	2.0	2.5	2.0	2.5	1.3
Serine	3.7	5.0	—	4.3	5.3
Threonine	3.9	5.4	5.5	3.3	2.5
Leucine	8.0	10.0	7.5	7.0	6.5
Isoleucine	3.4	5.0	6.0	4.0	4.5
Valine	6.1	5.0	5.8	4.3	4.1
Glutamic acid	—	11.5	14.7	29.0	—
Aspartic acid	—	5.3	—	—	—
Glycine	—	—	—	—	—
Alanine	—	—	—	—	—
Proline	—	3.0	—	—	—
Hydroxyproline	—	—	—	—	—

*Values assembled from tabular material by Block and Bolling. [5]

16 grams of amino acid per gram of nitrogen on a water- and ash-free basis. To convert the figures to actual amounts, it is necessary to find the per cent nitrogen content of the sample by analysis and to correct the figures by a factor obtained by dividing the per cent nitrogen by 16.

The proteins used most often in insect diets (albumin, casein, etc.) lack certain amino acids, making it necessary to fortify the proteins. Casein needs additional tryptophan, histidine, cystine, glycine, and possibly hydroxyproline. Gelatin should be fortified with tyrosine, tryptophan, and probably cystine or methionine. Zein requires the addition of arginine, histidine, lysine, tryptophan, cystine, valine, glycine, and hydroxyproline. Thus far, the amounts of each amino acid remain pragmatic, but like carbohydrate, there are quantitative as well as qualitative requirements. Some amino acids are toxic if used in excess. When racemic mixtures are used, it is the general practice to assume equal amounts of the D and L forms. Amino acid mixes that approximate synthetic proteins have been prepared for the nutrition of several insect species and are compared in Table 2-4.

TABLE 2-4. Amino Acid Mixes for Insect Diets

Amino Acid	l-form (mg./ml.)			
	German Cockroach[†] (B. germanica)	Onion Maggot[‡] (H. antiqua)	Pink Bollworm[§] (P. gossypiella)	Blowfly[#] (P. regina)
Alanine	5.5 mg./ml.	1.09 mg./ml.	0.38* mg./ml.	1.29 mg./ml.
Arginine	4.5	0.8	7.6	1.06
Aspartic acid	6.5	1.22	0.82*	1.53
Cystine	1.5	—	1.66*	0.36
Cysteine	—	0.48	—	—
Glutamic acid	23.0	4.42	2.18*	5.48
Glycine	3.0	1.75	2.50*	0.70
Histidine	3.0 (HCl)	0.48	3.8	0.70
Hydroxyproline	2.0	0.38	—	0.48
Isoleucine	6.5	1.26	1.02	1.53
Leucine	12.0	2.35	2.96	2.80
Lysine	7.5	1.34 (HCl)	1.18 (HCl)	1.76
Methionine	4.0	0.34	0.60	0.94
Phenylalanine	6.0	1.01	0.78	1.40
Proline	8.5	1.68	1.68*	2.0
Serine	7.5	0.88	0.08*	—
Threonine	4.0	0.38	0.92	0.94
Tryptophan	2.0	1.75	0.24	0.47
Tyrosine	7.0	1.24	0.52*	1.64
Valine	7.0	1.36	1.04	1.65

*"Dispensible"

[†]Data from House, H. L. 1948. *Some essential amino acids for Blattella germanica* (L.) *under aseptic conditions.* Cornell University Library, thesis for the doctorate.

[‡]Data from Friend, W. G., Salkeld, E. H., and Stevenson, I. L. 1959. Ann. N.Y. Acad. Sci. 77: 384.

[§]Data from Vanderzant, E. S. 1958. J. Econ. Ent. 51: 309.

[#]Data from Cheldelin, V. H., and Newburgh, R. W. 1959. Ann. N.Y. Acad. Sci. 77: 373.

Some of these amino acids are sold commercially as hydrochlorides. The hydrochloride form adds stability to the compounds, but their incorporation into diets may make the food unacceptable to insects.[1]

More is known about the amino acid requirements of insects in a qualitative way than is known about any other nutritional group. The results of the many investigations are difficult to interpret and compare because of the differences in the sources and in insect species, and in a number of cases because of the incorporation of amino acids into the diet from unsuspected sources. Table 2-5 summarizes the known requirements of several species.

The order of protein requirement for the confused flour beetle compares closely with that of the rat. Arginine, histidine, isoleucine, leucine, lysine, methionine, phenylalanine, threonine, tryptophan, and valine are essential for growth and development of the onion maggot, the pink bollworm, and many other species.[20] House[18] and Hilchey[16] showed that alanine, valine, leucine, isoleucine, serine, lysine, histidine, proline, tryptophan, and probably arginine are required for growth and development of the German roach under the conditions of their experiments. These conditions included the rearing of isolated insects from externally sterilized eggs on autoclaved diets that were nearly holidic (white dextrin—a nitrogen-free, but chemically undefined, carbohydrate source—was included). Some differences in the requirements of each sex were also noted in this work.[16] In a comparable assay under xenic conditions, a minimal amino acid mix was shown to require arginine, lysine, leucine, histidine, threonine, tryptophan, and glutamic acid.[14] Faster growth resulted if valine was included in the mix, and isoleucine and tryptophan were found to be partly replaceable by phenylalanine. Addition of amino acids classed as nonessential (serine, glycine, or proline) also appeared to accelerate growth. When the criterion of essentiality is *growth in terms of increase in weight,* the qualitative requirements derived from the nearly axenic culture and the xenic culture are remarkably similar. Alanine can replace glutamic acid, which is considered to be a major source of nitrogen,[14] which may explain the unusual alanine requirement of the German roach.

These data have been cited to show that the differences in protein requirements which exist are subtle. For the present, many of these differences can be explained on the basis of technology, including the quantitative relationships of the amino acids. Balance is very important for optimum growth, and some nonessential amino acids, including those that have iodine in the molecule, improve growth rates. Methionine and some other amino acids are toxic in moderately high concentrations. Ordinarily, the sulfur-bearing compounds are necessary for integument formation and normal molting, but it has been shown clearly that the German roach can synthesize these compounds by incorporating inorganic sulfur into an amino acid molecule.[17]

Fats and Sterols.   By definition, fats are esters of one or more fatty acids and glycerol, a trihydroxy alcohol. Enzymatic hydrolysis in the digestive tract splits the fatty acids from the glycerol, and each is metabolized separately. Sterols are compounds, with a complex ring structure, that always contain hydroxy groups. Sterols are associated with fats, but they are not esters, they will not saponify, and they are not split by lipases or

TABLE 2-5. Amino Acid Requirements for Several Insect Species*

Amino Acid	Phormia (flesh fly)	Pseudosarcophaga (parasitic dipteron)	Musca (housefly)	Calliphora (blowfly)	Drosophila (fruit fly)	Aedes (larvae) (mosquito)	Hylemya (onion maggot)	Blatella (German roach)	Apis (honeybee)
Alanine	–	stim.	–	–	–	–	–	(glut.)	–
Arginine	+	+	+	+	+ (cit.)	+	+	+	+
Aspartic acid	(glut.)	–	–	–	–	–	–	+	–
Cystine	–	–	–	–	–	– (+ pupa)	–	–	
Cysteine	(meth.)	–	–	–	–	–	–	–	–
Glutamic acid	(asp.)	stim.	–	–	–	– (+ pupa)	–	–	–
Glycine	–	+	+	+	stim.	+	+	+	–
Histidine	+	+	+	+	+	stim.	–	+	+
Hydroxyproline	+	+	+	+	+	–	+	–	+
Isoleucine	+	+	+	+	+	+	+	+ 2nd gen.	+
Leucine	+	+	+	+	+	+	+ pupa	+ 2nd gen.	+
Lysine	–	stim.	–	+	+	stim.	–	–	stim.
Methionine	(cysteine)	+	+	+	+	+	+ pupa	+ eggs	+
Phenylalanine	+	+	+	+	+	+	+ 3rd instar	–	stim.
Proline	+	+	–	–	–	stim.	–	–	–
Serine	stim.	stim.	–	–	stim.	stim.	–	–	
Threonine	+	+	+	+	+	+	+ 3rd instar	+ 2nd gen.	+
Tryptophan	+	+	+	–	+	+	–	+ 2nd gen.	+
Tyrosine	–	stim.	–	–	–	–	–	+ eggs	–
Valine	+	+	+	+	+	+	+	+ 2nd gen.	+

*Data abridged from Prosser and Brown.[28]

Abbreviations

+pupa, etc. = required for this specific stage of development.
(glut., etc.) = amino acid that will substitute.

+ = required.
– = not required.
stim. = stimulates growth, not required.

esterases. Through the activity of the hydroxy groups, it is possible for sterols to react with fatty acids to form esters. A number of esters are found in animals, and most of these compounds have physiological activity. The sterols are closely related to bile acids, and they are a constituent of many hormones. Ergosterol, which in its irradiated form is vitamin D, is a sterol.

So far as is known, all insects have a requirement for sterol, but only a few have been shown to have a clear-cut fat requirement. This does not preclude the possibility that fats or fatty acids can be utilized by insects; in fact, it is well established that many insects digest, assimilate, and metabolize fats.

The sterol requirement for insects can be satisfied with cholesterol, 7-dehydrocholesterol, and stigmasterol.[4] Plant feeders usually have a broader tolerance for sterols other than cholesterol, than do the flesh feeders and omniverous species.

In the purified state, cholesterol is highly insoluble in water. This poses a serious problem when it must be incorporated into a liquid or gel for a diet. Friend solved this problem by dissolving the required amount in hot 95 per cent ethyl alcohol, precipitating the cholesterol by adding water, and stabilizing the suspension with Tween 80.[12] The alcohol was removed under vacuum. Gordon impregnated his insect diet with an ether solution and evaporated the solvent,[14] and Beck and co-workers used cholesterol acetate, which is relatively soluble in water.[3]

Lipids that are associated with sterols are often added to insect diets as purified vegetable oils. Corn oil, linseed oil, soya bean oil, and wheat germ oil are the common choices. Corn oil is approximately 45 per cent oleic acid, 40 per cent linoleic acid, 7 per cent palmitic acid, and 3 per cent stearic acid. Linseed oil has 35 per cent linoleic acid, 45 per cent linolenic acid, 9 per cent oleic acid, 6 per cent palmitic acid, 4 per cent stearic acid, with traces of myristic, arachidic, and isolinoleic acids. Soya bean oil contains 30 per cent oleic acids, 55 per cent linoleic acid, 9 per cent palmitic acid, 4 per cent stearic acid, with traces of myristic and lignoceric acids. Wheat germ oil is composed of 44 per cent linoleic acid, 30 per cent oleic acid, and 10 per cent linolenic acid. All of these oils have an unsaponifiable residue composed of sterols and high-carbon alcohols. The total residue varies from about 3 to 5 per cent, a small part of which is made up of tocopherols, sitosterols, dehydrositosterols, and stigmasterol.[23]

From these data, it would seem that the plant oils are not an effective source of metabolizable sterols, but insects grow and develop on diets in which plant oils are the only source of sterols. Only trace quantities of these sterols are required in insect diets. From this it seems obvious that some conversion of the plant sterols takes place in insects, either through the intervention of symbionts or through a more fundamental metabolic process.

Cholesterol is required by insects for larval growth and oogenesis, and its function is similar to that of the juvenile hormone, which is an unsaponifiable constituent of insect lipids. Cholesterol may act as a precursor to the various steroid hormones. A sterol deficiency deprives insects of some of their natural immunity toward bacterial infections.[21]

Most Lepidoptera have a requirement for an exogenous fatty acid, as well as a sterol requirement. Certain moths require linoleic acid for larval growth and development, the German roach shows deficiency symptoms in the progeny of deprived parents, and a species of locust requires linoleic acid for normal wing formation.[20] As the criteria for sufficiency become more critical, it is probable that the number of insect species with a fatty acid requirement will increase.

Nucleic Acids. These compounds, present in the nuclei of all cells as ribonucleic acid (RNA) or deoxyribonucleic acid (DNA), exhibit an ever increasing number of metabolic functions. There is no reason to believe that nucleic acids do not have equal importance in insects as in vertebrates. Thus far, it has been demonstrated that the addition of RNA increases the growth rate in various dipterous insects.[20] Requirements for other insect groups have not been demonstrated but might well be anticipated.

Vitamins. Vitamins are organic molecules of diverse chemistry that are required in minute amounts for the growth and normal functioning of cells.[13] They play an important part in metabolic processes, in which they function principally as parts of enzymes.

The vitamin requirements of insects have been the subject of many studies, but little clear-cut information is available. It is generally conceded that the water-soluble group (B series), including thiamin, riboflavin, niacin, pyridoxine, pantothenic acid, biotin, and cyanocobalamin, is required by most insects. Ascorbic acid (vitamin C) is essential for the migratory locust.

A major source of confusion in the literature of vitamin nutrition comes from the use of common nomenclature. The alphabetic system by which they were originally classified has largely given way to the use of a chemical name. Common names still exist and have rather broad synonomy.

THIAMIN. The first of the series is thiamin. It is also known as B_1, thiamine hydrochloride, betabion, and aneurine. Similar synonomy is common with most of this series, but it can be resolved by consulting a handbook such as the *Merck Index*. Thiamin occurs in plant and in animal tissues, grain cereals, yeast, liver, eggs, milk, and in green leaves. Most of the commercial product is synthetic. Since growth is the principal criterion by which thiamin deficiency is measured in insects, a thiamin deficiency results in poor growth. From vertebrate nutrition it is known that thiamin functions as a coenzyme for pyruvate metabolism, and it is a reasonable assumption that this is its role in insects. Thiamin can be produced by the symbionts normally present in the insect body so that the deficiencies are most pronounced in axenic culture.

RIBOFLAVIN. Riboflavin is a slightly soluble pigment that occurs in trace amounts in all plant and animal cells. Good sources are milk, eggs, malted barley, liver and kidney tissue, and yeast. Riboflavin is available in a purified commercial preparation. In insects this vitamin is concentrated in the Malpighian tubes, in the free form in the lumen, and in a phosphorylated form in the cell walls. Riboflavin is never excreted as an intact molecule.[24] The principal known function of riboflavin is as a prosthetic group for the flavoprotein enzymes. Insects may be raised in xenic culture on a riboflavin-free diet, which indicates that the symbionts can furnish a part of the requirement. The mortality under these conditions usually is high.

NIACIN. Niacin (nicotinic acid amide) occurs in reasonably high concentrations in liver, yeast, milk, white meat, alfalfa, legumes, and whole grain cereals. Whole wheat flour averages about 60 micrograms of niacin per gram. Like the other vitamins, niacin is available commercially in a purified form. In vertebrates it functions as part of dehydrogenase coenzyme.

PYRIDOXINE.   Pyridoxine occurs in yeast, liver, and cereals and is available in a pure form. There is no requirement established for vertebrates, but pyridoxine takes a part in the process of amino acid conversion in the role of a coenzyme. It is considered essential for most insects.

PANTOTHENIC ACID.   Pantothenic acid was discovered as an essential for chicks. It is found in all living tissue, is commercially available in purified form, and is found in liver. One of the most potent natural sources of pantothenic acid is the royal jelly of the honeybee. The commercial product is synthetic. Pantothenic acid is part of coenzyme A (CoA) and as such probably is required in a number of metabolic processes. It is considered essential for insects.

BIOTIN.   Biotin, a vitamin found in liver, kidney, yeast, and milk in low concentrations, is either essential or beneficial to the nutriment of all animals. It is available in pure form, and its incorporation into insect diets improves growth. Biotin's cellular function is as a coenzyme in the fixation of carbon dioxide in 4-carbon acids.[13]

CYANOCOBALAMIN.   Cyanocobalamin, or cobalamin is often referred to as vitamin B_{12}. It was first isolated from liver in 1948, is commercially available and is used empirically in insect diets. In cellular processes cyanocobalamin functions as a coenzyme for an enzyme that is active in the methyl transfer and nucleic acid metabolism.[13]

OTHER B VITAMINS.   Other B series vitamins have been studied in insect nutrition, and some have been found to improve growth or development. Among these is vitamin B_T (carnitine), which is the only one of the group isolated from studies with insects. Carnitine has been found important to the development of Tenebrionidae[11] and *Aedes aegypti*.[29] The requirements of carnitine are variable with different species, and the qualitative requirements, as they are known, are tabulated for reference in Table 2-6. The mixes that have been used with several species are included in Table 2-7.

Mineral Salts.   Various mineral salts are nutritionally essential for insects, but this field has received relatively little attention. The obvious approach to the problem is to ash insects and determine the salt content of the residue. The results have not been too enlightening because they show such a wide spectrum of elements; many of the elements are of questionable importance, because the analyses include the unassimilated food in the digestive tract. There is general agreement that the ash of insects contains potassium, sodium, magnesium, calcium, zinc, copper, aluminum, silicon, phosphorus, arsenic, sulfur, chlorine, manganese, and iron. Some of these are found in trace quantities and if they are utilized at all, it is in very minute quantities.

The most common practice in diet formulation is to use one of the commercially prepared nutritional salt mixes for vertebrate work. These are designated as USP formulations (e.g., USP, XI Edition), or under the initials of the name of the person who described the original preparation (e.g., salt W is Wesson's salt mix). All of the mixes contain the same elements in approximately the same concentrations; the principal difference

TABLE 2-6. Vitamin Mixes for Insect Diets

Vitamin	Phormia (blowfly) 5* µg./ml.†	Musca (housefly) 1.2 µg./ml.††	Drosophila (fruit fly) 1.5 µg./ml.§	Hylemya (Onion maggot) 1.5 µg./ml.§§	Tenebrio (mealworm) 25.0 µg./gm.‖	Pyrausta (corn borer) 12 µg./gm.‖‖	Blatella (cockroach) 134 µg./gm.#	Schistocerca (locust) 25 µg./gm.##
Thiamine HCl	5*	1.2	1.5	1.5	25.0	12	134	25
Riboflavin	15*	1.6	2.4	2.4	12.5	18	150	25
Pyridoxine	15*	9.0	3.0	30.0	12.5	16	82	25
Inositol	100	59.6	–	–	–	2000	180	250
Nicotinic acid	15*	3.0	10.0	10.0	50.0	100	197	100
Choline chloride	100*	20.0	20.0	20.0	500.0	1000	340	1250
Pantothenic acid (Ca salt)	15*	4.4	6.0	6.0	25.0	40	88	50
p-Aminobenzoic acid	15	9.0	–	–	–	50	137	25
Folic acid	5.0	3.4	–	6.0	2.5	5.0	88	25
Biotin	0.025	0.09	0.02	0.02	0.25	1.0	4.8	1.0
Cyanocobalamin			0.04	0.040			2.7	
Dl-Carnitine		–			–	–	–	–
Dl-6-Thioctic acid		–	–	0.5	5.0	–	–	–

*Essential.

**The author's figures are cited as mg./gm.

†Data from Cheldelin, V. H., and Newburgh, R. W. 1959. Ann. N.Y. Acad. Sci. 77:373.

††Data from House, H. L. and Barlow, J. S. 1958. Ann. Ent. Soc. Amer. 51: 299.

§Data from Hinton, T. 1952. Science 116: 708.

§§Data from Friend, W. G., Salkeld, E. H., and Stevenson, I. L. 1959. Ann. N.Y. Acad. Sci. 77: 384.

‖Data from Fraenkel.[11]

‖‖Data from Wiessell, H. B. 1955. Ann. Report of the Ent. Soc. of Ontario. 86: 10.

#Data from Gordon.[14] Note: Powdered cellulose was used as a carrier and amounts were expressed in terms of micromoles per gram. The figures in the table are recalculated to conform with other data.

##Data from Dadd, R. H. 1960. J. Ins. Physiol. 5: 301.

TABLE 2-7. Water Soluble Vitamin Requirements Reported for Insects*

Vitamin	Pseudosarcophaga	Caenorhabditis	Tenebrio	Aedes aegypti	Calliphora	Musca	Drosophila	Phormia	Hylemya	Tribolium	Lasioderma	Patorus	Blatella
Thiamine	+	+	+	+	+	+	+	+	+	+	+	+	+
Riboflavin	+	+	+	+	+	+	+	+	+	+	+	+	+
Pyridoxine	-	+	+	+pupa	+	+	+?	+	+	+	-	+	+
Inositol	-			-	-		+?				-	-	+
Niacin	+	+	+	+stim.	+	+	+	stim.	+	+	+	+	+
Choline	+		+	+stim.	+		+	+	+	+	+stim.	+	+= betaine
Pantothenate	+	?	+	+	+	+	+	+	+	+	+	+	+
PABA	-												
Folic acid	+	+?	+	+pupa	+	+growth	+	stim.	+	+	+	-	+eggs
Biotin	+	?	+	+	+?		+	stim.	+	+	+	+	+eggs
Cyanocobalamin	-stim.	?		+pupa	-?	-			stim.	stim.		-	+eggs

*These data abridged and rearranged from tabular material by Prosser and Brown.[28]

Abbreviations

+ = required.

- = not required.

stim. = stimulates growth, not required.

+pupa, etc. = required for this specific stage of development.

(glut., etc.) = amino acid that will substitute.

comes from the method of formulation. Because of the lack of better information, salts are added to insect diets in empirical amounts by a trial and correction method. There is no reason to assume that the salt balance satisfactory for the mineral requirements of vertebrates should be the same or even close to that of insects.

From the available literature on the subject, there seems to be very little agreement on mineral salt requirements of the various species except that they require phosphorus and potassium. This is probably due more to the lack of critical studies than to the lack of actual requirements. Potassium, sodium, calcium, and magnesium are always present, and they undoubtedly function to maintain the ion balance necessary for the control of permeability of tissue membranes. Magnesium and potassium have been found in comparatively high levels of concentration in insects, particularly in the phytophagous forms. Magnesium may partially replace calcium as a divalent ion in insects. That the magnesium ion does not exert the anesthetic effect on insects that it has for many other invertebrates indicates an intrinsic difference in the permeability relations of the insect nerve sheaths.

Zinc in trace quantities is an activator for some enzyme reactions and except for this its function is unknown. Copper occurs in fairly high concentrations in some insects, and it has been speculated that it may be a part of an unidentified respiratory pigment. No such pigment has been isolated from insects.

Phosphorus in the form of a phosphate radical is the medium of exchange of energy, and it must be available for the synthesis of the phosphogen reserve. Chlorine is present as a chloride in salts of various anions, particularly potassium, sodium, calcium, and magnesium. The amount of chlorine found in insects is not sufficient to combine with the anions, so that these must be present in other than chloride salts. Iron, the last of the trace elements, is a part of the cytochrome system.

PRACTICAL ASPECTS OF NUTRITIONAL STUDY

The foregoing discussion should indicate clearly that research in insect nutrition may be simple or complicated, depending upon the end result desired. When insect production is the principal requirement, the best procedure is to find a commercially available product that can grow the most individuals with the greatest size and vigor, probably in the shortest period, and with no diminution of the reproductive potential. Most of this work is entirely pragmatic. The results of a typical experiment of this type are shown in Figure 2–1. This series of curves compares the rate of growth with weight increase of nymphs of the gray house cricket (*Acheta domesticus*) reared under similar conditions of crowding, temperature, and humidity and provided with a series of commercially available animal feeds. Here, only positive results are definitive. The reasons for poor growth are obscured by the variables incorporated in a completely nondefined diet, and from experience, it is apparent that an examination of the manufacturer's specifications does not give a dependable basis for prediction. That growth rates on one diet are low at the outset and become rapid in the later stages, or vice versa, may indicate that basic requirements change during growth

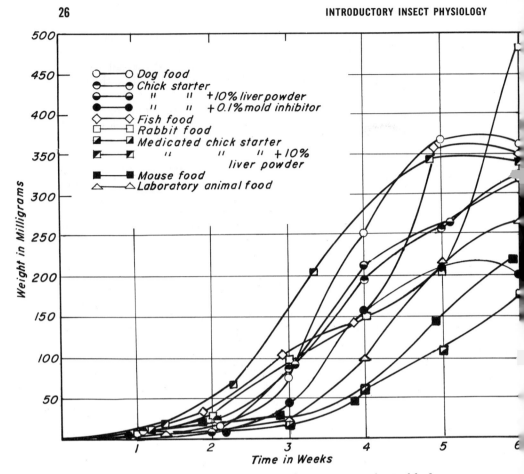

FIG. 2-1. Growth of the gray house cricket on commercial animal feeds.

of the nymph. This experiment demonstrates, when combined with observations of wing formation and ability to produce successive generations, that several commercial feeds are approximately equal in their requirements for this insect. Very little more can be gained from this experiment.[26]

The obvious refinement of this experiment is to prepare diets that are nearly holidic (achieving a strictly holidic diet is possible, but it may be impractical), and to rear the insects as individuals in axenic culture, taking into consideration the possibility of intervention of intracellular symbionts.

INTRACELLULAR SYMBIONTS AND NUTRITION

The intestinal fauna-flora in insects that act symbiotically can be removed by external egg sterilization and rearing under aseptic culture techniques. This is not true for the intracellular symbionts. These *bacteroids,* which are found in specialized cells usually at the edges of the segmented fat body adjacent to the midgut or deep in the fat body, have been observed frequently. The cells that contain bacteroids are described as *mycetocytes* or *mycetomes.*

Intracellular symbionts have never been cultured nor completely identified. They have been described as Rickettsia-like, bacteroid, or like fungi or yeasts. One of the most complete studies of bacteroids demonstrated that it is possible to prevent the transovarial transmission of these bodies in the German cockroach by subjecting the parents to high temperatures (approximately 37° C.), or by feeding the parents aureomycin (chlortetracycline) or sulfathiazole.[7] A concentration of 0.1 per cent aureomycin, fed to the parents during their entire life, assures aposymbiotic nymphs, and the lack of symbionts can be demonstrated by histological technique. In tests conducted by Brooks and Richards, aposymbiotic nymphs were virtually incapable of growth on a natural diet that was adequate for symbiotic nymphs.[7]

These observations bring up several problems that complicate nutritional study, even when conducted under aseptic conditions. The transmission of bacteroids through the egg makes external sterilization ineffective, and it seems apparent that these poorly defined bacteroids function in supplying essential nutritional factors. Two courses are open. Either the investigator must assume that since bacteroids are intracellular and since the symbiosis that appears to exist is of great antiquity in the evolutionary origin of the symbionts, they are an intrinsic part of the animal; or an attempt must be made to remove the symbionts by one of the methods described, and essential nutrients must be added to supplement the diet. The latter idea, although attractive from an academic point of view, offers a serious obstacle to the progress of nutritional study. A great deal more needs to be known about intracellular symbionts and their functions before their possible activity can be compensated for. Evidence indicates the procedures necessary to eliminate symbionts could confuse the results because of side reactions.

Aureomycin-treated chick mash, for example, with the drug level as low as 10 grams per ton has significantly inhibited the growth and development of the gray house cricket,[26] confirming earlier observations with the American cockroach (Periplaneta americana). In the case of the cricket, the addition of powdered liver increased both the growth and development rates. From these data, it may be argued that an essential growth factor is removed by the drug, and the powdered liver furnishes these essentials, or that the pathogenic, as well as the symbiotic flora, are destroyed, and the elimination of the pathogenic flora increases the growth and development rate when nutrition is adequate.

It is also of possible significance that cockroaches reared at high temperatures (above 36° C.) show a sharp break in their excretory efficiency at about 37° C.[28] This indicates the inhibition of a chain of enzyme reactions.[27]

There is no doubt that the intracellular symbionts of insects exist, but their presence as symbiotic organisms that are not an intrinsic part of the insect is debatable.

PHAGOSTIMULATION IN NUTRITION

Preparing either meridic or holidic diets that are physically and chemically attractive and acceptable to the various insect species is a technical obstacle in nutritional studies. Some insects are selective in their feeding, and observation of the residue left in the feeding dishes of a colony of cockroaches or crickets shows that these insects have selected the smaller particles and left the larger ones. Some plant feeders require an edge upon which to chew, and seed-feeding insects may refuse food until it is formed into a hard pellet. Methods of correcting these difficulties include such expedients as grinding the food (commercial animal feeds, for example) to a fine uniform particle size, formulating the food in dried gelatin or agar sheets, and forming the food into hard pellets in a pharmacist's pill press. No doubt other physical subterfuges have been used to induce feeding by altering physical properties of the food.

Chemical factors also induce feeding, and in some cases when the attractant is present, insects feed readily on a totally inadequate diet. The silkworm, for example, will feed on agar if one of several hexanols plus mulberry leaf extracts is included.[20] The larvae of the varied carpet beetle (*Anthrenus verbasci*) were observed to eat nylon in preference to wool after the nylon had been treated with certain finishing agents.[25]

Newly hatched larvae or nymphs are the most sensitive to phagostimulation; after the feeding pattern is established, phagostimulation may become less important. The acceptance of the diet by the insect species is of great importance in nutritional work, and many attempts have failed because of refusal of the insects to feed.

SUMMARY

Nutrition is the study of the food materials that insects normally eat and of the components of these food materials that are necessary for the best growth and development. Because food is the fuel for energy production and because there are a number of factors that must be supplied continuously to maintain normal metabolic cycles, a thorough knowledge of nutrition should be a precursor to any physiological study of insects.

The problems of insect nutrition may be approached from several points of view. The production of populations for experimental study requires an adequate but not necessarily defined diet. The study of nutritional factors may be made with purified or chemically defined diets, but the results must be definitive to have unequivocal value. The intervention of the unknown synthesis potential of the symbionts in the digestive tract or intracellular bodies must be taken into account.

LITERATURE CITED

1. Auclair, J. L. 1949. Amino acid metabolism in insects. Cornell University Library, Ithaca. Thesis for the doctorate.
2. Auclair, J. L., and Patton, R. L. 1950. The occurrence of D-alanine in the hemolymph of the milkweed bug. Rev. Canad. de Biol., 9:3–8.
3. Beck, S. D., Edwards, C. A., and Medler, J. T. 1953. Feeding and nutrition of the milkweed bug. Ann. ent. Soc. Amer. 51:283–287.

4. Beck, S. D., and Kapadia, G. G. 1957. Insect nutrition and metabolism of sterols. Science, *126:* 258.
5. Block, R. J., and Bolling, D. 1951. The Amino Acid Composition of Proteins and Foods. Charles C Thomas, Springfield, Ill.
6. Bowers, R. E., and McCay, C. M. 1940. Insect life without vitamin A. Science, *92:*291.
7. Brooks, M. W., and Richards, A. G. 1955. Intracellular symbiosis and production of aposymbiotic cockroaches. Biol. Bull., *109:*22–39.
8. Brues, C. T. 1946. Insect Dietary. Harvard University Press, Cambridge.
9. Dadd, R. H. 1960 and 1961. Nutritional requirements of locusts. J. ins. Physiol., *4:*319–347, *5:*161–168, *5:*301–316, *6:*126–145.
10. Dougherty, E. C. 1959. Introduction to axenic culture: A goal. Ann. N. Y. Acad. Sci., *77:*27–54.
11. Fraenkel, G. 1959. History of insect nutritional requirements. Ann. N. Y. Acad. Sci., *77:*267–274.
12. Friend, W. G. 1958. Nutritional requirements of phytophagous insects. Ann. Rev. Ent., *3:*57–74.
13. Giese, A. C. 1962. Cell Physiology. 2nd Ed., W. B. Saunders, Philadelphia, p. 56.
14. Gordon, H. T. 1959. Minimal nutritional requirements for the German roach. Ann. N. Y. Acad. Sci., *77:*290–351.
15. Gordon, H. T. 1961. Nutritional factors in resistance. Ann. Rev. Ent., *6:*27–54.
16. Hilchey, J. D. 1953. Qualitative amino acid requirements for the German roach. Contribs. Boyce Thompson Inst., *17:*203–219.
17. Hilchey, J. D., Block, R. J., and Miller, L. P. 1955. Utilization of inorganic sulfur by the German roach. Contribs. Boyce Thompson Inst., *18:*109–123.
18. House, H. L. 1949. Nutritional studies with the German roach under aseptic conditions. Can. Entomologist, *81:*105–112, 133–139.
19. House, H. L. 1961. Insect nutrition. Ann. Rev. Ent., *6:*13–26.
20. House, H. L. 1962. Ann. Rev. Biochem., *31:*653–672.
21. Levinson, Z. H. 1960. XI Internationaler Kongress für Entomologie, *3:*145–153, 154–156. Istituto di Entomologia Agraria dell'Università di Pavia, Italy.
22. Lipke, H., and Fraenkel, G. 1956. Insect nutrition. Ann. Rev. Ent., *1:*17–44.
23. Merck Index of Chemicals and Drugs. 1960. 7th Ed., Merck and Co., Rahway, N. J.
24. Metcalf, R. L., and Patton, R. L. 1942. Riboflavin metabolism in the Malpighian tubes of *P. americana.* Jour. of cell. and comp. Physiol., *19:*373–376.
25. Patton, R. L. 1945. Insect damage to nylon. Jour. econ. Ent., *38:*522–523.
26. Patton, R. L. 1963. Rearing the grey house cricket on commercial feeds. Ann. ent. Soc. Amer., *56:*250–251.
27. Patton, R. L., Anderson, A. D., and Gardner, J. 1959. Excretory efficiency in the American roach. J. ins. Physiol., *3:*256–261.
28. Prosser, C. L., and Brown, F. A. 1961. Comparative Animal Physiology. 2nd ed. W. B. Saunders, Philadelphia.
29. Singh, K. R. P., and Brown, A. W. A. 1957. Nutritional requirements of *Aedes aegypti.* J. ins. Physiol., *1:*199–220.
30. Trager, W. 1953. Insect nutrition. *In* Insect Physiology (K. D. Roeder, ed.), John Wiley, New York.
31. Uvarov, B. P. 1928. Insect nutrition and metabolism. Trans. Ent. Soc. London, *76:*255–343.

DIGESTION AND ASSIMILATION

Digestion is the process by which food in its ingested form is broken down into assimilable components. The process takes place in a specialized organ system, the digestive tract, through the hydrolytic action of digestive enzymes. As one would expect, considering the divergence of form and feeding habits among insects, the digestive tracts and their enzyme complements have many variations. Obviously, insects have a means of producing enzymes to digest their normal food.

ORIGIN AND STRUCTURE OF THE DIGESTIVE TRACT

The digestive tract is divided into three principal sections. Starting at the anterior, there is a foregut, or stomodeum, which may be enlarged to function as a crop; a midgut, mesenteron, or ventriculus, where most of the digestion takes place; and a hindgut, or proctodeum, which with the exception of the specialized section called the rectum, is primarily a duct for the elimination of the spent food bolus (Figs. 1–1 and 3–1).

Embryologically, the foregut and the hindgut arise from invaginations of the ectoderm; the midgut is formed from the endoderm. From a physiological standpoint, the structure of the foregut and the hindgut is the same as that of the integument and the tracheae, and the lumen of the digestive tract must be considered to be external. The structure of an insect is therefore like a double-walled tube, with the physiologically functional parts in the body cavity between the digestive tract and the integument.

Wigglesworth described eight structural types representing the variations in the digestive tracts of various insects.[26] A slight modification of this scheme is shown in Figure 3–1.

Type A is the primitive type. The foregut is essentially a duct leading to the midgut chamber, and the hindgut is only slightly developed into the specialized organs that exist in the more complicated forms. This is a structure typical of immature forms such as caterpillars.

The type B digestive tract is similar to A except that the foregut has become expanded into a storage chamber called a crop. This is typical of the

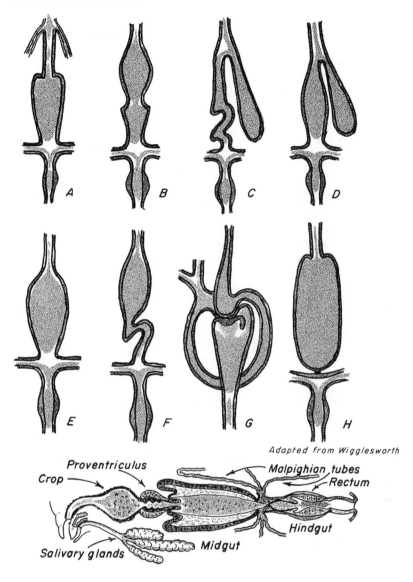

Adapted from Wigglesworth

Proventriculus

Crop

Malpighian tubes

Rectum

Salivary glands

Midgut

Hindgut

FIG. 3-1. *Top:* Diagrammatic representation of the anatomy of of the various typical digestive systems found in insects (see text for discussion) (adopted from Wigglesworth.) *Bottom:* Composite, showing the arrangement of the various digestive structures (redrawn after Roeder).

Orthoptera, many of which are plant feeders, and there is need for a storage chamber to hold a food reserve until the food can be moved to the midgut for completion of the digestive process. Some digestion takes place in the crop through the action of enzymes secreted by the salivary glands and possibly by the activity of bacteria.

The type C digestive tract is found in some of the higher Diptera. These insects feed on liquids, and the foregut has developed to a saclike diverticulum that would appear to function in food storage. The midgut in type C is more or less elongated to provide a long travel path for the liquid food, which presumably enhances digestion. The hindgut usually has well developed rectal glands in the expanded region (rectum) near the distal end of the tract.

Type D is found in the simpler Diptera (Nematocera) and in the adults of the Lepidoptera. This type of digestive tract also has a saclike diverticulum on the foregut, but the rest of the system is like that of the more primitive types A and B.

The type E digestive tract is found in the Siphonaptera. There are only slight differences between type E and the primitive type A; in fact for most purposes, they can be considered identical.

Types F, G, and H are highly specialized and are found in the Hemiptera, Homoptera, and in the larvae of some Hymenoptera and Neuroptera. Most Hemiptera feed on plant juice, and the long midgut serves to digest nutrients and assimilate them in the same manner as was suggested for the blood-sucking forms of type C. The type G digestive tract is peculiar to members of the family Homoptera, particularly aphids and coccids. Type G probably has evolved to function in the removal of excess water and sugar from the plant juice on which the insect feeds through a by-pass filter between the foregut and the hindgut. Removal of excess water would concentrate the protein, but this function has not been established; in fact, the presence of amino acids in honeydew makes this unlikely, since it indicates an excess of protein.[1] There are no Malpighian tubes in aphids, and Gersch[11] observed that fluorescein injected or fed is picked up and excreted at the level of the rectal glands.

The type H digestive tract is found in larvae only. There is no direct connection between the midgut and the hindgut during this stage. Insects of this type are fed a very concentrated diet by the adults of the colonies so that there is very little residual material. The metabolic wastes are removed from the body fluid by the Malphigian tubes, and the food residues remain in the midgut until metamorphosis is complete. During this time, the junction is completed and elimination is possible.

FUNCTIONS OF THE PARTS OF THE DIGESTIVE TRACT

Each section of the digestive tract has a principal function, which is similar in all forms. The esophagus is the food duct connecting the mouth to the crop. As the food is ingested, it is mixed with enzyme secretions from the salivary glands. Some additional mixing and digestion take place in the crop by the action of the salivary enzymes, and possibly enzymes from the midgut are also moved forward into the crop to further the digestive process.[8] Although this process seems illogical, it may well occur. It seems more likely that digestion takes place in the crop as a sort of rumination with the aid of symbionts, but experimental evidence for this is lacking.

The possibility of assimilation of nutrients in the crop has been suggested. Babers showed a sharp increase in blood glucose within 15 minutes after feeding the larvae of the southern army worm (*Prodenia eridania*) leaf sandwiches spread with glucose.[3] The lapsed time between the feeding of sugar and the appearance of increased concentration in the blood was sufficiently short that absorption through the foregut was the only logical explanation. Eisner demonstrated that in the American cockroach (Periplaneta americana) fat is partially hydrolyzed in the foregut and that the resulting fatty materials can be demonstrated in the cells of the wall of the foregut.[10] The histochemical technique used to demonstrate the concentration of the fatty material in the cells gives evidence that is beyond question, but it does not prove that the material leaves the cells and is picked up by the blood.

On the side of the argument that food is not absorbed through the wall of the foregut or crop are experiments showing that aqueous solutions may be exposed for days in the dissected crop of mosquitoes without drying out, indicating that the crop is impermeable to food materials and to water.[5] A more elaborate experiment indicates that absorption of sugar (in Schistocerca) takes place entirely through the gastric ceca and the ventriculus.[21]

It is easy to demonstrate that the crop of the American roach acts almost like an osmometer and is nearly semipermeable.[15] Even though the results of these experiments seem to be directly opposed, these contraindications do not mean that one of the results has to be in error. This seeming contradiction may be nothing more than a demonstration of the functional differences that exist between insect groups and emphasizes the fallacy of translating physiological details from one group of insects to another without verification.

Proventricular Structures.   Between the crop and the midgut, many insects have a specialized structure called the proventriculus. The proventriculus is lined with cuticle that may be soft but more often is very hard and sometimes equipped with spines. These spines may act as a sieve to occlude the passage of large particles into the midgut, and in the omniverous cockroaches the proventriculus has been described as a grinding organ. The muscles of the gut wall are powerful and can exert a tremendous grinding force. Snodgrass suggested that the actual mouth of the insect (specifically the honeybee) is the proventriculus.[20] This concept is worth considering for all insect forms.

In the honeybee, the proventriculus is the site of the honey stopper, which prevents the bee from swallowing the nectar it has gathered but allows the bee to swallow pollen. The proventriculus is a complicated valve with mechanics difficult to visualize. The mechanics of the proventriculus were worked out by Schreiner[19] and by Bailey,[4] who observed the action of the stomodeal valve through an aperture cut in the back of the insect.

The stomodeal valve consists of four proventricular lips, which are equipped with spines. The crop is in continuous pulsating motion so that the supension of pollen in the nectar is kept uniform. The proventricular lips do not work simultaneously but individually snap open and close rapidly. As they work, grains of pollen are separated from the nectar and collected into a compact mass that forms a bolus as it enters the ventriculus.

All insects have some sort of stomodeal valve that tends to prevent the regurgitation of food from the ventriculus to the crop, but the structure is most highly developed in the social insects. According to Waterhouse, the development of the filtering ability in social insects is probably secondary, but this ability provides a distinct advantage to the insects that must digest protein in the presence of relatively high sugar concentrations by concentrating the proteins and reducing the dilution of the proteolytic enzymes.[23]

The Peritrophic Membrane. Both the foregut and the hindgut have a chitinous lining that protects the cellular structure from the abrasive action of rough food particles. The midgut, being of endodermal origin, does not have this chitinous lining, and the cells of the midgut lining are soft and vulnerable. To protect these cells evolutionary processes have developed the peritrophic membrane.

The origin, structure, and function of the peritrophic membrane have been described in detail by Waterhouse.[22] This membrane may be of a single or multiple layer; it contains chitin; and it serves as a sheath that encloses the food in the midgut of many insects. The peritrophic membrane is produced in several ways. In the older literature this membrane is described as arising either from a ring of cells at the anterior end of the ventriculus or from a periodic delamination of the membrane from the midgut epithelium. Both sources may be present in the same insect. The principal function of the peritrophic membrane is to protect the midgut epithelium from mechanical damage in a manner comparable to the action of mucus of mammals.

There are some contradictory ideas regarding the presence or absence of the peritrophic membrane in various species. Generally, it was believed that the peritrophic membrane is lacking in insects that feed primarily on fluids because these insects have no need for such protection, but this is not the case. This membrane is also reported to be lacking in dermestids of the genus *Anthrenus,* the larvae of which feed on hair, feathers, and other keratinaceous materials.[9] These materials are very abrasive. More critical work has shown that neither of these generalities is true and that the confusion has come primarily from the lack of a suitable chemical method for detecting the presence of the peritrophic membrane.

The peritrophic membrane is produced by the midgut epithelium—an example of a chitinous structure originating from an endodermal tissue—and even mosquitoes surround the blood meal with a membrane that remains intact in the gut. If a second meal is taken before the first is completely digested, the mosquito forms a second layer around the first making a double membrane. These peritrophic coverings arise in situ either by delamination from the cell surface or by the secretion of a fluid precursor that condenses into solid membrane around the food.

Electron microscopy has given some valuable information as to the fine structure of the peritrophic membrane. This technique was applied by Richards and Korda, who observed that in most insects the characteristic and most resistant part of the structure is a fibrillar network formed of three systems of parallel strands placed at 60° to each other.[18] This structural formation results in a hexagonal symmetry. As an alternative to this, two sets of strands may be produced that are at right angles to each other. Various intermediate arrangements also exist. In *Periplaneta* each fibril is about 100 Å in diameter, and several fibrils may exist in each strand. Separate strands are about 0.15 to 0.20 μ. apart. An amorphous film fills the interstices and probably overlays the network.

The network membranes are produced from the surface of cells that have a striated border. It has been suggested that the holes in the network correspond to the spaces occupied by the individual rods of the border and that fibril formation and orientation occur within the striated borders of the cells. During detachment of the peritrophic membrane from the cells, the net is impregnated with a secreted amorphous layer. To spoil this generality, it has been observed that in various insects not closely related taxonomically, there is no network. To explain this, it has been postulated that the membrane is composed of nonoriented fibrils impregnated with a matrix that is secreted as a fluid to cover the food bolus where it hardens. The necessity for an explanation of observed phenomena is the only proof of the existence of this method of formation.[22]

Use of the electron microscope to determine the structure of the annular type of peritrophic membrane is hampered by the thickness of the membrane; however, after treatment with pepsin or alkali, which removes some of the excess material, reticulations appear. It would not be expected, and it is certainly difficult, to visualize the method of production of a fibrillar membrane from an annular process, but many insects that produce membranes in this manner appear to achieve this. The probable explanation is that some midgut membrane is contributed to the structure.

Regardless of the method of formation, most insects have a peritrophic membrane, and considering the observations of Waterhouse it is apparent that this membrane serves functions other than a purely mechanical protection of the midgut epithelium from abrasion. In blowfly larvae, the rate of flow of food may be 10 times as great as the rate of production of the membrane. The space between the membrane and the gut wall is filled with fluid that must contain digestive enzymes and absorbed products. This fluid also moves slowly compared to the flow of food through the digestive tract. This differential tends to increase the efficiency of the absorption process.

Structure and Function of the Midgut.   The midgut functions as the principal site of digestion and assimilation of digested food. It is divided into regions with secretory and absorptive functions, and the secretory part of the midgut has a vesicular structure in the cells of the wall. The cells are active and appear to secrete digestive enzymes. The secretion may be endocrine, in which the cells remain intact with the secretion elaborated through the cell membrane; the secretion may be merocrine, in which the cell wall ruptures and discharges some of the contents; or the secretion may be holocrine, in which case the cell wall ruptures and the entire contents are discharged. Holocrine cells are replaced immediately by new cells, which enlarge and repeat the process.

Many histological studies have been made on the epithelium of the insect gut, but surprisingly little is really known about the functions of the cells within the major regions, since orthodox histological methods yield very little information on the function of these cells. Unlike mechanics, in which the physical function of a part may be visualized by its appearance, it is impossible to look at a fixed cell and describe its chemical activity. Some advances have been made by histochemical technique; these advances have been summarized by Waterhouse.[23]

The various regions of the gut are subdivided into zones that function in various ways. The midgut of the blowfly is divided into an anterior, posterior, and midregion; and the midsection can be further subdivided into five distinct zones of activity. The most interesting and unusual of these is the second zone, which is a mosaic of two cell types. One cell type is packed with lipoid spheres and glycogen, contains a cytoplasmic acid phosphatase, and has a distinct striated border. The other cell type accumulates copper and iron, and contains esterases, cytochrome oxidase, and active dehydrogenases. Glycogen and lipid are absent, acid phosphatase is weak, and a distinct striated border is present. The full significance of these observations, which have come from histochemical study, remains to be determined, but these observations represent a distinct advance over those made by classic histological techniques.

There is still a great deal to be learned about the digestive function of insects. For the present, the only thing that can be stated with certainty is that the midgut is the principal site of digestion and assimilation of food.

The Hindgut.   The hindgut is ectodermal and has a structure similar to that of the foregut. Very little, if any, digestive function can be associated with the hindgut; it is primarily a duct to carry the spent food bolus away from the midgut. Passage through the hindgut is usually quite rapid. When a capsule of excreta reaches the expanded region of the rectum, it is often held for an appreciable period. The water and some essential elements (salts, amino acids, etc.), which have been removed from the blood by the Malpighian tubes, are reclaimed at this point. Critical studies of the function of the hindgut are few, and possibly the neglect is justified, but Waterhouse found that the hindgut epithelium in the blowfly larva is an active tissue that plays an important role in metabolism and in the regulation of the products of excretion.

In the blowfly the hindgut is divided into a short proximal region and a short distal region, which function as sphincters for the elongated central part. The central part is unusual in that it is composed of three types of cells, each forming a longitudinal band. The bands produced by cell types A and B each form about one half of the hindgut, while the bands of type C form two narrow longitudinal strips one cell wide situated at the junctions of the bands formed by cell types A and B. The A type cells are rich in potassium, acid phosphatase, dehydrogenases, and acetyl esterase. The cells of the B type react strongly to ammonia and stain diffusely for barium in larvae fed on a barium enriched diet. The C type cells react very strongly to ammonia and accumulate barium-rich granules. The central part of the hindgut takes up ammonia rapidly, when ammonia is liberated by the activity of deaminases from the blood; the B and C type cells are especially active in this process. Much of the ammonia is finally eliminated in the form of a bicarbonate.

From these observations, it is clear that the hindgut is not just a tubular duct but that it is an active tissue which has an important function in the regulatory process in the insect. Ramsey has found evidence to support this with observations that the hindgut of mosquito larvae acts in controlling the osmotic relations between the internal and external environment.[17] In this regard, it is important to clearly distinguish between the structure that comprises the rectum, which is an active part of the hindgut of almost all insects, and the remainder of the structure, which may still prove to function only as a tubular duct.

THE DIGESTIVE PROCESS

The digestion of food by insects, or any other animal, involves the action of enzymes, which are secreted by various cells that comprise the tissues of the digestive tract. The sites of enzyme secretion vary so with different species that there is no basis for generalizations. The important point is that enzymes are produced, and the conditions in the different parts of the digestive tract are so adjusted and controlled that the enzymes are able to act.

Enzyme Function

Enzymes are often defined as biological catalysts that are capable of initiating reactions as well as accelerating them. Enzymes usually enter into the chemical process that they catalyze, and they may be used up in the course of their function. Enzymes are proteins or compounds in which a protein molecule is the principal component. Frequently nonprotein groups are essential to their activity. If these nonprotein groups are attached to the molecule, they are called prosthetic groups; but if the nonprotein groups exist as entities not part of the protein molecule, they are coenzymes.   .

Classification and Nomenclature of Enzymes.   Enzymes are classified acording to the type of reaction they catalyze. In the broadest possible terms enzymes are divided into two groups. These are the hydrolyzing enzymes, which include the principal enzymes of digestion, and the desmolyzing enzymes, which include all the others.

Enzymes are named according to the substrate on which they act by adding the suffix *ase*. Thus a proteinase hydrolyzes a protein, a peptidase splits a peptide linkage, and a lipase splits fat into fatty acids and glycerol. The use of common nomenclature may be confusing, but it is fortunate that the study of the enzyme systems of insects is sufficiently recent not to be hampered significantly by the use of common names.

The Chemistry of Digestion.   Digestive enzymes are hydrolases, and as such they split complex molecules into simpler ones by hydrolysis. Hydrolysis can be defined as a double decomposition reaction involving the splitting of water into its ions with the formation of a weak acid, a weak base, or both.[6] Because all enzymes are proteins, they respond to physical and chemical factors that affect proteins. These factors can become critical in the function of an enzyme and are of especial importance in the process of assaying enzyme activity.

The results of an enzyme assay are almost always expressed as the rate of the reaction that is catalyzed, so that an assay of the activity of a digestive enzyme is made on the basis of a quantitative estimate of the formation of one of the hydrolysis products at successive time intervals. With animals as small as insects, this procedure imposes severe technological problems.

The usual procedure involves grinding fresh tissue by some physical means to produce a uniform homogenate called a *brei*. Both skill and advanced knowledge of anatomical structure are required to obtain homogeneous tissue samples from insects. The enzyme potency of many of the tissues is extremely high, so that accidental inclusion of an unknown tissue (a section of Malpighian tube in a fat body sample, for example) can lead to spurious results. A common method for circumventing this problem has been to reduce whole insects, or arbitrary divisions of insects (heads, thoraces, etc.), to a brei and to use this brei for the assay. This technique is bound to give results, but the value of these results is comparable to finding gold in alluvial drift. Doubtlessly the material sought is present somewhere, but there is very little direction toward the source.

Quantitative assay is also hampered by the necessity for determining sample size. Wet weights are notoriously inaccurate and difficult to determine, particularly at the submilligram level. A common substitute for wet weight is a chemical weighing procedure in which total protein in the sample (or a comparable sample from the same brei) is used to compare the amount of enzyme present in successive determinations.

If all other conditions are favorable, the rate curve of an enzyme-controlled reaction shows a gradual rise with an increase in temperature until an optimum is reached. Above this optimum temperature, there is a sharp cut-off, caused by the denaturation of protein of the enzyme. At suboptimal temperatures, an enzyme-controlled reaction is slow, but at these low temperatures the enzyme is more stable and lasts longer. When the temperatures are optimal or slightly above, the reaction proceeds more rapidly, but the enzyme is spent more quickly. The temperature optimum is not a fixed point. As the temperature rises, several things happen simultaneously. The rate of the reaction increases, and at the same time the enzyme breaks down, so that if the measurements are made over short periods, the optimum determined may be somewhat higher than if incubation is carried out over a longer period.

Proteins are composed of amino acids linked together. A single amino acid, or a chain of them, has a double-ended characteristic in that a carboxyl group is on one end and an amino group is on the other end. This means that two opposite reactive groups are exposed, and the degree of influence of one or the other is emphasized by the direction in which the molecule dissociates. Molecules of this type are variously known as *hybrids, ampholytes,* or *zwitterions.* The degree of dissociation in one direction, or the other, depends upon the concentration of hydrogen ions in the system. The degree of dissociation is expressed as the negative logarithm of the hydrogen ion concentration, or *pH.* The rate of an enzyme reaction is controlled by the degree of dissociation of the enzyme protein and the direction in which it goes. The pH at which the undissociated part of the molecule is at its greatest concentration (the dissociation is at a minimum) is the *isoelectric point.* Every amino acid and protein has an isoelectric point.

The curve that relates pH to enzyme activity is bell shaped, and the optimum shifts up and down the pH scale, depending upon the nature of the enzyme protein. Pepsin and trypsin, for example, are both proteinases, but pepsin functions at an acid pH and trypsin is active at neutrality or in a slightly alkaline medium.

Because enzymes enter into the reactions that they catalyze, the rate of the reaction can be controlled by the relative concentrations of the enzyme and substrate. If the quantity of enzyme is more or less fixed, the reaction velocity increases with an increase in substrate concentration up to the point at which no more enzyme molecules are available to combine with the substrate. When this level is reached, the rate of the reaction levels off. The rate of an enzyme activity can be altered in some cases by products of its own reaction. These factors have their greatest effect in vitro. Enzyme studies in vivo are difficult to perform quantitatively because the function of the various vital systems of the insect tends to stabilize enzyme reactions.

Digestive Enzymes in Insects. Insects produce digestive enzymes, and it is a safe generalization that the enzymes that must be present in the digestive tract to take care of the food normally consumed are produced either by digestive secretion or by symbionts. With this as the starting point, it is possible to arrive at a procedure for the determination of the digestive enzymes of almost any insect, but first it must be recognized that there are a number of types of carbohydrates, proteins, and fats and that the enzymes may be very specific.

CARBOHYDRASES. Carbohydrates exist as monosaccharides, oligosaccharides, or polysaccharides, depending upon the number of simple sugar molecules in the structure. The carbohydrates are split first into their monosaccharide components, usually hexoses, before they are assimilated. Starch is hydrolyzed through a series of dextrins to yield glucose and maltose. Three specific enzymes act in sequence on starch to produce α-glucose as the end product. α-Glucose is a hexose that exists as a six-membered oxygen-bearing ring structure (pyranose) that has two (α and β) spatial configurations. The α configuration usually has more biological activity than the β. One of the enzymes that act on carbohydrate is α-amylase (the others are α-oligosaccharase and maltase), and this group of three enzymes is sometimes referred to in loose terminology simply as *amylase*. The same enzymes that hydrolyze starch also split glycogen.[16]

Cellulose, which makes up the bulk in plant tissue, consists of a series of β-glucoside units in long chains. This long-chained structure makes the material undigestible to most animals, but some insects that bore in wood and ingest relatively large quantities of cellulose either secrete a cellulase in the digestive tract or depend upon symbionts for the digestion of cellulose.

PROTEASES. Proteases are enzymes that act principally by hydrolytic splitting of the protein molecules at the peptide linkages. Proteases differ according to the size of the molecule they split, the groups adjacent to the peptide linkages that they attack, the pH at which they function, the presence of metallic prosthetic groups, and the effects of activating and inhibiting factors.[16] In animals most proteases are of the L-series, but this may not be entirely the case with all insects.[2] The proteases are classified as *endopeptidases* and *exopeptidases*, depending upon the location of the linkages in the protein molecule they attack.

Endopeptidases include such specific enzymes as pepsin, trypsin, chymotrypsin, and cathepsin. Pepsin acts in an acid medium (a pH from 1.0 to 5.0) and is rarely, if ever, found in insects. Pepsin attacks linkages adjacent to an aromatic amino acid and at neutrality is inactivated.

Trypsin, a proteinase found in insects as well as in other animals, is most effective in a slightly alkaline medium (a pH from 7.0 to 9.0). It is secreted as a trypsinogen that is activated autocatalytically or by a specific enzyme such as enterokinase. Trypsin characteristically attacks peptide linkages adjacent to arginine or lysine.

Chymotrypsins—there are at least four—originate in the pancreas of mammals. Chymotrypsins act in alkaline media and attack peptide linkages with adjacent aromatic amino acids, particularly tyrosine, phenylalanine, tryptophan, and to a lesser extent methionine. Chymotrypsins are inhibited by organic phosphates (isopropylfluorophosphate) and by benzoyl derivatives of several amino acids.

As the result of studies, several cathepsins are known to exist as intracellular proteases of the liver, kidney, and spleen of mammals, and cathepsins are also known to exist and function extracellularly in a number of invertebrates. These enzymes act most effectively in an acid medium (a pH from 4.0 to 6.0). The various cathepsins resemble pepsin, trypsin, and chymotrypsin in their substrate requirements. Proteinases that act in the pH range between 4.0 and 6.5 are arbitrarily classified as cathepsins. Some cathepsins require reducing substances for activation, but some do not. The identification of this group of enzymes in insects is incomplete.

Exopeptidases are enzymes that attack the terminal peptide linkages (substrates with free polar groups), most of which arise as the result of proteinase activity. Usually exopeptidases have a metal in the molecule or are activated by the presence of a metallic ion. The exopeptidase group is further divided into carboxypeptidases, aminopeptidases, and dipeptidases.

Carboxypeptidases remove a terminal amino acid with a free carboxyl group, the aminopeptidases split a peptide linkage next to a terminal amino acid that has a free amino group, and the dipeptidases are active in splitting the linkage that holds two amino acids together to form a dipeptide. The pancreatic carboxypeptidase of mammals has been shown to contain one zinc atom per molecule, the aminopeptidases require manganese, and the dipeptidases are activated by cobalt, manganese, or zinc, depending upon the nature of the enzyme. Most of these exopeptidases act in a slightly alkaline medium.

LIPASES AND ESTERASES. Neutral fats are by definition esters of one or more higher fatty acids and glycerol, and the enzymes that accomplish a hydrolytic split of the acids and the alcohol are called lipases. Fatty acids also form compounds (esters) with other alcohols or with sterols. The enzymes that split esters are called esterases. Thus lipase is a more or less specific esterase. Both the lipases and the esterases act effectively throughout a broad pH range and are relatively nonspecific. They usually act best in an alkaline medium.

Insects can utilize (although they may not require) fats, and in some cases intact fats may be assimilated by cells, in which they are further metabolized. Both lipases and esterases are found in insects, either in the digestive tract or in various tissues. The esterases have received a great deal of attention during the last 10 years because of their interaction with organophosphate insecticides. A great deal is still to be learned, both from the qualitative and quantitative standpoint, about esterases and their functions in insects.

When evaluating the literature on digestive enzymes, it should be remembered that enzymes found from an assay of the brei of the whole digestive tract and its contents may be somewhat different from those enzymes elaborated into the digestive tract. It is important to differentiate the contents from the tissues. This has not always been the practice, and the resulting data may be misleading. Enzymes demonstrated from the digestive tracts of a series of insects are summarized in Table 3–1.

THE DIGESTION OF UNUSUAL FOOD

Of all the animals, only insects can feed successfully on and digest such refractory materials as keratin—the protein of wool, hair, and feathers; and only a few insects can digest cellulose without the intervention of symbionts. These subjects have been given considerable attention because they are exotic.

Cleveland is usually credited with the experimental proof that wood-feeding insects (termites) are able to survive on nearly pure cellulose and that they are dependent upon the activity of symbiotic protozoa for the production of cellulase.[7] He used high oxygen tensions to defaunate his test insects, and some of the luster was removed from his experiments because the defaunating treatment also altered the growth rate of the termites. Even so, the fact remains that termites are dependent upon their symbionts for their nutrition.

The digestion of keratin offers another problem. This material is characterized by a high, but varying, content of cystine, and the sulfur of this amino acid forms disulfide bonds between adjacent polypeptide chains. The disulfide bridges contribute greatly to the stability of the keratin molecule, and the destruction of these bridges renders keratin more readily digestible.

A number of factors contribute to the digestion of keratin by various of the Mallophaga, Dermestidae, and Lepidoptera (Tineidae). Disulfide linkages are less stable in an alkaline pH such as exists in the insect gut, but this is a minor factor in keratin digestion. Linderstrøm-Lang and Duspiva demonstrated that one essential difference between the larvae of the genus *Tineola* (clothes moth) and insects unable to digest wool is the unusually strong reducing potential in the midgut of the larvae.[13] This reducing potential varies from -200 mv. to -250 mv., and under these conditions reduction of the disulfide bonds to sulfydryl groups occurs so that a cystine moiety becomes two molecules of cysteine. The reduced keratin formed in this way can be digested by the proteases of the digestive tract. The origin of the reducing potential is not known. Waterhouse has presented a more recent discussion of this process.[24]

The digestion of wax by the larvae of two species of Lepidoptera that infest stored honeycomb has been a subject of attention because, like keratin, beeswax is a refractory material. Waterhouse has summarized the extensive literature on this subject,[23] and Niemierko and Wlodawer have discussed the subject in a long series of journal papers.[14]

From the available data, it is most logical to conclude that the lipolytic enzymes that digest beeswax arise from bacterial symbionts and not from the larval tissue. Final proof of this idea must await the strictly axenic culture of these wax-digesting insects. Waterhouse has discussed the problems and progress in this line of endeavor.[25] Haydak proved that larvae of *Galleria* do not require beeswax for normal growth and development over many

TABLE 3-1. Digestive Enzymes in Insects*

Part of Digestive Tract — Enzyme

Insect	Salivary Gland	Foregut Tissue	Foregut Contents	Gastric Ceca	Midgut Tissue	Midgut Contents	Hindgut Tissue
American Locust, *Schistocerca americana*	amylase	maltase invertase	amylase maltase invertase	maltase invertase lipase protease	maltase invertase lipase protease	amylase maltase lipase protease	amylase maltase invertase lipase protease
Oriental Cockroach, *Blatta orientalis*	amylase	maltase invertase lipase	amylase maltase invertase lipase protease	maltase invertase lipase protease	maltase invertase lipase protease	amylase maltase invertase lipase protease	amylase maltase invertase protease
Chinese Mantis, *Paratenodera sinensis*	amylase maltase invertase	maltase invertase protease	amylase maltase invertase protease	maltase invertase lipase	maltase invertase lipase protease	amylase maltase invertase lipase protease	maltase invertase lipase protease
Dragonfly, *Libellula luctuosa*		maltase invertase	maltase invertase lipase protease		maltase invertase lipase protease	maltase invertase lipase protease	maltase invertase lipase protease

TABLE 3-1. (continued)

Insect	Salivary Gland	Part of Digestive Tract — Enzyme					
		Foregut Tissue	Foregut Contents	Gastric Ceca	Midgut Tissue	Midgut Contents	Hindgut Tissue
Spotted Grapevine Beetle, *Pelidnota punctata*		maltase invertase	maltase invertase amylase lipase protease		maltase invertase lipase protease	maltase invertase lipase protease amylase	maltase invertase lipase protease amylase
Red Milkweed Beetle, *Tetraopes tetra-ophthalmus*		maltase invertase	maltase invertase protease		maltase invertase	maltase invertase lipase protease	maltase invertase lipase
Promethea Moth, *Callosamia promethea*		maltase lipase	maltase lipase		maltase lipase	maltase invertase	maltase
Bumblebee *Bremus fervidus*	amylase	maltase invertase protease	amylase maltase invertase protease		maltase invertase lipase protease	maltase amylase invertase lipase protease	amylase maltase invertase lipase protease

*Data from Swingle, H. S. 1925. Ohio J. Sci. 25: 209-218; and 1931. Ann. Ent. Soc. Amer. 24: 147-184.

generations;[12] however, Young observed improved growth of *Galleria* larvae over short periods when beeswax, certain fatty acids, or even paraffin wax was added to the diet.[27]

SUMMARY

Digestion in insects takes place in a specialized organ consisting of: a foregut, which may be modified into a storage unit or crop; a midgut where most of the digestion and assimilation takes place; and a hindgut, which serves both as a duct and a reabsorbing organ. Enzymes are produced by secretions of the salivary glands and by specialized cells in the midgut. A large number of insects possess highly evolved adaptations to specialized diets, including some highly refractory materials. Often, the explanation of these adaptations leads back to the presence of intestinal symbionts that produce the enzymes required for the process.

Digestion in insects is an elementary process that is usually taken for granted; however, it offers fascinating study for further research.

LITERATURE CITED:

1. Auclair, J. L. 1958. Honeydew excretion in the pea aphid. J. ins. Physiol., *2:* 330–337.
2. Auclair, J. L., and Patton, R. L. 1950. Occurrence of D-alanine in the hemolymphs of the milkweed bug. Rev. Canad. Biol., *9:* 3–8.
3. Babers, F. H. 1941. Glycogen in *Prodenia eridania* with special reference to the ingestion of glucose. J. agr. Res., *62:* 509–530.
4. Bailey, L. 1954. The filtration of particles by the proventriculi of aculeate *Hymenoptera.* Proc. R. ent. Soc. Lond., (A) *29:* 119–123.
5. Boissezon, P. de. 1930. Histophysiology of the gut, larva of *Culex.* C. R. Soc. Biol., *103:* 567.
6. Chemical Rubber Handbook (Hodgman, C. D., Weast, R. C., and Selby, S. M., editors). 1957–1958. 39th Edition. Chemical Rubber Publishing Co., Cleveland, p. 2861.
7. Cleveland, L. 1923. Digestion of cellulose by termites. Proc. nat. Acad. Sci. U. S. *9:* 424–428; 1924. Biol. Bull. *46:* 177–225; 1924. Biol. Bull. *48:* 455–468.
8. Day, M. F., and Powning, R. F. 1949. A study of digestion in certain insects. Australian Jour. sci. Rec. B., *2:* 175–215.
9. Day, M. F., and Waterhouse, D. F. 1953. Functions of the alimentary system. *In* Insect Physiology (K. D. Roeder, ed.), John Wiley, New York, p. 306.
10. Eisner, T. 1955. Digestion and absorption of fats by the American cockroach. J. exp. Zool., *130:* 159–181.
11. Gersch, M. 1942. Distribution and excretion of fluorescein, Aphids. Zeitschr. vergleich. Physiol., *29:* 506–531.
12. Haydak, M. H. 1936. Diets for wax moth larvae. Ann. ent. Soc. Amer., *29:* 581–588.
13. Linderstrøm-Lang, K., and Duspiva, F. 1936. Digestion of keratin by the clothes moth. C. R. Trav. Lab. Carlsberg, Ser. chim., *21:* 53–83.
14. Niemierko, W., and Wlodawer, P. 1950. Studies on biochemistry of the wax moth. Acta Biol. Exper. *15:* 69–78. (See also: 1952. Acta Biol. Exper. *16:* 157. III Congress of the Pol. Physiol. Soc. in Wroclaw. 219; and Wlodawer, P. 1956. Acta Biol. Exper., *17:* 221–230.)
15. Patton, R. L. Permeability of the crop of the American cockroach. Unpublished research.
16. Prosser, C. L., and Brown, F. A. 1961. Feeding and Digestion. 2nd Ed. W. B. Saunders, Philadelphia. Ch. 5.
17. Ramsey, J. A. 1950. Osmoregulation by mosquito larvae. Jour. exp. Biol., *27:* 145–157.
18. Richards, A. G., and Korda, F. H. 1948. Electron microscopy of extracted cuticle. Biol. Bull., *94:* 212–235.

19. Schreiner, T. 1952. Food transport in the gut of the honeybee. Zeitschr. vergl. Physiol., *34:* 278–298.
20. Snodgrass, R. E. 1956. The Anatomy of the Honeybee. Comstock Press, Ithaca, New York.
21. Treherne, J. E. 1958. The absorption of sugars by *Schistocerca.* Jour. exp. Biol., *35:* 611–625.
22. Waterhouse, D. F. 1954. Rate of production of the peritorophic membrane. Australian J. Biol. Sci., *7:* 59–72.
23. Waterhouse, D. F. 1957. Digestion in insects. Ann. Rev. Ent., *2:* 1–18.
24. Waterhouse, D. F. 1953. Digestion of wool by insects. Australian J. biol. Sci., *6:* 257–275. See also: Aust. J. Sci. Res. B. *5:* 143–168; and *5:* 178–188.
25. Waterhouse, D. F. 1959. Axenic culture of wax moths. Ann. N. Y. Acad. Sci., *77:* 283–289.
26. Wigglesworth, V. B., 1938. Principles of Insect Physiology. Dutton, New York, ch. 11.
27. Young, R. G. 1961. Effects of beeswax and wax components on the larvae of the wax moth. Ann. ent. Soc. Amer., *54:* 657–659.

4

THE FUNCTION OF
TRANSPORT—BLOOD
AND CIRCULATION

Insects, like other animals, have an internal medium of transport for food elements and waste products of metabolism, which also serves as a water reservoir. This medium is called the blood, visceral fluid, or hemolymph. The term *hemolymph* is in common use and implies a combined function of the blood and lymph as they exist in mammals. Hemolymph contains cells, salts, proteins, free amino acids, and water. It is circulated by an organ that acts as a simple heart. There are no closed vessels, but the fluid is circulated in the body cavity. Contrary to what might be visualized, the body cavity is rarely, if ever, full of blood, and the volume of blood can vary significantly.

A number of physiological functions have been described for this circulatory system. Some of these functions are obvious and important; others may seem obscure. The most obvious function is the transport of food materials and waste products of metabolism. The hemolymph also serves as a reservoir for water and probably amino acids, and it functions as a lubricant and hydraulic medium within the animal. The cellular inclusions are generally capable of phagocytic action against invading bacteria, they carry nutrients and possibly hormones, and they have enzymes that can detoxify some biologically active chemicals.

COMPOSITION OF THE SERUM FRACTION

The blood of insects has been the subject of many analyses, and like studies of other tissues, the results show great variation among taxonomic groups. A typical analysis compiled by combining data from various sources is shown in Table 4–1. Comparable values for human serum are used for reference. Many of the figures quoted are subject to correction according to the method of analysis, the stage of the insect sampled, the sex, or the food upon which the insect was fed. Most of the values for insect serum are from analyses of whole blood, which introduces an obvious error when these values are compared with those for mammalian serum.

There are several noteworthy differences between insect blood and mammalian serum. The first is the relatively high amino nitrogen content of

46

TABLE 4-1. The Chemical Composition of Insect Hemolymph
(in mg./100 ml.)

Compound	Hemolymph*	Human Blood[†]
Total nitrogen	1400-1700	3000-3700
Protein nitrogen	700-900	1000-1265
Total protein	4375-5625	6500-8200
Nonprotein nitrogen	300-500	25-35
Amino nitrogen	200-300	5-8
Urea nitrogen	1-10	10-15
Uric acid	12-14	2-3.5
Potassium	20-40 (omniverous)	178
	160-180 (foliage)	
Sodium	20-60	330
	300 (aquatics, adults, and some parasites)	
Calcium	35-40	9-11.5
	150 in some species	
Magnesium	10-25	1-3
Phosphorus (total)	64-245	34.9
Chloride	50-100	450-500
Reducing substances (as glucose)	0-25	70-100
	1000 (honeybee)	
Glycogen	24	5.5
Trehalose	700-800	
Lipids	398	652

*Values from Altman, P. L., and Dittmer, D. S. 1961. Blood and other body fluids. Federation of American Societies for Experimental Biology, Washington, D. C.

[†]Values from Hawk, P. B., Oser, B. L., and Summerson, W. H. 1947. Practical Physiological Chemistry., 12th edition, Blakiston, Philadelphia.

insect blood, the second is the low or inverted sodium-potassium ratio, and the third is the relatively high magnesium content. Insect blood nearly always has a high uric acid content, which may reach the supersaturation point.

Amino Acids in Insect Hemolymph

The amino acid content of insect hemolymph has been a subject of intense study. The results reported in the early literature were often qualitative or semiquantitative, owing to the technological problems in quantitative analysis for these compounds. The development of paper partition chromatography has done a great deal to overcome this. Table 4–2 shows a summary of the amino acid content of the blood of several insect species.

It is not possible to appraise the importance of the high amino acid content of the blood. Many of the results have come from microbiological assay, and there is little doubt that some of these results are subject to correction. With one exception, the values for the blood of immature stages have been selected, the reason being that these values are more likely to remain constant than those of adult blood, which show significant variation with age.

Free amino acids are probably derived to a great extent directly from

TABLE 4-2. Amino Acid Composition of Insect Hemolymph*
(in mg./100 ml.)

Insect Amino Acid	Aeschna sp.	Schistocerca sp.	Bombyx mori (3rd and 4th Instar Larvae)	Bombyx mori (Late 5th Instar Larvae)	Galleria mellonella (Larvae)	Leptinotarsus decemlineata (Adult)	Apis mellifera (Larvae)	Caliphora sp.
Alanine	47	31	13	50	225	34	58	118
Arginine	23	20	22	28	39	19	63	T
Asparagine	6	9	47	59	13			35
Aspartic acid	8	5	11	10	38	21	33	14
Glutamic acid	20	0	17	10	22			48
Glutamine	43	166	228	143	369	611	78	109
Glycine	33	84	69	73	51	17	78	29
Histidine	12	28	104	273	136	43	24	0
Isoleucine	17	23					25	
Leucine	26	21	16	29	42	12	28	20
Lysine	11	45	115	164	68	42	90	T
Methionine	7	3	6	14	27		22	T
Phenylalanine	8	13	3	11	11	9	11	20
Proline	24	88	14	36	520	637	393	92
Serine	24	50	93	111	47			25
Threonine	17	17	19	36	62	21	38	T
Tyrosine	8	17	9	31	76	0	3	134
Valine	26	41	19	23	29	25	59	16

*Average values calculated from data by Duchateau and Florkin (1958).

the proteins in the food. Some free amino acids, however, are produced as a result of metabolic synthesis in the individual, since they appear in the blood of insects that have been fed on diets deficient in free amino acids.

One characteristic of amino-acidemia in the blood of insects is its constancy, a subject discussed by Florkin.[11] When concentrations of free amino acids are plotted against the concentrations of amino acids resulting from either hydrolyzed or nonhydrolyzed blood samples of a number of insects, the resulting curve is relatively uniform and distinctive.

The free amino acids found in the blood in the largest quantities are not those amino acids essential to the nutrition of the insect. From this, it can be suggested that the high amino acid concentration in the blood of insects represents the storage of nitrogenous materials that can be drawn on, according to the needs of the tissues; or it may indicate that an excess of amino acids are produced from the diet and that the amino acids are stored in the blood until they can be eliminated by normal excretion. A great deal of information is available on what takes place in the amino acid metabolism of the insect, but relatively little is known about why it takes place.

The Sodium-Potassium Ratio

That this ratio is inverted in some insects has led to speculation on its importance, but most of this has been due to the popularity of emphasizing the exotic as it is observed in insects. Some insects that feed on plants with an unusually high potassium content show this inversion, but insects that feed on diets with less potassium do not. Boné showed that the potassium content of hemolymph is a function of the amount of potassium ingested with the food.[4] Tobias reported further information on this factor for the American cockroach.[32] His interest in the subject came from the study of water interchange of tissues, which interchange should be altered by the amount of potassium in the blood.

From these data,[32] it can be stated that the serum of the American cockroach has more sodium than potassium but that the ratio (6.2) is low compared to that of man (29.2). Tobias did find, however, that irritable tissues of the cockroach can function at a relatively high serum potassium level; but it can also be shown that a saline solution with an inverted sodium-potassium ratio is quite toxic to dissected preparations, particularly those made using insects in which the inversion is not normal.

Duchateau[9] arrived at the following conclusions in discussing the mineral salt content of the blood of insects: The results of determinations of the sodium, potassium, calcium, and magnesium concentration of the blood of a series of insects indicate the existence of two types of blood, which are extremes. The first blood type is probably the primitive type, which may be characterized by the Odonata. It is like that of other animals in which the concentration of sodium is somewhat greater than the concentration of potassium and magnesium. The second blood type is interpreted as a biochemical specialization, which is characterized by the Lepidoptera, Coleoptera and some other groups. In these groups, there is a low concentration of sodium and a high concentration of potassium and magnesium. The other insects fall more or less into one or the other of these types as a function of their evolutionary development and their nutritional habits. The content of inorganic bases in the food causes a departure from this normal condition, and insects deviate in varying degrees dependent upon the concentration or dilution of these inorganic bases in the blood but end up with a specific composition of the base as one might predict from the taxonomic position.

The high content of magnesium in the blood of insects as compared to that in some other invertebrates is worthy of attention since this element has an anesthetic effect upon most invertebrates. This anesthetic effect is not important in insects.

Uric Acid in Insect Hemolymph

Most insects are uricotelic. Uric acid is produced principally in the cells of the fat body and released into the blood, which transports it to the Malpighian tubes to be excreted. In a normally functioning insect, the ability of the Malpighian tubes to remove uric acid is balanced by uric acid production, and the concentration of uric acid remains at about the saturation point. When a disturbance causes the blood volume to decrease because of water loss, if the excretory function is impaired or if the metabolic rate is unusually high, crystals of uric acid may appear in the blood, indicating a supersaturation. The high uric acid content of the blood probably has no significance beyond indicating that the serum fraction functions as a transport mechanism.

Other Differences in Insect Blood

Two more differences between the chemical composition of the blood of insects and the serum of humans are apparent from the data in Table 4–1. One is the low chloride content of insect blood, which is much too low to account for combination of the base elements to form chlorides. The other difference is the presence in relatively large quantities of the glucoside, trehalose.

It is usually assumed that the basic elements in animal fluids are present in the form of chlorides, and the basic elements are furnished in the form of chlorides in most physiological salines and in diets. The analyses reported of insect fluids do not show enough chlorine to nearly account for the amount of sodium, potassium, calcium, and magnesium if these were to exist as chlorides. Thus it is logical to assume that these elements are present, at least in part, as carbonates, bicarbonates, or phosphates. This idea is of use later in explaining other phenomena that take place in insects, and it might be borne in mind when preparing experimental salines for in vitro work with insects.

Trehalose is a glucoside, (α-D-glucosido)-α-D-glucoside, which has been found in cocoons of certain parasitic beetles for some years, and it is also found in nature in certain fungi. Trehalose is soluble in water and does not reduce copper but is fermentable by yeast. As the technology for analysis improves, trehalose likely will be reported from the blood of more and more insect species, in which it may serve as a storage form of carbohydrate, possibly replacing glycogen. Trehalose is not found in the blood of mammals.

The Proteins of Insect Blood

The total blood protein has been recorded for a number of species. These have been tabulated by Buck.[6] Wide discrepancies exist in the values for different species, and many of them show a low protein level. A reason for these differences lies in the analytical procedure and the method of collecting blood samples. These procedures may exaggerate differences that exist, and in some cases the low values may be artifacts. Patton demonstrated that heat fixation before sampling reduces the blood protein titer of the gray house cricket (*Acheta domesticus*) by a factor of six.[26]

The proteins in the blood are usually conjugated. They are intimately bound to or associated with triglycerides, phospholipids, sterols, or other non-protein compounds. The properties of insect blood proteins have been reported in a number of miscellaneous papers. Blood proteins have been classified on the basis of their solubility in salt solutions, by serologic reactions, by ultracentrifugation, by free electrophoresis, by histochemistry, and by paper and starch block electrophoresis. The results of a series of studies using these methods were reported by Siakotos.[29]

Five fractions of proteins were separated from the blood of the American cockroach. By various staining procedures these proteins were shown to be conjugated. Two fractions (II and IV) were readily identified by their phospholipid, carbohydrate, and protein composition. Fraction III, characterized by a high neutral lipid and sterol content, was found to be present in greater quantity in males than females. Fraction I also contains neutral lipid and sterol but has a greater mobility than III. Fraction V is the least mobile and has properties similar to those of human fibrinogen when subjected to electrophoresis. Siakotos was quite specific in pointing out that the electrophoretic similarities observed between insect and human proteins do not necessarily indicate functional similarities.

By its electrophoretic properties, fraction I is comparable to albumin and fraction II to α-globulin, and fractions III, IV, and V are like β-globulins. From these observations it was concluded that the β-globulin-like proteins may be important in the transport of lipid to and from the fat reserves. The plasma glycoproteins may be important in the transport of carbohydrate particularly during the molting process. Except for osmotic control and transport of unsterified fatty acids, which are controlled by the albumin fraction of vertebrate blood, the fractions of insect blood and vertebrate blood appear to have comparable functions when the adjustments necessary to compensate for the requirements of the insect system are considered.

PHYSICAL AND CHEMICAL PROPERTIES OF INSECT HEMOLYMPH

The hemolymph is the internal environment of the cells that comprise the tissues and organs. As such, the physical and chemical properties and the constancy of the hemolymph are important. These properties include: volume, pressure, specific gravity, osmotic pressure, hydrogen ion concentration (pH), and oxidation-reduction potential.

Blood Volume

Considering the functions of insect blood, it is apparent that the volume is of importance to the efficiency, particularly for transport and translation of pressure from one part of the body to another. The body cavity is rarely filled with blood, and the blood volume varies with the physiological state.

Tabular figures showing the blood volume relationships for a number of insect species are found in Altman and Dittmer.[2] These data were collected from several sources and represent measurements made by a variety of methods. These methods include: exsanguination, cell dilution, chloride dilution, dye (amaranth) dilution,[44] Carbon-14 (inulin) dilution,[33] and specific gravity changes with saline dilution.[27] The results of these determinations are usually related to body weight following the convention used in mammalian physiology. The correlation is poor, but there is general agreement that the blood of an average normal insect accounts for between 16 per cent and 20 per cent of its total weight. If the specific gravity is known, it is possible to calculate the volume; and it is well within the limit of error for this calculation to assume that the specific gravity of the hemolymph is 1.000.

Blood volume can be altered by many factors. The volume of the blood is more variable in male nymphs of the gray house cricket than in the female,[27] and it is usually reduced severely in adults that have completed their reproductive cycle. Blood volume decreases sharply when intoxication with some biologically active chemicals causes water shifts between the blood and the tissue.[16]

Thus far, the only methods used for the blood volume determination that do not require sacrificing the insect are the chloride dilution, the dilution of carbon-14 (this method has been deemed unsatisfactory because of self-absorption of the low-energy beta from the carbon isotope[33]), and the determination of the change in specific gravity with saline injection.

Blood Pressure

Mammals with their closed circulatory system use blood pressure to drive some other processes, but insects must find other means since their blood is not enclosed but free in the body cavity and circulated by a relatively low-efficiency system. The pressure of the blood of insects probably varies considerably, depending upon the point on the body at which it is measured. The muscles of the body wall can force the blood to one part of the body and exert appreciable hydraulic pressure at one point, but the average pressure over the entire insect must be low. The idea that the average blood pressure of insects is negative has been suggested by the observation that a drop of saline placed over a small wound in the integument is drawn into the body cavity.[5] It is possible for a temporary partial vacuum to exist in the body cavity of an insect because of the forcible expulsion of air from a tracheal sac, and this could account for the observed phenomenon.

Specific Gravity of the Hemolymph

Specific gravity is the mass per unit of volume compared to the mass of an equal volume of water at the same temperature. For practical purposes, specific gravity and density may be considered to be synonymous although they are equal only at 4° C. Specific gravity is very easy to measure precisely with small amounts of blood and serves as an index of the physiological state of individual insects. Many physiological conditions bring about shifts in the internal water balance, and all of these shifts are reflected in a change of blood specific gravity.

Specific gravity measurements have been reported from data obtained by direct weighing (pycnometry),[16] the application of Stoke's law of falling bodies,[42] and the Linderstrøm-Lang gradient column.[21, 26] Specific gravities of the blood of several common laboratory species measured by the latter method are shown in Table 4–3. The values are listed as a mean, plus or minus the standard deviation. The range so described includes two thirds of the individuals in a normal distribution, which can be considered to describe the normal range for the group. Specific gravity values outside this range are abnormal. For most insects, the hemolymph specific gravity lies between 1.015 and 1.060 (usually calculated in grams per milliliter). Considerable variation

TABLE 4-3. Specific Gravity of the Hemolymph of
Several Insect Species

Insect	Sex	Stage	Mean Specific Gravity	Standard Deviation
Orthoptera				
Acheta domesticus	male	adult	1.021_5	$.004_5$
Acheta domesticus	female	adult	1.019_5	.003
Acheta domesticus	male	nymph	1.018_8	$.002_5$
Acheta domesticus	female	nymph	1.019_2	$.002_6$
Periplaneta americana				
	male & female	nymph	1.029_7	$.003_7$
Leucophacd madiera	male & female	nymph	1.029_3	$.006_4$
Hemiptera				
Oncopeltus faciatus	male & female	nymph	1.024_3	$.000_2$
Diptera				
Musca domestica		larva	1.047_9	$.004_1$
Lepidoptera				
Galleria mellonella		larva	1.054_6	$.003_7$
Coleoptera				
Tenebrio molitor		larva	1.033	.004
Hymenoptera				
Apis mellifera	worker	larva	1.038	.006
Apis mellifera	drone	larva	1.050	$.005_4$

*Data from Patton, R. L. 1962. Specific gravity of insect blood. J. Ins. Physiol. 8: 537-544.

between species is evident, and the period during which an insect is molting is always marked by an increase in the specific gravity of the blood.

Osmotic Pressure of the Hemolymph

Osmotic pressure is numerically equal to the hydrostatic pressure difference required to prevent penetration of a solvent through a semipermeable membrane into a solution. In biological systems the penetrating solvent is always water. All tissues and organs of insects are bathed in the blood, which according to the figures tabulated by Altman and Dittmer,[2] ranges from 84 per cent to 94 per cent water. Since the blood is the internal environment of the insect, osmotic pressure is of great importance.

Osmotic pressure is related empirically to the specific gravity since both of these values depend upon the amount of water present. Osmotic pressure is directly related thermodynamically to the freezing point depression, the boiling point elevation, and the vapor pressure. These are the colligative properties of matter, and any one of these properties that can be measured can be translated into another.

Data describing osmotic pressure are expressed in several ways. Depression of the freezing point is the most common method of describing osmotic pressure, because it is the most popular method of measurement. When testing insect blood, the depression of the freezing point must be determined with caution. The proteins of the blood are denatured by freezing so that a second freezing point obtained from a single sample differs from the value of the first reading. The coagulation of a sample also alters the freezing point

TABLE 4-4. Osmotic Pressure of Insect Blood
(Expressed as NaCl Equivalent)*

Species	NaCl Equivalent (Per cent Wt./vol.)	Stage
Orthoptera		
Acridia nasuta	1.48	Adult?
Blatta orientalis	1.12	Adult
Carausius morosus	0.83	Adult
Decticus albifrons	1.06	Adult
Gryllotalpa gryllotalpa	1.25	Adult
Locusta viridissima	1.12	Adult
Hemiptera		
Nepa cinerea	1.17	Adult?
Notonecta glauca	0.88	Adult
Pyrrhocoris apterus	1.18	Adult
Ranatra linearis	1.12	Adult
Lepidoptera		
Bombyx mori	0.72	Larva
Ephestia elutella	1.68	Larva
Galleria mellonella	1.71	Larva
Galleria mellonella	1.58	Pupa
Prodenia eridania	1.26	Larva
Saturnia pyri	1.15	Larva
Diptera		
Aedes aegypti	0.6-0.75	Larva
Aedes detritus	0.6-1.2	Larva
Anopheles maculipennis	0.85-1.11	Larva, pupa, adult
Culex pipiens	0.6-0.75	Larva
Gastrophilus intestinalis	1.30	Larva
Coleoptera		
Carabus intricatus	1.42	Adult ?
Dytiscus circumcinctus	0.83	Adult
Hydrophilus pistaceus	1.05	Adult
Melolantha vulgaris	1.22	Larva
Oryctes nasicornis	1.14	Larva
Popillia japonica	1.53	Larva
Silpha carinata	1.32	Adult
Tenebrio molitor	1.7-2.2	Larva
Tenebrio molitor	1.46	Adult
Temarcha tenebrecosa	1.11	Adult
Hymenoptera		
Apis mellifera	1.29	Larva
Vespa crabro	1.30	Adult
Odonata		
Aeschna sp.	0.83	Larva

*Data recalculated from tabular material by Buck. [7]

depression significantly. Another method of expressing data describing osmotic pressure is in terms of millimeters of mercury (pressure) or atmospheres. None of these methods is of direct value in experimental work, in which the application most needed is a guide to the concentration of a salt solution prepared so that it is isosmotic with the blood and tissues. The most useful value for this is the equivalent concentration of sodium chloride. Data for the osmotic pressures of the hemolymph of a number of insects were tabulated by Buck.[7] Table 4–4 is derived from these data with the values recalculated to the sodium chloride equivalent.

The pH of Insect Hemolymph

pH is the negative logarithm of the hydrogen ion concentration of the blood, or a measure of the degree of acidity or alkalinity. Following the invention of measuring methods, determination of the pH of almost every measurable substance became popular, and the blood of insects was no exception. A summary of the data of insect blood pH is found in the work of Altman and Dittmer.[2] These values were derived by a number of methods, and many of the variations in results undoubtedly come from the technology. Repetition of this work is unnecessary because the pH range for almost all insects lies between 6.0 and 8.0. A safe generality is that the pH of insect blood is near neutrality.

Shifts in pH occur with some physiological disturbances as a reflection of the failure of a vital system. These shifts are usually small and are rarely a limiting factor in the normal function. If the excretory system is intact, the concentrations of the various metabolites that might alter the pH of the blood are regulated.

Of more importance than pH is the buffer capacity or buffer index of the blood. The buffer capacity is the ability of the blood to resist changes in pH that might come from the production of acidic or basic metabolites.

Experimental measurements show that the buffer capacity of insect blood is only slightly greater than that of water.[14, 20] The maximum buffer index usually lies at a pH somewhat acid to the normal pH. This is explained by noting that the range of greatest buffer capacity is coincident with the isoelectric points of the amino acids that are present in high concentration. For the most part, the pH of these amino acids ranges between 3.0 and 5.0. The buffering capacity at neutrality, such as it is, comes from the small amounts of carbonates and phosphates in solution in the blood.

The Oxidation-Reduction Potential of Insect Hemolymph

The oxidation-reduction potential is a function of the electron potential (free negative charge) present by virtue of the constituents of the solution. The oxidation-reduction potential has received very little attention, but it is a property with considerable importance in the mechanics of action of many biologically active chemicals, because it exerts a controlling force on the valence state of various elements in the system. Many toxicants are sensitive to oxidation or reduction and may be rendered either toxic or nontoxic by changes.

Systems that oxidize or reduce other things depend upon the oxidation potential, which is symbolized by E_0, the normal or molal electrode potential for the system, with the molal hydrogen electrode referred to as a standard. In physical chemistry E_0 is determined at pH $= 0.0$, but this is impossible in biological systems so that, instead, it is determined at pH $= 7.0$. Any system with an E_0 value more positive than that of a second system will oxidize that second system, becoming reduced itself in the process. There are two opposed conventions used in this designation; however, the above usually applies to biochemical measurements. Oxidation-reduction potentials can be measured electrometrically with an appropriate electrode potentiometer system, but in biological application it is easier to obtain an estimate by bracketing the value with oxidation-reduction–sensitive dyes. These dyes change color from the oxidized to the reduced state, and with a series of these compounds the oxidation-reduction potential of the blood can be determined.

Most attention to oxidation-reduction potentials of the blood of insects has been given to the determination of the total reducing substances. The results of this moderately popular study have been reported in terms of fermentable reducing substances (primarily sugars). That other reducing substances exist seems apparent, but they have not been positively identified. A tabulation by Buck summarizes the information on the reducing substances in insect blood.[6] The variations in the values and in the methods of determination, and lack of information on the stage of development as well as the nutritional history of the insects from which the samples were taken make the data difficult to use.

CELLULAR INCLUSIONS OF INSECT HEMOLYMPH

The hemolymph of insects has cellular inclusions called hemocytes, and in many insects, small globules of fat or oil called lipomicrons. Hemocytes have been studied extensively because they are easily mounted for microscopic examination; a number of cell classifications have been suggested. The early literature on hemocytes was summarized by Ermin[10] and by Rooseboom.[28] More recent reviews have been presented by Jones,[17] Munson,[23] and Wigglesworth,[37] and a summary of current concepts has been offered by Jones.[18]

Classification of the hemocytes has followed three patterns, which depend somewhat upon the technique used for preparation of the material for observation. The largest number of cell types have been described from smears stained with a mammalian type blood stain—Wright's stain or Giemsa's stain. From such a series, Yeager described 10 classes and 32 types of cells but failed to arrive at a workable classification.[41] Sarkaria et al. developed a simpler and more direct staining method for use in clinical investigations and recognize two or possibly three types of cells.[30] Gregoire studied the coagulation process under phase contrast and described a cell type that he called a *hyaline hemocyte,* which is responsible for the initiation of the coagulation process as it exists in insect blood.[13]

The classification of insect blood cells is still confused. By far the greatest number, by all classifications, are in the form of an ovoid disk with a well defined cytoplasm and nucleus. This is the *plasmatocyte.* The cytoplasm of this type of cell may be relatively clear, or it may contain granules and vacuoles. The granular condition appears to be evidence of aging and degeneration and is an important criterion in the differentiation of chemically injured cells. If the plasmatocyte is viewed edgewise, it becomes *spindle shaped;* if the disk is twisted at the ends, it becomes *vermiform.* In vivo observations indicate that these cells can send out pseudopods, which change them into *podocytes.* These observations strongly suggest that many of the cell types that have been described are different physical forms, stages of development, or even artifacts produced from one cell type by the technique of preparation.

Proleukocyte   Plasmatocyte   Spindle shape   Spherule

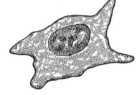
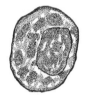
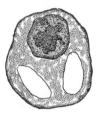

Podocyte   Granular leukocyte   Enocytoids

Vermiform   Plasmatocyte with
phagocytized erythrocytes

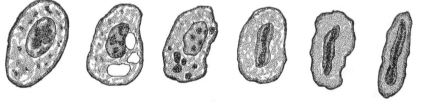

Normal cell   Ist stage   2nd stage   3rd stage   4th stage   5th stage

Stages of chemical injury

FIG. 4-1.   Common types of insect hemocytes, both normal and abnormal.

Next in number to the plasmatocytes are cells that appear to have a very large nucleus and very little cytoplasm. These cells are *proleukocytes,* which are probably juveniles that will develop into plasmatocytes. Examples of the various cell types are shown in Figure 4–1.

The proposed genealogy of the blood cell types has been suggested by Jones[17] for *Tenebrio molitor,* by Rooseboom,[28] and by Hrdỳ.[15] There is general agreement that all cell types arise from one basic juvenile. Jones describes all cell types as coming from the proleukocytes, which later differentiate into the various other forms that he described. Rooseboom states that the cells all arise from macroleukocytes (the plasmatocytes of others), which divide and give rise to the proleukocytes. When the proleukocytes grow, they become macroleukocytes, and the other cell types are derived from these.

Much of the existing confusion in the description of insect blood cells comes from differences in nomenclature. Nittono tabulated the various names used by different investigators to describe the same cell type.[24]

Histochemical Differentiation of Insect Hemocytes

Nittono used histochemical as well as histological properties to differentiate the cell types of the silkworm larvae (*Bombyx mori*).[24] This is a new approach that may offer clues to the functions of the various cell types.

The proleukocytes are round or oval cells with deeply staining nucleus (Delafield's hematoxylin) and a small amount of basophilic cytoplasm. These cells measure from 6 to 8 μ. in diameter with a 4 to 6 μ. nucleus. The cytoplasm gives a strong positive reaction for RNA (ribonucleic acid), and the mitochondria give a positive reaction for phospholipids. There is cytochrome oxidase around the nucleus. Mitotic figures occur with moderate frequency.

The plasmatocytes of the silkworm are described as spindle shaped when they are withdrawn from the insect, but they rapidly change their form by retracting their spindle ends, rounding up, spreading out, and sending out filamentous processes of cytoplasm. The spindle shaped cells, which are fixed immediately after withdrawal, are from 8 to 20 μ. in diameter. Often a cytoplasmic band is observed across the nucleus. Mitochondria surround the nucleus, and these give positive reactions for phospholipids and cytochrome oxidase. One or more glycogen deposits may be present in the cytoplasm near the nucleus. At the pupal stage, lipid granules from 1 to 3 μ. in diameter appear. These granules give positive reactions for phospholipids or neutral fats.

The granular cells are round or oval. They are from 5 to 12 μ. in diameter with nuclei 3 to 5 μ. across. They contain a number of round or oval inclusions in the cytoplasm that are 1 to 3 μ. across, and these inclusions increase in number and size during the molting period. Only a few of the granules give a positive reaction for protein or lipid, but most of the granules were positive when tested for mucopolysaccharides or mucoproteins. The mitochondria give positive reactions for phospholipids and cytochrome oxidase. After the onset of pupation, lipid granules 1 to 3 μ. in diameter appear that give positive tests for phospholipids or neutral fats. In the pupal stage, the granular cells are quite large, 12 to 17 μ. in diameter with nuclei 6 to 8 μ. across. They are loaded with larger inclusions than in the larvae. Most of the inclusions show positive reactions for mucopolysaccharides, and some of them give positive tests for proteins or lipids. Frequently the nuclei of the histolyzing larval tissues give positive reactions for DNA (deoxyribonucleic acid). These disappear 2 days before emergence. Mitotic figures are present in both larval and pupal granular cells.

The spherule cells are round or oval with a diameter of 6 to 12 μ. and a nucleus of 3 to 5 μ. They have coarse spherules that practically occupy the whole cell. Spherule cells give strong positive reactions for mucopolysaccharides but not for proteins or lipids. At the pupal stage, small lipid granules appear that test positive for phospholipids or neutral fats. Mitotic figures are rare in spherule cells.

The imaginal spherule cells described by Nittono occur only in the adult, or rarely in the pupal blood the day before emergence. These cells are elliptic or oval, about 8 to 20 μ. in diameter. The cytoplasm is filled with spherules that are smaller and more numerous than those of the larval spherule cells. The spherules test positive for mucopolysaccharides.

The enocytoids are large round or oval cells with strongly basophilic cytoplasm and large central or slightly eccentric nuclei. One or two large nucleoli may be present that give positive reactions for RNA, and the chromatin granules are relatively coarse. Often the cytoplasm contains one or more inclusions that are either spindle or crescent shaped. These inclusions are poorly defined when the blood is first drawn but become more distinct shortly afterward, and these inclusions accept cytoplasmic or nuclear stains. The cytoplasm is strongly positive when tested for RNA, but the inclusions give negative reactions. The granules give a positive reaction for proteins but do not show a reaction when tested for polysaccharides or lipids. In fixed smears the cytoplasm of enocytoids often has coarse vacuoles, and there are often glycogen deposits. At the pupal stage, enocytoids possess lipid granules that contain phospholipids or neutral fats. Binucleated enocytoid cells have been observed in some cases, but mitotic figures are not present.

These data open many lines of possible research in the study of the hemocytes, their classification, development, and function.

The Total Hemocyte Count

Counting insect hemocytes is a simple procedure with the aid of a standard hemocytometer such as is used in mammalian white cell counting. Tauber and Yeager recorded the total counts for a number of insect species.[31] These usually are of the order of 30,000 to 50,000 cells per cubic millimeter of blood, but the variation is large even within species. One source of variation is the stage of development.

Patton and Flint counted the hemocytes of a large number of nymphs of the American cockroach during molts and during the periods between molts.[27] Their data show that a tenfold reduction in the total hemocyte count may take place just before a molt, with the lowest count occurring at ecdysis. Immediately following ecdysis, but before the integument develops its pigmentation, the count increases rapidly and usually overshoots the normal value. After several days, the cell count returns to the normal level.

During the period before ecdysis, when the blood cell count is reduced, the plasma is filled with cellular debris and what appear to be large grampositive rod shaped bacteria. The latter have been described by Wheeler as fragments of disintegrated cells.[34] They have never been cultured successfully nor positively identified as bacteria so that this may be a reasonable explanation for their existence.

When the insect regains its normal hemocyte count, the debris is removed from the plasma by the phagocytic activity of the cells, and the blood becomes clear. Immediately following a molt, the proleukocyte type of blood cell predominates, and later the plasmatocytes become more prominent. This is interpreted as evidence that the proleukocytes are the juveniles from which the plasmatocytes develop.

The Origin of Hemocytes

Wigglesworth pointed out that there are many variations among different insects as to the percentage of the total hemocyte population that circu-
lates.[38] In many insects, only a part of the cells are circulating; the remainder
are more or less sessile. The sessile cells are loosely attached to various body
tissues. Many intermediate stages between adherent cells and circulating cells
exist in insects, and there are some permanent aggregations that may be
regarded as hematopoietic organs. Several of these aggregations have been
described from different insect species, and the rapidity with which the total
cell count can be rebuilt after a molt is evidence for their existence.

The Functions of Hemocytes

Several functions have been described for the hemocytes of insects. The
most frequently mentioned include phagocytosis and encapsulation of foreign
bodies in the insect body cavity, coagulation to prevent loss of blood, transport of food elements and possibly hormones, and detoxication of metabolites
and biologically active chemicals.

Phagocytosis.   Phagocytosis is by far the most spectacular of the
hemocyte functions. Hemocytes readily pick up foreign bodies in the hemolymph, whether they are bacteria, cell fragments, or foreign bodies injected
for experimental purposes. Hemocytes also aggregate and encapsulate larger
bodies such as parasites or eggs of parasites. No one has successfully differentiated the hemocyte cell types in terms of their phagocytic activity, and until
proved otherwise, it may be generally assumed that the principal phagocytic
activity is a function of the plasmatocytes.

Yeager et al. injected lamp black into the blood of the American cockroach and observed that the particles were picked up by the cells.[43] If the
number of particles injected is great enough, the hemocytes become heavily
loaded with the engulfed material and eventually disintegrate. This hemocyte
disintegration causes an experimental leucopenia which suggests possibilities
for further study of hemocyte function. Even more effective than lamp black
as a blocking agent are mammalian erythrocytes.[3] These cells, injected at
the rate of about five to one, will almost eliminate the hemocytes from the
blood of an experimental insect.

Coagulation.   Coagulation and the role of hemocytes in this process
were studied most extensively by Gregoire, who used the phase contrast
microscope for in vitro observation of coagulation as it progressed in a hang-
ing drop preparation.[13] Three hundred specimens from 61 species were included in this study, and in each were found specialized cells called *hyaline
hemocytes*. These hyaline hemocytes are spherical with a relatively small
nucleus and a hyaline, pale cytoplasm, in which there are dispersed numerous small granules. These cells were indistinguishable using other techniques.

Hyaline hemocytes are present in the blood of all species examined, but
some insects have blood that does not coagulate. In these insects, the hyaline
hemocytes are present but inactive. Where coagulation is observed, the cells
appear to be highly sensitive to contact with a foreign surface, and they
rapidly undergo alterations in structure when contact is made. These altera-

tions in structure play an important part in the plasma coagulation that follows. There are at least two mechanisms involved.

In the first mechanism of plasma coagulation, a succession of local changes in the cytoplasm of several hyaline cells results in the development of a thin "fog" in the surrounding cytoplasm. This "fog" rapidly thickens into an island of coagulating material. Extension of this process may result in general coagulation of the blood. This mechanism has been observed in Orthoptera, Dermaptera, and in scattered species from different orders. There is some difference in the amount of coagulating substance that is formed.

The second type of mechanism produces a coagulum by the extrusion of threadlike pseudopodial expansions from the hyaline hemocytes. These threadlike expansions form networks of varying complexity. These developments in coagulation are followed by, or in some cases accompanied by, the formation of thin, transparent, slowly developing veils of plasma that eventually surround the original site of coagulation. This type of coagulation is typical of various species of Odonata, Lepidoptera, and Coleoptera.

Anticoagulants.   Several physiological measurements can be seriously hampered by coagulation of the hemolymph, and means of preventing this process have been studied. Gregoire listed a series of compounds that inhibit the coagulation process.[12] Among these, the most effective are potassium oxalate and cocaine hydrochloride. Any means that can be used to kill or inhibit the activity of the hyaline hemocytes should be effective in preventing coagulation. The most popular method is heat fixation, a process by which the insect is killed by immersion in hot water (about 65° C.) for periods ranging from 1 to 5 minutes. This is effective in preventing coagulation of the blood, but it has the obvious disadvantage of killing the test animal so that further examination is precluded. Other moderately effective anticoagulants include acetic acid, citric acid, ammonium acetate, and Sequestrene (ethylenediamine tetraäcetic acid, sodium salt). Coagulation can also be slowed enough to allow a quick volumetric measurement by chilling the insect and using a chilled pipet.

Transport.   Knowledge of the functions involved in transport by hemocytes is based primarily on results of indirect measurements and circumstantial evidence. Wigglesworth observed that if he blocked the hemocytes of *Rhodnius* by injecting India ink, trypan blue, or iron saccharate, the result was a prolonged delay in molting.[36] He also observed that the block must be placed before the fourth day after feeding, and once the thoracic gland hormone is released, there is no effect. There are several possible explanations for the observed phenomena, but it seems reasonably certain that hemocytes must be involved in some way in the transfer of the hormone from the site of its elaboration to the tissues. The function of nutrient transfer by hemocytes is also circumstantial. Histochemical studies show the presence of glycogen in the cells, and insects with a severe leucopenia cannot survive for long periods, but the active transfer of nutrients by the hemocytes is more of an assumption than proved fact.

Detoxication.   Also based on circumstantial evidence, it seems clear that the hemocytes are capable of effecting detoxication, a property usually assigned by definition to the liver tissue in mammals. Yeager et al. attempted to prove this function by injecting lamp black or trypan blue into cockroaches to determine the effect of blocking the hemocytes on the toxicity of arsenite.[43] They concluded that the removal of the hemocytes potentiated the toxicity, but they could not offer an explanation for the mechanism. Patton observed that the toxicity of many insecticides is greater during the premolt period when the blood cell count is naturally low.[25] Experimental reduction in the cell count by the injection of erythrocytes or by inducing leuçopenia by injecting small quantities of ethyl alcohol also caused a dramatic increase in the observed toxicity of parathion applied topically to nymphs of the gray house cricket.

To explain and verify these observations, the enzymes of the blood cells were assayed qualitatively. The results showed the presence of a normal complement that might be expected in any living tissue, but the activity of the nonspecific esterases was very high. It can be reasoned with some experimental backing that the enzymes of the blood cells detoxify the phosphate insecticide through a competitive reaction for the phosphate radical with both the enzyme and the insecticide becoming inactivated.[22] That this conclusion is reasonable was demonstrated by a sharply reduced esterase activity in the blood cells of insects 24 hours after they had been treated with a sublethal dose of phosphate insecticide.

Connective Tissue Formation.   Wigglesworth in his 1959 review of the functions of insect hemocytes points out that hemocytes may function in the formation of connective tissue and in intermediary metabolism beyond functioning in detoxication. The cells that comprise the thin strands and sheets of connective tissue, such as those of the basement membranes and membranes surrounding the fat body, resemble the granular hemocytes in their cytological and histochemical properties. At each molting period these cells multiply and migrate in large numbers to the epidermis before the new cuticle is formed. These connective tissue cells settle below the basement membrane where they spread out and discharge some of their inclusions, which merge to form the membrane proper. At this time these cells show a strong histochemical test for PAS (periodic acid–Schiff), a reaction that indicates the presence of mucopolysaccharides. The same process has been observed in the formation of muscle sheaths, and it may be speculated that this process also occurs in the formation of sheaths around nerves and ganglia.

Undoubtedly there are functions of the blood cells that have not been defined clearly, and it is very apparent that the blood cells are an essential part of the vital mechanism. Patton pointed out that a reduction in the total blood cell count by 35 per cent, brought about by any experimental means, could be critical to the survival of the individual.[25]

CIRCULATION OF THE HEMOLYMPH

Insect hemolymph is circulated mechanically in a posterior to anterior direction by the action of a pulsatile organ called the *dorsal vessel*. This organ lies along the dorsal midline and extends from the abdomen to the head (Fig. 1–1). In the abdomen this pulsatory organ is divided segmentally into simple chambers, each of which is equipped with a slitlike pair of lateral openings called *ostia.* The thoracic tube connecting the abdomen to the head is called the *aorta*. Extending laterad from the dorsal vessel in the abdomen are thin sheets of cells of the transverse muscle fibers, which form two wings, or *alary muscles*. Beneath the alary muscles lies a dorsal diaphragm. The alary muscles are attached to the body wall along the lateral parts of the dorsum and are not always the typical delta or wing shape. They are believed to function more or less as elastic bands that bring about the expansion (diastole) of the heart following each contraction (systole).

The dorsal vessel is composed of contractile tissue, and the motion used in pumping the blood is a paristaltic wave that originates at the posterior end and moves in an anterior direction. Blood is drawn into the vessel through the ostia during the diastole and is forced forward during the systole. As the wave of contraction progresses, the ostia close, and the lips are pushed inward to form a sort of simple valve that partially prevents the backflow of the blood.

In addition to the dorsal vessel, a number of other pulsatory organs that presumably aid in the circulation have been described. The ventral diaphragm has been described as pulsating in a gentle undulating motion that could mix the blood. At or near the attachment of most of the appendages, there are pulsating membranes that have been suggested to function as auxiliary hearts whose purpose is to pump the blood into the tubular appendages.[36] It is easy to observe these pulsating membranes near the coxal joints of flies and grasshoppers, but it is difficult to prove if these pulsations are driven by a contractile mechanism or if they are pulsating because of changes of pressure corresponding to the action of the dorsal vessel.

Innervation of the Dorsal Vessel

The dorsal vessel is innervated by a pair of lateral nerves that run along the heart with branches extending into the heart wall, into the alary muscles, and into the lateral vessels, if they are present.[36] Contributing to these nerves are fibers from the paired cardiac ganglia of the stomatogastric system and nerves from the ganglia of the ventral nerve cord. It has been suggested that these elements form an autonomic nervous system.[1] Segmental nerves carry accelerator fibers from the central nervous system; sensory filaments reach the heart on the dorsal side from the sensory branches that are directed toward the dorsal body wall. In some insects the lateral cardiac nerves are not present.

The foregoing is the classic description, but the fact remains that the heartbeat of insects can be maintained for many hours in vitro with the central nerve connections completely removed. The stomatogastric system and particularly the corpus cardiacum are usually left at least partially intact in such a dissected preparation.

Various studies with chemicals known to stimulate or inhibit the heart action of other animals led Krijgsman and Krijgsman-Berger to conclude that the heartbeat of insects is controlled by a neurogenic pacemaker with adrenergic properties, which is controlled by a cholinergic accelerating nerve.[19] Davey enlarged on the mechanism further with a series of experiments in which he demonstrated that a secretion from the corpus cardiacum reacted upon cells of the pericardial tissue causing them to produce a hemic substance that brings about an increase in the rate of the heartbeat.[8]

Rate and Amplitude of the Heartbeat

The rate of the heart contraction is affected by a number of factors, both external and internal. Among these are: ambient temperature, rate of metabolism, stage of development, and the presence of various of the biologically active chemicals used as insecticides.

The effect of temperature upon the rate of heartbeat has been recorded frequently because it gives a convenient index for the study of the thermodynamics of physiological processes. Within limits, the rate of the heartbeat increases with an increase in temperature. At both extremes of temperature, the rate slows or the heart stops beating entirely. The high and low extremes tolerated by the insect depend somewhat upon the normal environmental range for the species. Within the range of activity, there is usually a gradual decrease in the temperature coefficient. Attempts to convert these data to a μ value according to the Van't Hoff-Arrhenius formula as a means of proving a myogenic or neurogenic origin of the heartbeat have yielded nonconclusive results.

Various biologically active compounds, including some used as insecticides, alter the rate or amplitude of the heatbeat. This criterion for pharmacologic action was suggested by Yamasaki and Ishii, who pointed out that there are very few cases in which the circulatory mechanism was primarily affected.[38] In general, any material that increases metabolic rate or acts upon the nervous system will alter either the rate or the amplitude of the heartbeat.

Efficiency of Hemolymph Circulation

Normally the blood is circulated toward the head through the dorsal vessel and then forced back through the body cavity by displacement, possibly aided by the movement of the undulating membranes. It is unusual to find a hard-bodied insect that has a blood volume equal to the volume of the body cavity, so that there is always ample space for the blood to flow and sufficient gaseous space for pressures to be equalized.

Only a few studies have been made on the rate of circulation, but this factor is very important, and it is a value that may become limiting in experimental work. Craig and Olson presented quantitative data on circulation rate in terms of the lapsed time between injection of radiophosphorus and the appearance of the isotope in uniform quantity at several sampling points on the body.[7] The complete mixing time of the blood was variable with species. For *Tenebrio molitor* the mixing time was estimated to be between 8 and 10 minutes. For the squash bug (*Anasa tristis*) and the harlequin cabbage bug (*Murgantia histrionica*), the time required was about 20 to 30 minutes. This is very slow when it is considered that the time required for complete mixing of the blood in man is estimated at between 2 and 4 minutes.

Nature of the Insect Heartbeat

Cardiographic records of the heartbeat of larger insects have been made by several methods, but so far these records have served more as a novelty than as a criterion of physiological function. Yeager used a delicate mechanical device with optical levers to produce a mechanocardiogram of the heart of the American cockroach,[39] and Crescitelli and Jahn showed the similarity between the electrocardiogram and the mechanocardiogram, with the simultaneous recording of the action of the heart of a grasshopper.

There is nothing unusual or outstanding about the cardiogram of the normal insect heart. The beat consists of a contraction phase followed by the relaxation phase. Between each beat and just before the onset of the systole, there is a very brief period of relaxation called the presystolic notch.[40] The cause and possible significance of the presystolic notch was discussed by Yeager. It may be either a contraction of the body wall muscles, or it may be a passive dilation of the dorsal vessel, caused by the contraction wave in some other part of the heart. Analysis of EKG values for insect hearts has never been explored thoroughly, so that the real value of this measurement is unknown.

SUMMARY

The hemolymph of insects is a circulating fluid composed of a serum fraction with cellular inclusions. Functionally, hemolymph is the medium of transport, the internal environment of the cells that comprise the tissues and organs, a storage site for water and amino acids, and the principal lubricant and hydraulic medium. The cells protect the insect from invading bacteria and parasites by a phagocytic action that may extend to encapsulation, and they initiate coagulation to close wounds. Other functions of the cells may include the transport of nutrients and hormones and the detoxication of metabolites or biologically active chemicals. The cells are not all circulating in the normal insect. Some of them are sessile, attached to various tissues, from which they can be released as required.

Hemolymph is circulated by a dorsal vessel aided by various pulsating organs. The general direction of movement is from posterior to anterior, but the efficiency is low.

LITERATURE CITED

1. Alexandrowicz, J. S. 1926. Innervation of the insect heart. J. comp. Neurol., 41: 291–309.
2. Altman, P. L., and Dittmer, D. S. 1961. Blood and other body fluids. Federation of American Societies for Experimental Biology, Washington, D. C.
3. Bettini, S., Sarkaria, D. S., and Patton, R. L. 1951. Fate of erythrocytes and hemoglobin in the American roach. Science, 113: 9–10.
4. Boné, G. J. 1945. Sodium potassium ratio and diet. Ann. Soc. roy. Zool Belg., 75: 123–132.
5. Brocher, F. 1931. Respiration and circulation. Arch. Zool. exptl. Gen., 74: 25–32.
6. Buck, J. B. 1953. Physical properties and chemical composition of insect blood. In Insect Physiology (K. D. Roeder, ed.). John Wiley, New York, Ch. 6.
7. Craig, R., and Olson, N. A. 1951. Rate of circulation of body fluid. Science, 113: 648–650.
8. Davey, K. G. 1961. Mode of action of heart accelerating factor from the corpus cardiacum. Gen. and comp. Endocrinol., 1: 24–29.
9. Duchateau, C., Florkin, M., and LeClercq, J. 1953. Concentration of fixed bases and total base in the blood of insects. Arch. inter. Physiol., 61: 518–549.

10. Ermin, E. 1939. The structure and function of hemocytes. Z. Zellforsch. mikros. Anat., *29:* 613–669.
11. Florkin, M. 1961. The free amino acids of insect hemolymph. IV. Internat. Congr. Biochem. (Proc.), *12:* 63–77.
12. Gregoire, C. 1953. Reactions of insect hemolymph to vertebrate coagulation inhibitors. Biol. Bull., *104:* 372–393.
13. Gregoire, C. 1955. Blood coagulation in arthropods. Arch. Biol., *66:* 104–108.
14. Hastings, E., and Pepper, J. H. 1943. Buffers and pH of body fluids. Jour. econ. Ent., *36:* 857–864.
15. Hrdỳ, I. 1959. Development of the blood picture of *Acheta domesticus.* Acta Symposii de evolutione Insectorum, Praha, pp. 106–110.
16. Jochum, F. 1956. Changes in reaction chains in insects caused by diethyl-p-nitrophenyl thiophosphate. Blood sp. g. by pycnometry. Höfchenbr. Wiss., *9:* 289–348.
17. Jones, J. C. 1950. The normal hemocyte picture of the yellow mealworm. Iowa State Coll. Jour. Sci., *24:* 355–361.
18. Jones, J. C. 1962. Current concepts concerning insect hemocytes. Am. Zool., *2:* 209–246.
19. Krijgsman, B. J., and Krijgsman-Berger, N. E. 1951. Physiology of the heart of Periplaneta. Bull. entomol. Res., *42:* 143–155.
20. Levenbook, L. 1950. Buffer capacity of the blood, Gastrophilus larvae. Jour. expt. Biol., *27:* 336–346.
21. Linderstrøm-Lang, K. 1937. Gradient method for sp. g. Nature, *139:* 713.
22. Metcalf, R. L. 1955. Organic Insecticides. Interscience Publishers, New York, Ch. 11.
23. Munson, S. C. 1953. Hemocytes, pericardial cells, and fat body. *In* Insect Physiology (K. D. Roeder, ed.). John Wiley, New York, Ch. 8.
24. Nittono, Y. 1960. The blood cells of the silkworm. Bull. ser. expt. Sta. (Tokyo), *6:* 171–266.
25. Patton, R. L. 1961. Detoxication function of hemocytes. Ann. ent. Soc. Amer., *54:* 696–698.
26. Patton, R. L. 1962. Specific gravity of insect blood. J. ins. Physiol., *8:* 537–544.
27. Patton, R. L., and Flint, R. A. 1959. Variation in blood cell count with a molt. Ann. ent. Soc. Amer., *52:* 240–242.
28. Rooseboom, M. 1937. Studies of the blood of certain insects with general consideration. Arch. Neerl. Zool., *2:* 432–559.
29. Siakotos, A. N. 1960. The conjugated plasma proteins of the American cockroach. Jour. gen. Physiol., *43:* 999–1013, 1015–1030.
30. Sarkaria, D. S., Bettini, S., and Patton, R. L. 1951. Staining cockroach blood cells. Canad. Ent., *83:* 329–332.
31. Tauber, O. E., and Yeager, J. F. 1936. On the total hemolymph cell counts in insects. Ann. ent. Soc. Amer., *28:* 229–240; 1935. *29:* 112–118.
32. Tobias, J. M. 1948. Sodium, potassium, and water exchange in *P. americana.* J. cell. and comp. Physiol., *31:* 125–142.
33. Wheeler, R. E. 1962. Hemolymph volume during the molting cycle of *P. americana.* Federation Proc., *21:* 123.
34. Wheeler, R. E. 1963. Studies on the total hemocyte counts in *P. americana.* J. ins. Physiol., *9:* 223–236.
35. Wigglesworth, V. B. 1939. Principles of Insect Physiology. Methuen, London; E. P. Dutton, New York.
36. Wigglesworth, V. B. 1955. Role of hemocytes in growth and molting. J. expt. Biol., *32:* 649–663.
37. Wigglesworth, V. B. 1959. Insect blood cells. Ann. Rev. Ent., *4:* 1–16.
38. Yamasaki, T., and Ishii, T. 1957. Mechanism of action of insecticides and how to study it. Inst. of Insect Control, Kyoto University (WHO publication).
39. Yeager, J. F. 1938. Mechanographic recording of insect cardiac cycle. J. agr. Res., *56:* 267–276. (See also Crescitelli and Jahn. 1938.) Jour. cell. comp. Physiol., *11:* 359–375.
40. Yeager, J. F. 1939. Significance of the presystolic notch. Ann. ent. Soc. Amer., *32:* 44–48.
41. Yeager, J. F. 1945. Blood picture of the southern armyworm. J. agr. Res., *71:* 1–40.
42. Yeager, J. F., and Fay, R. W. 1935. Specific gravity of insect blood. Proc. Soc. exper. biol. Med., *32:* 1667–1669.
43. Yeager, J. F., McGoveran, E. P., and Munson, S. C. 1942. Effect of blocking hemocytes on resistance to arsenite. Ann. ent. Soc. Amer., *35:* 23–40.
44. Yeager, J. F., and Munson, S. C. Blood volume of *P. americana.* Arthropoda, *1:* 255–265.

RESPIRATION

Respiration includes both the processes by which gaseous oxygen is introduced into the insect and the processes by which this oxygen is combined with the substrates to produce energy. The first process includes the mechanisms of gaseous exchange, or ventilation—the subject that is discussed in this section. The second process—respiratory metabolism—is treated in Chapter 6.

The mechanics by which oxygen is introduced into animals is basically the same for all forms. Oxygen always comes from the atmosphere regardless of the habitat, and it always crosses the membranes to reach the cells in the animal where it is utilized, in an aqueous solution. Carbon dioxide is produced as an end product of the metabolic activity and is eventually liberated, at least in part, in a gaseous state. In insects in which the liberation of carbon dioxide tends to be sporadic, there is evidence that some of the gaseous product is converted to carbonate and excreted as such.

GROSS STRUCTURE OF INSECT RESPIRATORY SYSTEMS

The respiratory system of insects is unique among animals, and it more closely resembles that of plants in that it combines the respiration function of the circulatory system and the respiratory system of other animals into one anatomical unit.

In insects, air is transferred in the gaseous state throughout the body to the proximity of the site of assimilation. The respiratory system is made up of a series of reinforced tubes—the tracheae—which are of ectodermal origin. The tracheae open to the air in terrestrial forms through segmentally paired ports—the spiracles—located near the pleural line of the abdomen and the thorax. Internally, the tracheae ramify as they penetrate more deeply into the tissues. When the size of the tracheae is reduced to a diameter of 1 or 2 μ., these tubes are called tracheoles. Tracheoles are variously defined by morphologists, but the distinctions used are not in agreement with observed fact so that the size of the tubes remains as sound a criterion for definition as any.

The degree of development of the tracheal system depends upon the evolutionary position of the species. In the higher forms, a network formed with the tracheae of adjacent segments is connected by one or more special adaptations. In some of the more primitive forms, each segment has its own system with no connection to the tracheation of the adjacent segment.

Since tracheae are of ectodermal origin, they have a structure similar to

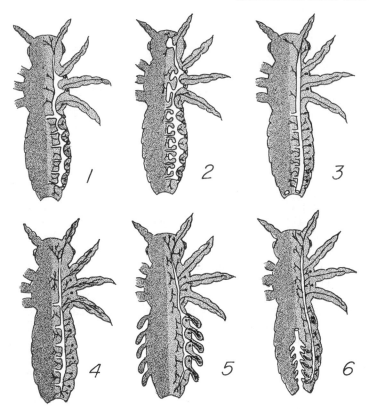

FIG. 5-1.   Diagrammatic representation of the gross anatomy of insect tracheal systems (redrawn after Wigglesworth).

that of the integument; they are lined with the same type of epicuticular substance, which contains chitin and protein. Tracheae are underlaid with large epithelial cells. A supporting structure—the taenidium—prevents the collapse of the larger tubes and is present as a series of rings of thickened material or as a helical structure reminiscent of the spring placed inside a vacuum cleaner hose to prevent its collapse under vacuum. The tracheoles are presumed (and so defined by some morphologists) to have no taenidium, but Richards and Anderson observed taenidia in tracheoles with a diameter as small as 0.3 μ.[9]

Wigglesworth described six types of tracheal systems, with appropriate variants, existing in insects.[16] These six types are shown in Figure 5-1.

In the first type a series of anastomosing tracheae connect externally with paired spiracles on each segment of the abdomen and two pair on the thorax. The second type has expansions in the form of air sacs that lie between intersegmental connections. The third type, which is found in larvae that inhabit semifluid media, has all of the spiracles closed except for the terminal ones on the last abdominal segment. This third type of tracheal system is a metapneustic type typical of many of the Diptera. The fourth type has all of the spiracles closed but contains gaseous air throughout the system. In this type gaseous exchange has to take place through the integument. The fifth type is found in some aquatic insects; all of the spiracles are closed, but there are gill-like structures on the abdomen that have been assumed to function like the gills of some crustaceans. These gill-like structures are called tracheal gills, but there is reasonable doubt that they function to absorb oxygen. The sixth type is a variation of the fifth in that the gill-like structures are inside the digestive tract in the hindgut. Water is drawn into the rectal region and gas exchange is believed to take place. When water is expelled by contraction of the gut muscles, it forms a jet that propels the insect in the water. Regardless of the type of tracheal system, the contents of all tracheal systems is always a gas, and the oxygen is distributed in the gaseous state throughout the body.

VENTILATION

Ventilation is the process by which air is brought into the tracheal system and circulated throughout the body. In many insects. particularly the immature forms, simple diffusion is sufficient to supply the needs of the animal. It was on the assumption that simple diffusion accounted for the oxygen supply at the level of the tissues that Krogh showed that on a theoretical basis this factor could limit the size to which insects could grow.[5]

Many insects of the higher orders have the ability to control diffusion by opening and closing the spiracles. This has been observed in fleas, whose skeletal structure is so rigid that active ventilation through movements of the abdomen is impossible.[16] When the insect is at rest, the sphincters on two pairs of spiracles are kept open, and the remainder are closed. When active movement is necessary, the insect requires more oxygen, and all spiracles are opened. Except under extreme activity, all spiracles are not held open, but show a rhythmic opening and closing action with periods of 5 to 10 seconds.

Control of the Spiracles

The opening and closing mechanism of the spiracles was discussed at length by Wigglesworth, who pointed out that control of closure lies in the respiratory centers of the central nervous system outside the head.[16] The opening and closing mechanism is also controlled by a nerve center that is not associated with the central nerve cord. More recent work, reviewed by Buck,[2] has added more detail to the knowledge of spiracle control but has not added a great deal to the basic information. That spiracle control is governed by a neurosecretion and not necessarily by direct innervation could explain some of the observed phenomena, but no positive proof of the existence of this mechanism exists.

Full details of the stimulation that triggers the action of the spiracles are not clear; however, it seems apparent that the stimulation is related to the oxygen–carbon dioxide tension in the insect blood. The duration of the open period is determined by the amount of carbon dioxide that has accumulated during the closed period, and conversely the open period is more or less proportional to the oxygen content of the air being taken in. When the carbon dioxide content of the air is high, the spiracles remain open most of the time; but when the oxygen tension is raised, the spiracles are closed. Knowledge of this control mechanism has been used for practical purposes in the fumigation of insects with hydrocyanic acid gas. If carbon dioxide is injected into the fumigation chamber before the toxicant, the spiracles are opened, and the fumigation is more effective.

The greatest weakness of the insect respiratory system is the ease with which water can be lost through the open spiracles. If it were not for the development of basket-like structures and the action of the sphincters that close the spiracles, water loss could easily become critical for terrestrial insects. Fleas placed in a 5 per cent carbon dioxide atmosphere lose water at twice the normal rate because of the enforced opening of the spiracles. Considering the physical size of insects and the volume of their water reservoir, they cannot stand an increased rate of dehydration for prolonged periods.

Directed Ventilation

The larger insects are not entirely dependent upon diffusion to supply oxygen to the tissues but supplement diffusion with a directed flow of air through the tracheal system, usually from anterior to posterior. The air flow may be increased by a pumping action of the abdomen, brought about by either a dorso-ventral flattening, a telescoping action, or a sort of peristaltic compression controlled by the muscles of the body wall.

McCutcheon studied this pumping action in the grasshopper and noted that the spiracular valves are related mechanically to the abdominal respiratory movements so that an inspiratory and an expiratory phase takes place.[6] Flow of air is controlled by three distinct phases in the normal respiratory cycle. These phases are: an inspiratory phase, which is short, about one quarter of a second; a compressatory phase lasting about 1 second; and an expiratory phase, which also lasts about 1 second. The thoracic spiracles are open during the last one or two tenths of the inspiratory phase and remain closed during the rest of the cycle. The abdominal spiracles remain closed during the compressatory phase and open during the last three tenths of a second of the expiratory phase. Under conditions of high activity and forced (dyspneic) breathing, the compressatory phase tends to fuse with the inspiratory and the expiration phase becomes indistinct.

Generally it has been assumed that the air sacs in larger insects serve to increase the vital capacity of the system and thus that they expand and empty with the abdominal movements. This is the case with the large sacs that lie near to the spiracles, but according to McCutcheon, quite a different situation exists in the distal sacs.[6] The distal sacs tend to collapse during inspiration, which suggests a ventilation mechanism that had not been seriously considered before. The mechanics of this ventilation mechanism were worked out using a model, the classic physiological approach. The proposed action of this system is as follows:

A resistance gradient exists along the trachea, owing to the diminishing size. As the resistance gradient approaches a maximum in the very small tracheae, the resistance is high—much higher than the intratracheal pressure resulting from the pressure decrease created by abdominal expansion. Inspiration involves only the main trunks and sacs, but the subsequent compression increases the pressure suddenly to the degree that the resistance along the tracheal branches is partially overcome. As the intratracheal pressure increases, the resistance in the smaller tubes of the system is overcome and they expand. The air surges through the expansion to fill the next distal air sac, which expands because of a momentary increase in pressure. This increase occurs because the resistance of the tracheae leading away from the air sac is greater than the resistance in the sac itself. Subsequent compression and decompression phases tend to force the air deeper and deeper into the tracheal system with the intersac tracheae acting as valves. Since the tracheal system is never entirely closed, it is presumed that this mechanism forces fresh oxygenated air deep into the system and allows some of the spent air to diffuse back to be expelled through the posterior spiracles. Watts later confirmed most of McCutcheon's observations and added some detail to the understanding of the mechanism by using a more sensitive recording system.[12]

Ventilation in the Tracheoles

As the tracheae decrease in size to become tracheoles, diffusion must account for the oxygen supply. These finer branches carry oxygen directly to the cells and tissues.

The tracheoles arise from processes that develop from special cells at the termination of the tracheae. The finer branches that are formed have walls less than 0.01 μ. in thickness.[9] Wigglesworth described the tracheoles that supply the epidermis in *Rhodnius* as simple branched tubes that end blindly when they diminish to a diameter of about 0.2 μ. The terminus of each tracheole is a single cell, and once the tubes are established they persist throughout the life of the insect. The tubes do not shed their cuticular lining with each molt, and they are never converted to tracheae. Wigglesworth further observed that the tracheoles are not inert structures, but that they can migrate toward an oxygen-deficient zone that might develop as the result of serious injury or implanted tissue.[13] Movements of up to 1 mm. have been observed. The tips of the tracheoles appear to be attracted to sites where the oxygen tension is low. If an insect is reared in an atmosphere in which oxygen is deficient, an increase in the number of tracheoles develops. This is evident particularly in the wing lobes; the pattern of wing venation could be altered in a minor fashion by such movements.

Tracheole Fluid. All tracheoles are filled with fluid at their distal ends. Wigglesworth reviewed the processes in the absorption of tracheole fluid and by combining the observations of a number of experiments has suggested a working hypothesis to explain the process of absorption and filling of the tracheal systems.[14]

In most insects the tracheal system opens to the exterior through functional spiracles, but in aquatic and parasitic forms the spiracles remain closed. As far as the initial filling of the system with gas is concerned, no really functional distinction between the open and the closed systems exists. In the closed system, the gas first makes its appearance while the insect is immersed in fluid. Such is the case with *Corethra*, members of the family Chironomidae, and the Odonata. Even in insects with an open tracheal system, gas usually appears throughout the respiratory system while the insect is still bathed in the fluid contents of the egg.

As the tracheal system fills with air, fluid is absorbed into the tissues. This is almost certainly the result of an active transfer by a secretory process, as evidenced by observations that filling does not take place when oxygen tension is low, nor does it take place under narcosis. The absorption of fluid from the tracheal system is effected only during a brief period after the insect emerges from the egg.

The tracheole fluid is never entirely withdrawn from the tracheole system but varies in the degree of withdrawal into the tissues with the need for oxygen. The forces that are involved, if considered on the basis of capillary pressure, are tremendous and must be explained on some basis other than mere absorption to account for the movement.

ABSORPTION OF TRACHEOLE FLUID.   Tracheole fluid is not an ultrafiltrate of the hemolymph. It more closely resembles the amniotic fluid, and in the embryo tracheole fluid is isosmotic with amniotic fluid.[14] The same filling process takes place with each molt, during which time the fluid advances to the level of the trachea, and after the molt, the fluid is again withdrawn toward the tissues. At this time the fluid is continuous with the molting fluid and must be assumed to be of the same composition.

The molting fluid of *Rhodnius* is a protein solution, free of chloride. This fluid can be transferred by an active secretory process but not by osmosis, so that the absorption process for the tracheole fluid must be similar to that of the molting fluid. This idea is supported by observations with *Aedes* larvae, in which the main tracheal trunks are connected by transverse members, which possess no tracheoles. During the process of filling with gas, the gas simultaneously enters both ends of the transverse structures.

There is no doubt that the fluid in the system is removed by active absorption, which requires the expenditure of energy. The problem is to find the source of energy sufficient to produce enough force to withdraw the fluid against the resistance of capillarity. Wigglesworth has proposed the most logical hypothesis.[14]

In order to break a continuous column of liquid or to cause the dissolved gases to revert to the gaseous phase, the required force would have to be approximately 3000 psi, if an aqueous medium is assumed. This figure is based on the cohesion force of water in a chemically clean system in which all parts are completely wetted. This is not the situation in the tracheole system, because the intima has a very low adhesion and the lining is almost nonwettable, owing to the presence of the thin layer of wax peculiar to the integumental structures of insects. Under these revised circumstances, dissolved gas will appear at a relatively low pressure reduction. If the deposition of wax or the tanning of the cuticle coincides with low gas tension brought about by active absorption, it is not surprising that gas is liberated from the fluid. When the first bubble forms, it continues to grow rapidly to fill the entire system. Wigglesworth demonstrated this principle effectively with a simple model.

If a microscope slide is coated with paraffin and immersed in a beaker of water that has been saturated with air, gas bubbles will appear quite soon on the coated area but not on the uncoated surfaces. If distilled water that has been boiled to free it from dissolved gas is used, no bubbles will form on either surface unless the pressure is reduced, but a reduction of as little as half an atmosphere (7.5 psi) releases gas from the water, and bubbles will collect on the coated surface. This simple physical model clearly demonstrates that the hypothesis suggested by Wigglesworth for the formation of gas in the tracheal system is feasible.

Differences in the ability of the various insect species to fill their tracheal systems with gas depend upon the differences in the wettability of the lining, the intensity of the absorptive activity, and the gas content of the fluid in the system.

PENETRATION OF AIR INTO THE TRACHEOLES.   Thus far the tracheae and the tracheoles have been treated more or less interchangeably as regards their fluid content. If the tracheoles alone are considered, the question arises as to how far the air penetrates into them and what controls the level of the fluid.

It has been generally conceded, following the work of Wigglesworth, that the column of air ends abruptly and that the fluid fills the smaller divisions of the tracheole system to the extent dependent on the oxygen requirement of the tissue. As the requirement increases during activity, the fluid is withdrawn almost to the end cell of the tracheole. This phenomenon is also observed under asphyxiation, and it can be brought about by exposure of the tracheole endings to hypertonic solutions such as those of sodium or potassium chloride and lactic acid. If death of the animal intervenes, the tracheoles fill with fluid immediately.

From experimental observations, osmotic pressure could be considered to furnish the basic control for the level of the tracheole fluid, and if certain assumptions are made, the opposing forces just about balance. For this to be true, it must be assumed that the fluid is pure water, that it wets the walls of the tracheole with a zero angle of contact, and that the barrier between the fluid and the blood behaves as a perfect semipermeable membrane. None of these assumptions are valid, so that some other explanation must be used. Again, Wigglesworth set up a working hypothesis supported by use of both living and nonliving models.

If the larvae of *Aedes aegypti* that have been conditioned to fresh water are changed to sea water, the sodium chloride equivalent of the blood (osmotic pressure) is raised from about 0.75 per cent to about 1.5 per cent. The fluid in the tracheoles behaves the same in either situation. This precludes the idea that osmotic pressure is the direct basic control for the level of the tracheole fluid. Instead, it was suggested that the swelling pressure of the protein of the tracheole sheath could be the source of pressure for the fluid level control. To demonstrate this, a nonliving model was devised.

A glass tube was filled with a 10 per cent solution of gelatin in 50 per cent Ringer's solution. Before the gel formed, a capillary pipet was inserted so that the end extended to within 3 mm. of the bottom of the tube. The pipet was withdrawn after the gel had formed, leaving a tapered cavity. This model represented the lumen of the tracheole. The cavity was filled with 50 per cent Ringer's solution, and the tube was placed in a solution of the same concentration and allowed to stand until an equilibrium was established. Next the tube was transferred to a beaker of 100 per cent Ringer's solution and allowed to stand for 24 hours. The result was the removal of the fluid from the "lumen" of the tube. In this model the intensified concentration of the salt increased the swelling pressure of the gelatin, which absorbed the more dilute solution from the "lumen" of the tube. This process can be described in terms of the Donnan equilibrium, combined with the effects of specific ions that reduce the swelling. This model demonstrates how osmotic pressure changes in the blood could act indirectly through changes in the swelling pressure of the sheath to cause temporary absorption of the fluid from the lumen.

Even though this model demonstrates a principle that may exist, it must be borne in mind that the wall of the tracheole is more complex than the membrane represented by the gelatin model. The cytoplasmic sheath is bounded on the outside by a cell membrane that separates the sheath from the blood and on the inside by a modified cell membrane that is the wall of the tracheole. The osmotic pressure of the blood may operate through the outer membrane upon the cytoplasmic sheath, and the capillarity forces in the tracheoles operate against the swelling pressure or colloidal osmotic pressure of the cytoplasm in the sheath. It is possible to conceive a mechanism in which an increase in the osmotic pressure of the blood will cause temporary shrinkage of the cytoplasmic sheath. The gel of the sheath will thereby be compressed and will resume its normal volume by reason of its elasticity or colloidal osmotic pressure. If it is assumed that the inner wall of the sheath, which is the tracheole lining, is more permeable than the outer cell membrane, then the fluid would be absorbed from the lumen of the tracheole. The assumption of differential permeability between the outer and inner layers of the tracheole is very important in the absorption mechanism.

The movement of the fluid in the tracheoles is a key function in the respiratory process of insects. Wigglesworth suggested a working hypothesis that may be summarized as follows:

It may be concluded that the fluid contents of the tracheal system are absorbed by the walls of the system and that the gas may enter the system either from the air or from gas dissolved in tissue or fluid, the latter taking place with very slight negative pressure. Removal of the fluid from the endings takes place during activity and particularly with a deficient oxygen supply. This removal is brought about primarily by physical forces produced by the products of metabolism that are not immediately removed or oxidized at the site of the activity. There is evidence to support the idea that the tracheole fluid is a cellular fluid, whose passage up the tube is opposed by the elasticity or the swelling pressure of the cytoplasmic sheath of the tracheoles, and that there is greater permeability of the inner wall of the tracheole than of the outer membrane. Such an observation makes the proposed hypothesis possible.

Despite the minute size of the tracheoles, the forces of capillarity are quite small. This conclusion is reached because the tubes are lined with an oily film that reduces the wettability and thus reduces the capillary force. It is possible to show experimentally that control of the imbibition ability of the tracheoles is exerted by the osmotic pressure of the blood bathing the tissues and that this ability increases markedly during periods of asphyxiation, especially if the muscular activity is increased.

SPECIALIZED STRUCTURES FOR OXYGEN ABSORPTION

Several evolutionary developments have taken place in the adaptation of insects to various environments. Among these evolutionary developments are some interesting and novel structures that enable the terrestrial type of respiratory system in insects to supply the aquatic insects by absorbing gas from the surrounding water.

The blood gills of some aquatic larvae have been thought to absorb oxygen, mostly because there seems to be no other explanation for their development. These blood gills are thin cuticular sacs that contain hemolymph but have few tracheae.[4] Because the hemolymph has no known carrier and is incapable of carrying more oxygen than will dissolve in it, oxygen absorption by the blood gills is very doubtful. It is more likely that blood gills aid in eliminating carbon dioxide, which can diffuse out through the integument.

In the Plecoptera and Trichoptera, there are cuticular areas that are thin and richly supplied with tracheae. Again, it is assumed by relating structure with possible function that these areas act as gills in the absorption of oxygen from the water. On the same basis, the tube gills of *Simulium* have been assigned an oxygen-absorbing role.[3]

One of the most novel of the evolutionary adaptations, found in many aquatic insects, is the development of hydrofuge hairs. These hairs have a coating of nonwetting wax on one side and are wettable on the other so that when a ring of these hairs is spread like an umbrella, the larva can hang from the surface of the water and expose the posterior spiracles to the air. This adaptation is observed in the larvae of many mosquitoes. When one of these larvae is stimulated to dive, the hairs are deflected so that the nonwetting surface is no longer in contact with the water, and the animal sinks.

Another interesting adaptation is the plastron respiration observed in some aquatic beetles. The ventral side of these insects is covered with fine hydrofuge hairs. When the beetle dives, it takes a bubble of air down with it, but this air is not used just as an auxiliary supply. The invasion coefficient between water and air is about three times greater than that between nitrogen and water, so that there is a tendency for the oxygen to enter the bubble from the water to restore the equilibrium as the oxygen is used by the insect. The tendency for the oxygen to enter the bubble is much greater than the tendency for the nitrogen to leave, which could also restore the equilibrium that results in the plastron functioning as a gill. An insect can stay submerged for as much as 13 times longer by this means than would be possible if the insect were totally dependent on the oxygen it took down with it. Details of plastron respiration and its adaptations and importance have been reviewed recently by Thorpe and Crisp.[10]

Rate of Oxygen Consumption

The rate of oxygen consumption of any insect species is an elusive value that varies with many internal and external factors. Under carefully controlled conditions, the rate is not difficult to determine; however, some hazards in the technology of measurement must be taken into consideration when determing the rate or when interpreting data.

Standard equipment for all respirometry is the Warburg apparatus, which consists of a differential manometer type of respirometer in which the volume is kept constant. In the hands of a skilled operator and with insects that have a reasonably low rate of oxygen consumption, this device produces significant and dependable data; however, because the system must be closed, the gas concentrations of the atmosphere surrounding the test insect change significantly during the course of a measurement. If these atmospheric changes are great enough, the response of the insect will vary accordingly. The same difficulty can arise with any closed system.

Winteringham described a respirometer that circumvented this problem by using a closed system in which the oxygen consumed is constantly replaced by electrolysis.[17] The electric current used in the electrolytic process serves as the index from which the volume of oxygen consumed can be calculated by applying one of Faraday's laws. Measurements of 300-mg. nymphs of the gray house cricket with this device show a normal rate of oxygen consumption at 30° C. of 2 to 3 ml. per hour.[7] Under these conditions, the physiological state of the insect remains good (apparently normal) for periods up to 72 hours. This is a distinct advantage in experimental respirometry.

Any factor that increases activity or metabolic rate also increases the oxygen consumption. It should follow, therefore, that the rate increases with a rise in temperature. Over a limited range this usually is the case; however, when temperatures approach the thermal death point of the insect, breaks occur in the oxygen consumption curve. These breaks were the subject of an investigation by Fraenkel.[4] From his data, it was concluded that oxygen consumption at sublethal and lethal high temperatures is dependent upon oxygen tension at the outset of the determination.

It was also found that the oxygen concentration does not affect the consumption rate after approximately 1 hour, and that the optimum oxygen concentration lies between 10 per cent and 20 per cent partial pressure of oxygen. The rate of oxygen consumption at this level is higher than it is at either a 5 per cent or 100 per cent partial pressure. This occurs because of the complete consumption of oxidizable materials in the insect and the failure of the excretory mechanisms to remove waste products.

Various biologically active chemicals, including those used as insecticides, alter the rate of oxygen consumption—a change that is probably a reflection of metabolic activity. A summary of these chemicals can be found in the work reported by Brown.[1] Since the rate of oxygen consumption represents only a part of the metabolic process, oxygen consumption data alone are of questionable value in mode-of-action studies.

CARBON DIOXIDE ELIMINATION AND THE RESPIRATORY QUOTIENT

The carbon dioxide produced in respiratory metabolism must find its way out of the insect. Just how egress is achieved is somewhat of a question. Areas of the integument and probably the trachea are permeable to the gas,[3] and some of it may be exchanged through the spiracles.

In many insects, particularly during the pupal stage, the release of carbon dioxide is cyclic. The cycles of release can vary from 1-minute bursts occurring 25 times per hour to half hour bursts occurring once in 24 hours. Cyclic release of carbon dioxide is characteristic of several experimental insect species, but there is no reasonable explanation of the mechanics of this process, nor are there any data as to why this mechanism developed. A review of the available knowledge on the subject along with some speculation as to the mechanics of the system is found in the work of Buck.[2]

In mammalian physiology the rate of metabolism and the type of material metabolized are determined by dividing the volume of carbon dioxide given off by the amount of oxygen consumed by the animal over the same period. These determinations are expressed as the respiratory quotient (RQ). If, for example, the RQ is equal to one, it is assumed that the principal metabolite is carbohydrate. This determination is based on the stoichiometric relationship in which one molecule of carbon dioxide is released for every molecule of oxygen consumed in the oxidation of carbohydrate. Other values distinguish the metabolism of fat and protein.

Because the release of carbon dioxide in insects is cyclic, it is not easy to obtain a valid or meaningful RQ value. The only method that has been remotely successful is the titration of the carbon dioxide absorbent after a prolonged run. Continuous measurement, with carbon dioxide determination paralleling oxygen consumption, could be of great value in experimental physiology if it were possible to achieve. So far, attempts to make this type of measurement have yielded fantastic results.

ANAEROBIC RESPIRATION AND OXYGEN DEBT

Many species of insects are able to survive relatively long periods in inert atmospheres, and some insects have been able to resist the effects of fumigants by closing their spiracles.[8] This is often called anaerobic respiration. Actually, the insect does not have the ability to get along without oxygen but rather the ability to survive with greatly reduced activity and to use energy produced by the anaerobic phase of glycolysis. If oxygen supply is not restored within a certain time, the insect dies from asphyxiation.

When oxygen is available after a period of anaerobic respiration, the rate of consumption is increased until the oxygen debt incurred is paid off. The total consumption usually approximately equals the amount of oxygen that would have been used under normal conditions, and the increased consumption restores the balance in the glycolytic cycle. The ability of insects to suspend respiration and survive suffocation is variable with species and is not a universal characteristic. Anaerobiosis among the invertebrates was discussed by von Brand.[11]

SUMMARY

The process of attaining oxygen by insects shows many adaptations that are related to the normal habitat; however, the ultimate source of oxygen is always the air. In all insects, the tracheal system is filled with gas and the actual transfer of oxygen from the tracheoles to the tissues takes place by the diffusion of oxygen dissolved in an aqueous medium through the cells near the tracheole endings.

Air may diffuse through the system, which will supply sufficient oxygen under resting conditions, but in larger insects that are active, air is forced through the larger trunks by muscular contractions of the abdomen. When the gas reaches the fine branches (tracheoles), it is transported by diffusion.

The absorbing fluid fills the tracheoles to a degree dependent upon the requirements of the tissues supplied. The fluid resembles the molting fluid in composition and is not an ultrafiltrate of the hemolymph. The control of the fluid level in the tracheoles is an indirect function of the concentration of metabolites at the tissue level, which operates through the swelling pressure of the tracheole sheath.

The rate of oxygen consumption for various laboratory species has been determined for periods of inactivity and heavy activity such as flight, and under the influence of biologically active chemicals. Normal values are difficult to obtain because they vary greatly with external factors.

The determination of carbon dioxide is made difficult by its cyclic release, and RQ measurements are of questionable validity unless made over long periods to include the bursts of carbon dioxide.

REFERENCES CITED

1. Brown, A. W. A. 1951. Insect Control by Chemicals. John Wiley & Sons, New York.
2. Buck, J. 1962. Insect respiration. Ann. Rev. Ent. 7: 27–56.
3. Edwards, G. A. 1953. Respiratory mechanisms. In Insect Physiology (K. D. Roeder, ed.). John Wiley, New York, Ch. 4.
4. Fraenkel, G. S., and Herford, G. V. B. 1940. The physical action of high temperatures on poikilothermic animals. J. exp. Biol., 17: 386–395.
5. Krogh, A. A. 1920. Studies on tracheal respiration. Arch. ges. Physiol., 179: 95–120.
6. McCutcheon, F. H. 1940. The respiratory mechanism of the grasshopper. Ann. ent. Soc. Amer., 33: 35–55.
7. Patton, R. L. The oxygen consumption of Acheta domesticus. Unpublished research.
8. Pratt, F. S., Swain, A. F., and Eldred, D. N. 1931. Spiracular closure and fumigation. J. econ. Entom., 24: 1041.
9. Richards, A. G., and Anderson, T. F. 1942. Electron microscope studies of insect trachea. J. N. Y. ent. Soc., 50: 147–167.
10. Thorpe, W. H., and Crisp. D. J. 1949. Studies on plastron respiration. J. exp. Biol., 26: 219–260.
11. von Brand, T. 1946. Anaerobiosis in Invertebrates. Biodynamica, Normandy, Mo.
12. Watts, D. T. 1951. Intertracheal pressure in insect respiration. Ann. ent. Soc. Amer., 44: 527–538.
13. Wigglesworth, V. B. 1959. Migration of tracheoles. J. exp. Biol., 36: 632–640. (See also: 1953. Motility of tracheoles. Nature [London], 172: 247.)
14. Wigglesworth, V. B. 1954. Surface forces in the tracheal system. Quart. J. microscop. Sci., 94: 507–522.
15. Wigglesworth, V. B. 1954. Growth and development of the tracheal system. Quart. J. microscop. Sci., 95: 115–137.
16. Wigglesworth, V. B. 1939. Respiration. In Principles of Insect Physiology. Dutton, New York, Ch. 9.
17. Winteringham, F. P. W. 1959. An electrolytic respirometer. Lab. Prac., 8: 372–375.

6

INTERMEDIARY
METABOLISM

Metabolism is a word that denotes collectively all of the chemical processes that take place in an animal and ultimately result in the production of energy, the production of waste compounds, and the chemical reactions that render some of the waste compounds, which are toxic, innocuous. In the present context, production of energy is most important, although the other aspects hold the key to many of the problems of applied entomology. Intermediary metabolism denotes the processes that take place between the introduction of the energy source (the assimilated food or metabolite) and the liberation of energy. These reactions take place at the cellular level. Since intermediary metabolism involves conversion of the basic food elements, this metabolism is conveniently discussed in terms of the chemistry of degradation and synthesis of specific categories of compounds (carbohydrates, proteins, etc.).

The study of intermediary metabolism in insects is represented by an ever growing series of papers, many of which deal with isolated phases of one special system. Nevertheless, it is still impossible to achieve a clear-cut picture of what is actually happening, and a great deal of our present knowledge of intermediary metabolism exists only by assuming analogous reactions in insects with those reactions demonstrated to exist in either mammals or microorganisms.

If it were possible to draw a line of demarcation between physiology and biochemistry, it should be drawn at this level. In the discussion that follows, it is assumed that the reader is either familiar with current concepts of intermediary metabolism or that he will seek out the necessary background of information from recent textbooks of biochemistry[2, 6, 23] and cellular physiology,[9] or from the current literature. The details of the various metabolic pathways are changed frequently as new research is completed, and it is important to look for information in recent publications. In the following discussion, it should be unnecessary to repeat the various metabolic pathways in detail; however, an outline is desirable as a guide to the general nature of the processes that take place and as a basis for discussion.

ENERGY AND ENERGY PRODUCTION

In physiological discussion, the word *energy* can have just one meaning—the capacity to do work. Energy may result in the production of heat, may drive a chemical reaction, or may give rise to the mechanical force exerted by a contracting muscle; but energy is most often expressed in terms of *gram calories* (gm. cal.)—the amount of heat required to elevate the temperature of one gram of water one degree centigrade.

Regardless of the designation, it is apparent that the quantitative expression of energy has to be the product of two factors. First, the potential factor indicates the degree of force applied; and second, the capacity factor indicates how far or to what extent the reaction goes.[17]

In animals, most energy comes from the oxidative metabolism of carbohydrates. If a known mass of sugar or starch is burned in a calorimeter, the end products include carbon dioxide, water, and heat; all of these can be determined quantitatively. The heat produced from the reaction is the heat of combustion (ΔH), and from the heat of combustion can be calculated the heat of formation (ΔH_f) by making use of factors obtained through previous experimentation.[11] Under normal circumstances only part of the energy represented by ΔH is available to the animal in the processes of metabolism, and this is the free energy (ΔF), a value that exists only through mathematical deduction and that cannot be measured. The unavailable energy in the system is called *entropy*. The relationships and interrelationships of these terms and their applications are defined by the laws of thermodynamics, which may be found in any textbook of physical chemistry.

The important fact for this discussion is that if the value of ΔF is negative, the reaction results in the liberation of energy and the reaction will proceed spontaneously. Such a reaction is *exergonic*, and since it usually is accompanied by a simplification of a substrate, it is also *catabolic*. If ΔF is positive, the result is a reduction in the amount of free energy, and thus the reaction will have to be driven. This is accomplished at the expense of an exergonic reaction; a reaction that has to be driven is called an *endergonic* reaction. Endergonic reactions often result in the formation of a more complex material than the substrate and are thus *anabolic*. Both types of reactions take place simultaneously, with the energy from the exergonic reaction driving the endergonic reaction.

All energy-producing reactions are controlled so that energy is liberated at a rate slow enough to enable it to be utilized as it is produced and not be lost because an excess is produced at any one time. The energy production process in animals is complicated and subtle. In almost all cases, it is carried out through the intervention of enzyme catalysis; as a result of a chain of reactions, energy is harnessed.

In animals, the *ultimate* reaction that liberates energy is an oxidation, which in the final analysis utilizes atmospheric oxygen. Along the pathway traveled by the metabolite are many energy-trapping reactions that do not require oxygen, and energy-liberating reactions in which oxygen is not involved. The most important exchange reaction for the transfer (alternate trapping and liberating) reactions is the disruption of the high energy phosphate bond, most often the terminal phosphate on a molecule of adenosine triphosphate (ATP). When considering the various metabolic cycles, it is important to recognize that the desired end product is the production of as much ATP as possible and that the breakdown of ATP to give adenosine diphosphate (ADP) represents a loss rather than a gain in the potential energy released by the metabolism of the substrate.

Atoms, Molecules, and Bonds

The concept of high and low energy bonds in chemical molecules is fundamental to the energy-trapping mechanism of animals, but what makes a bond a high energy or a low energy system is usually glossed over in biological writing, and this lack prevents understanding of the whole process. This subject is generally not discussed thoroughly because the structures and the nature of chemical bonding constitute a very complicated subject. High and low energy bonds have been discussed in detail by Pauling.[18]

The terminal phosphate of ATP gives up between 8,000 and 12,000 gm. cal. per mole (depending upon the inclusion or exclusion of the molecular weight of water in calculation) when it is split off, and the same amount (or slightly more) of energy is required to form the bond. The closer the phosphate radical is to the central part of the molecule, the less energy that is required to put it into position, and the less energy it will yield when it is split. This is in no way an explanation but a statement of observed phenomena.

Molecules are made of atoms, and partly because of the relatively recent success of man in dissociating atoms, increasingly more has been learned of their structure. An atom may be divided grossly into two parts. It has a central, positively charged nucleus, resulting from the presence of the positively charged protons. The number of protons in the nucleus designates the atomic number. The nucleus also contains neutrons—particles with mass but no charge—which hold the protons together.[17] The total mass of the protons and the neutrons is the atomic mass (atomic weight) of the element, and the total mass of the electrons (in the order of 1/2000 of the total mass) is so small that it is disregarded.

Two atoms can have the same number of protons and a different number of neutrons in the nucleus. These atoms will also have the same number of electrons and thus the same chemical properties. The two atoms are called *isotopes;* the imbalance of protons and neutrons in the nucleus, if great enough, will give rise to radioactivity.

Surrounding the nucleus is a negatively charged region that contains the electrons, and it is the number and arrangement of these electrons that imparts the chemical properties to the atom. Chemistry, then, may be defined as the study of changes in the number and the arrangement of the electrons surrounding the nucleus of the various atoms.[17]

Arrangement of the electrons has been deduced by mathematical calculations, and the results of these calculations have been summarized in the Quantum Theory. This theory has resulted in a mathematical model of the atom somewhat different from the older mechanical model, in which the electrons were depicted as spinning around the nucleus in a definite pattern of orbits, or shells. According to the Quantum Theory, the electrons that surround the nucleus can exist only at certain energy levels, called *quantum levels.* These may be thought of in terms of concentric rings only so long as it is recognized that each shell represents the average distance from the nucleus to the electrons in that shell. The closer an electron lies to the nucleus, the less energy it contains; following the principle that in an equilibrium state the amount of free energy tends toward a minimum, the electrons seek a position as close to the nucleus as possible. As the inner positions are filled, more energy may be applied, and additional electrons are forced into positions further from the nucleus. These outer electrons have a higher energy content because they are in a state of greater "excitement." [17]

The concentric spherical shells that represent the possible energy levels around a nucleus are designated either by numbers (1, 2, 3, 4, etc.) or by letters (K, L, M, N, etc.). Within these energy levels there are sublevels known as *orbitals,* indicating that the electrons are arranged in a three dimensional pattern. The orbitals outline zones of probability of electron density, and their shapes are defined by a mathematical wave equation that predicts the approximate position, but not exactly where the electron is or how fast it is moving.[17]

Not more than two electrons can be held on each orbital, and if both are present, they must have opposite spin. Since an electron in motion is a reasonably accurate definition of an electric current, the spin results in the production of a magnetic field. If there are two electrons present, their fields cancel each other, and the atom is not attracted by a magnet. Such a situation is described as *diamagnetic.* If there is a single electron or an odd electron, the atom can be attracted by a magnet; such an atom is *paramagnetic.* If one knows the atomic number of an element, it is possible to predict the location of the electrons in the orbitals because the inner energy levels fill first and because a maximum of eight electrons can be held at any one energy level.[17] The number and position of the electrons give an element its chemical properties.

When atoms hook together to form molecules, the linkage is made through a bonding force called a *valence bond.* These bonds may be either *covalent* or *electrovalent,* and each has important variants.

In covalent bonding, two atoms mutually share a pair of electrons with both electrons attracted to the two nuclei. Even though the two electrons mutually repel each other, they occupy the same orbital. In some cases the pair of electrons comes from the same atom—a special case called *coordinate valence bonding,* or *dative bonding.*

In electrovalent bonding, linkage is achieved through an electron transfer. The atoms at the far left of the periodic table (metals) readily lose one or more electrons by transfer, and those at the right (nonmetals) act as willing acceptors. This release and acceptance of electrons gives rise to positively and negatively charged *ions,* which are mutually attracted through the electrovalent bond. Sodium chloride is an example of a molecule or compound held together by an electrovalent bond.

Various intergradations in the type of bonding are found in various compounds, depending upon their polarity. If it is possible to represent the electronic structure of a molecule in two or more ways, in which the positions of the atomic nuclei are unchanged and the energy of the various structures is approximately the same, the configuration becomes a hybrid with greater stability than any of the individual structures. This phenomenon is called *resonance* and is important in the stability of various structures (benzene, for example).

Under certain circumstances the hydrogen atom in one molecule can be attracted by an unshared electron pair in another atom to form a bond between two atoms. This *hydrogen bonding* is a type of covalent linkage that is very important in the formation of organic compounds. The bond formed is normally much weaker than the ordinary types, and it is readily broken by elevating the temperature.[11]

Bond types are mentioned in this discussion only to ensure that the reader is cognizant of their existence. For further information a textbook of physical chemistry should be consulted.

Every chemical reaction is an electrical transaction in which something gains electrons and something loses electrons. In this transfer process, energy is shifted, and some of it may be released. The most elementary reaction by which the energy of the sun is transferred to animals (indirectly) is the photosynthetic process of plants, wherein occurs a shuffling back and forth of electrons between carbon orbitals and oxygen orbitals. The first step is the release of hydrogen from oxygen.[17] When the hydrogens are torn away from the oxygen, energy is put into the system; if the hydrogens released are covalent bonded to carbon, more energy becomes potentially available. If, for example, methane is the result, it contains more potential energy than in the original covalent bonding with oxygen, and this can be recovered or released by recombining the hydrogen with oxygen. This energy is released when methane is burned.

Earlier it was pointed out that animals use bond energy as a medium of exchange in the energy-trapping reactions. They make use of the increasing stored energy by adding one, two, or three phosphate radicals to an organic compound (adenosine), with an increasing order of potential energy required to add each radical and a decreasing yield when the radicals are split off. In each case, the energy release has to be activated, just as it is necessary to activate energy release from methane by igniting it with a match.

In biological systems mechanisms have evolved for the controlled release of energy so that the energy is released slowly and is not lost in explosive bursts. A very large percentage of the enzymes, carriers, and adjuvants necessary for the control of energy release are included in the intracellular structure of the *mitochondria*.[9] For this reason, intermediary metabolism is the study of the chemistry of the individual cells that comprise the tissues.

THE INTERMEDIARY METABOLISM OF CARBOHYDRATES

Plant starch, the principal source of carbohydrates used by animals, may be ingested in various forms; it is always assimilated after being broken into a simple sugar, usually α-glucose. There are three common pathways through which energy is released from carbohydrates to be trapped for further use by the animal. These include: the anaerobic glycolytic pathway, often referred to as the Embden-Meyerhof pathway; the pentose pathway (hexose monophosphate shunt); and the Krebs cycle (citric acid or monocarboxylic acid cycle), which is an aerobic pathway that completes the breakdown of energy-containing fragments remaining from the first two pathways.

The Embden-Meyerhof Pathway

If starch or glycogen is the starting substrate, it is converted to glucose. The glucose is phosphorylated in the 1 position with a phosphate radical from inorganic phosphate   (Pi). This phosphorylation results in glucose-l-phosphate, which is converted to glucose-6-phosphate by shifting the position of the phosphate radical on the molecule. A rearrangement takes place to change the pyranose structure of glucose to a furanose structure as fructose-6-phosphate and another phosphate radical are added. The additional phosphate radical comes from the release of the terminal phosphate from a molecule of adenosine triphosphate (ATP) and gives rise to a molecule of adenosine diphosphate (ADP). The carbohydrate is now fructose-1,6-phosphate, which is converted to glyceraldehyde-3-phosphate and dihydroxyacetone phosphate, two compounds that can be interconverted. In mammals, the subsequent conversion of the dihydroxyacetone phosphate to α-glycerophosphate, and ultimately to glycerol, is of relatively little importance; this is not the case with insects.

The glyceraldehyde-3-phosphate (2 moles formed for each mole of glucose) proceeds through a series of steps involving oxidation and reduction reactions with a diphosphonucleotide (NAD and $NADH_2$ = DPN and DPNH + H+) in its oxidized and reduced forms and is transformed successively through a series of reactions in which energy is trapped. The first of these steps is the loss of one phosphate per mole, which reaction gives rise to ATP (2 moles). The 3-phosphoglyceric acid formed is converted to 2-phosphoglyceric acid, to phosphopyruvic acid, and finally to pyruvic acid. In the last step another phosphate is trapped to produce ATP (2 moles). Part of the pyruvic acid may be reduced further to give lactic acid. For each molecule of glucose at the start of the pathway, two molecules of ATP are expended and four are gained, leaving a net gain of two high energy phosphates trapped in the process. The scheme for the glycolytic pathway can be found in various forms in textbooks of biology,[22] physiology,[9] and biochemistry.[6] A superficial outline and comparison with the scheme that appears to be predominant in insects is shown in Figures 6–1 and 6–2.

The Pentose Pathway

Glucose-6-phosphate has an $H-\overset{|}{\underset{|}{C}}-OH$ configuration at the number 1 carbon, which is subject to dehydrogenation. Glucose-6-phosphate dehydrogenase in the presence of NADP (nicotinamide-adenine trinucleotide = triphosphopyridine nucleic acid, or TPN), which acts as an acceptor, catalyzes the reaction to give 6-phosphogluconic acid. The acid can likewise be dehydrogenated to form a product that undergoes further decarboxylation to give a pentose—ribulose-5-phosphate—a compound important in photosynthesis and a precursor of ribose-5-phosphate, which is a constituent of nucleotides and nucleic acids.

This dehydrogenation-decarboxylation type of reaction makes possible the rearrangement of the upper three carbons of the original molecule, which can give rise to 3-, 4-, 5-, 6-, and 7-carbon sugars. The pentose shunt is an aerobic pathway that in some organisms, including insects, can account for an appreciable part of the metabolism of glucose. The principal reactions are shown in Figure 6–3. High energy phosphates are trapped by the pentose shunt reaction, and while it is often subordinated to other metabolic path-

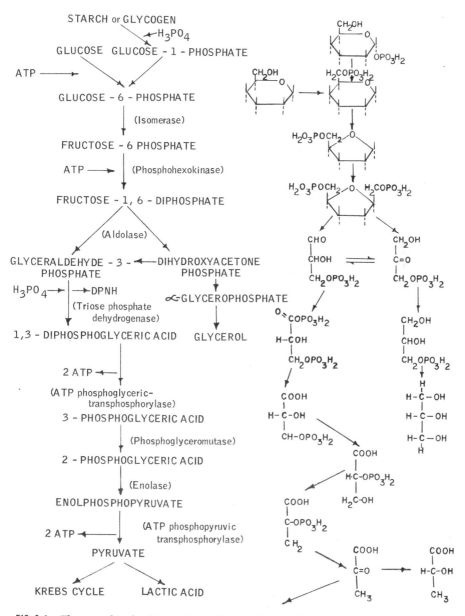

FIG. 6-1. The anaerobic glycolytic pathway (Embden-Meyerhof pathway) in vertebrate liver. The enzymes essential for this cycle have been demonstrated to occur in insects (adapted from Prosser).

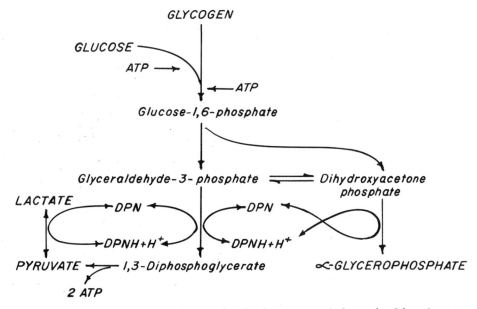

FIG. 6-2. Condensed scheme for anaerobic glycolysis in insects (redrawn after Gilmour).

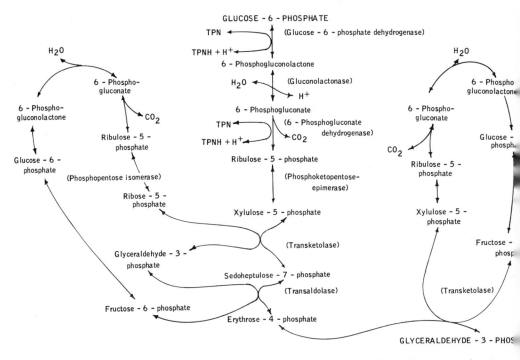

FIG. 6-3. Schematic representation of the hexose monophosphate pathway (the pentose shunt) (redrawn after Gilmour).

ways in animals, there is evidence that it may have an appreciable significance in insects.[3, 14]

The Krebs Cycle

The Krebs cycle is aerobic and is very important in the metabolism of the carbohydrate fragments left by the other pathways and in the metabolism of proteins and fats. The wide significance of the Krebs cycle in animals led Giese to refer to it as the "metabolic mill." [9] It is a cycle whereby fragments of organic compounds that are the result of various metabolic reactions in the degradation of carbohydrates, proteins, and fats are brought together and utilized.

Some of the fragments enter the Krebs cycle by way of acetyl-CoA plus oxaloacetic acid, which produces a 6-carbon acid identified as citric acid. The citric acid proceeds through a series of reactions, each of which is enzyme-controlled and during which there is a net gain of 15 moles of ATP. The Krebs cycle ends with production of malic acid, which is converted to oxaloacetic acid to renew the cycle. Along the route, the fragments are manipulated chemically so that carbon dioxide and water are given off, representing the final breakdown products of the original carbohydrate. The scheme for the various reactions of the Krebs cycle are shown in Figure 6–4.

Glycolysis in Insects

The study of glycolysis in insects has been a fertile field of comparative biochemistry, and the many isolated studies were summarized by Rockstein[19] and by Chefurka.[8] On the basis of the presence of enzymes and enzyme systems, all pathways known to be common to mammals and found in microorganisms are possible for insects. Most glycolysis, particularly in muscle, probably occurs by way of the Embden-Meyerhof pathway; however, the stoichiometry of the reactions indicates a strong tendency in insects for the metabolism to shift from anaerobic toward aerobic pathways.[3] This tendency is explained by the peculiarity of the respiratory system of insects, in which atmospheric oxygen is taken directly to the cells, making it more readily available for metabolic processes than is the case with mammals, in which oxygen is carried by a blood pigment.

Glucose, which is a starting point in glycolysis, comes from two sources in insects. For many years glycogen has been reported from the cells and tissues of insects, but recently it has been shown that the principal blood sugar of insects is a disaccharide called *trehalose*. Trehalose consists of two molecules of α-glucose and is also found to occur in certain species of fungus. A very active trehalase is present in the blood and fat body of Orthoptera.[5] The starting point of energy production in insects depends somewhat on the stage of development of the insect and on the type of energy required. For example, it has been shown that during active flight, glycogen, or in some cases fat, is the principal source.

The anaerobic glycolysis pathway in insects obviously follows the same pathway as in mammals, but the formation of α-glycerophosphate, which

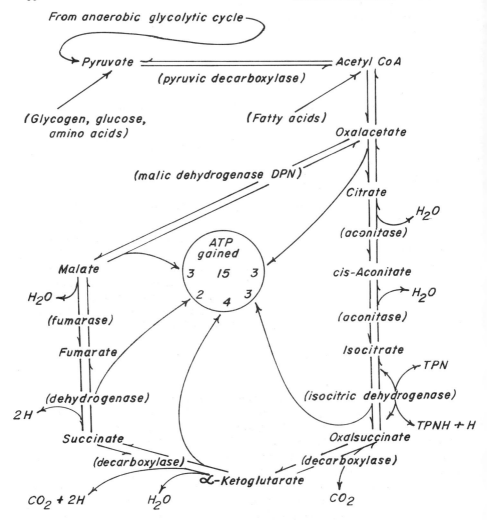

FIG. 6-4. The tricarboxylic acid (citric acid, or Krebs) cycle for aerobic glycolysis (adapted from Baldwin).

accumulates in insect muscle during strenuous activity, and the amount of lactic acid and carbon dioxide that are produced do not coincide with the reactions that would be necessary if glycolysis were to follow the same pattern to the same extent as in mammals. Gilmour states that glycolysis produces approximately equimolar quantities of pyruvate and α-glycerophosphate but that the latter appears much more rapidly.[10] A phosphatase is present in insect tissues that can convert α-glycerophosphate to glycerol, which tends to accumulate in diapausing insects. As an aside, glycerol may act as an antifreeze by increasing the osmotic pressure of the tissue fluids and thus contribute to the cold hardiness; but at the same time production of glycerol eliminates the important energy-trapping reactions of the Embden-Meyerhof cycle so that this departure would lower the energy yield in the overall process.

All of the enzyme systems necessary for the pentose pathway are found in insects[8] and in mites,[14] and available evidence indicates that this pathway may be of considerable importance in insects. Also, presence of these enzyme systems further indicates the tendency in insects of a shift of glycolytic metabolism from anaerobic toward aerobic pathways.

All data indicate the presence of the Krebs cycle as an active part of insect metabolism. Insect metabolism appears to follow a scheme similar if not identical to that of other animals.

THE METABOLISM OF AMINO ACIDS

Individual amino acids, which are derived from protein in the diet or synthesized by the animal or its symbionts, follow a degradation pattern that is fairly well established, and the reactions are characteristic. Deamination, transamination, decarboxylation, and peptide synthesis give rise to the formation of proteins typical of each animal species, of carbohydrate fragments that are metabolized through the Krebs cycle, and of keto acids, fats, and other compounds, some of which have intense physiological activity.

Giese groups the amino acids into categories depending upon their structural characteristics.[9] These include: (1) monoamino-monocarboxylic acids such as glycine, (2) monoamino-dicarboxylic acids such as glutamic, (3) diamino-monocarboxylic acids such as lysine, (4) hydroxyl-containing acids such as threonine, (5) sulfur-bearing amino acids such as methionine, (6) aromatic amino acids such as phenylalanine, (7) heterocyclic amino acids such as tryptophan, and (8) iodine-bearing amino acids such as iodogorgoic acid.* Each amino acid enters into specific metabolic processes typical either for the individual amino acid or for the type of structure of the individual amino acid. These metabolic processes are treated in detail in modern textbooks of biochemistry, and the reader is referred to these sources.

The Metabolism of Amino Acids by Insects

The available knowledge on the metabolism of amino acids by insects was reviewed by Bheemeswar[4] and later by Gilmour.[10] According to the former, information is relatively fragmentary on the distribution and properties of enzymes involved in amino acid metabolism in insects as compared to the same information for mammals and microorganisms. Four types of reactions have been confirmed for insects; these are the same as for mammals. Gilmour has summarized the literature and information for individual amino acids and their activity in the metabolic processes in insects.

Concentration of free amino acids in the blood of insects is high (Table 4–2), and these amino acids undoubtedly contribute to the osmotic pressure of the hemolymph. In addition to the amino acids that are components of proteins, a relatively large number, known only in the free state, are found in the hemolymph. These free amino acids include such compounds as α-amino-

---

* Giese does not include the iodine amino acids in his classification, but his repetition of one category indicates that this may be an oversight.

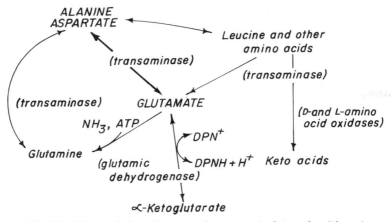

FIG. 6-5.   The metabolism of amino acids in insects (redrawn after Gilmour).

butyric acid, β-alanine, ornithine, and taurine. Of these, taurine is the only free amino acid that is widely distributed, but amino acid derivatives of tryptophan and tyrosine in the form of kynurenine, 3-hydroxykynurenine, and dihydroxyphenylalanine are found commonly in the blood of insects.

Transaminations in insects have been demonstrated that involve glutamic acid, aspartic acid, alanine, and their corresponding α-keto acids. In *Bombyx* transamination activity is highly developed, and the formation of glycine from glyoxylic acid and alanine from pyruvic acid has been proved.[10] The addition of chlormycetin to the diet of silkworms has resulted in an increase in the transaminase activity, which has been related to the increase in growth rate and silk production. In most animals, glutamate acts as the central transfer station between amino acids and keto acids for amino groups, but it has not been definitely established that this is true in insects. Other examples of transamination have been studied with various insect species, and the results indicate that the pathways are similar to those demonstrated for mammals. The greatest transaminase activity in insect tissues is found in the fat body and the Malpighian tube tissues.

The conversion of amino acids to their keto acids can be achieved through oxidative deamination as well as by transamination. Amino acid oxidases are the enzymes involved, and both D and L forms have been found in insects. In mammals these enzymes are flavoproteins, and it is a reasonable assumption that insect enzymes are of the same type.

Decarboxylation mechanisms in insects have not been given much attention, but it has been reported that extracts of both silkworm gut and silk gland catalyze the β-decarboxylation of aspartate to form α-alanine.[10] This reaction is usually found in bacteria, and it is surprising to find it in insects. The α-aminobutyric acid reported present in *Ephestia* probably indicates the activity of a glutamic acid decarboxylase, but this activity has not been verified. The general reactions for amino acid metabolism in insects are summarized in Figure 6–5.

Metabolism of individual amino acids by insects has been the subject of diverse and more or less isolated work. This metabolism involves detailed reactions in which the amino acids contribute fragments, or radicals, to the formation of other biologically active compounds. Gilmour has summarized the available data, and new information is appearing in the literature regularly. The advances in the last 10 years have been largely due to the availability of isotope-tagged compounds, which make it possible to trace fragments in the chemical processes in which they are involved.

Nitrogenous End Products

When the excreta of animals are examined critically, it is found that about two thirds of the total nitrogen eliminated is in the form of ammonia, urea, and uric acid. The remaining one third is composed of various nitrogen compounds including purine bases and xanthine. Also the nature of the nitrogenous end product is related to the habitat of the animal. Thus, an animal in an aqueous habitat can get rid of ammonia easily because of its ready solution in the surrounding water, but an animal in a dry environment must excrete a less toxic product, such as urea (mammals) or uric acid (birds and insects).

Table 6–1 shows a typical analysis of the feces of several insect species. These data show a predominance of uric acid but also a surprising amount of urea in the excreta of the yellow mealworm (*Tenebrio molitor*), which is notorious for its ability to live in a dry habitat.

Ammonia. Ammonia can be produced directly from the deamination of amino acids, or it may result from the action of urease on urea. Insects that inhabit fluid or semifluid media (houseflies and blowflies) excrete relatively large quantities of ammonia. This is very evident to anyone who has

TABLE 6-1. Analysis of Feces

Insects	Compounds										
	Adenine	Guanine	Uracil	Thymine	Cytosine	Hypoxanthine	Xanthine	Uric acid	Allantoin	Urea	Sodium chloride
Acheta domesticus All stages	−	−	−	−	−	−	−	+	−	−	+
Oncopeltus fasciatus All stages	−	−	−	−	−	−	−	+	−	+	−
Periplaneta americana All stages	−	−	−	−	−	−	−	+	−	−	−
Tenebrio molitor Larvae	−	−	−	−	−	−	−	+	+	+	−
Malacosoma americana Larvae	−	−	−	−	−	−	−	+	−	−	−
Galleria mellonella Larvae	−	−	−	−	−	+	+	+	−	Weak +	+
Galleria mellonella Adults	−	−	−	−	−	Weak +	−	+	−	−	−

From Nation, J. L., and Patton, R. L. 1961. Nitrogen partition in insect excreta. J. Ins. Physiol. 6: 299-308.

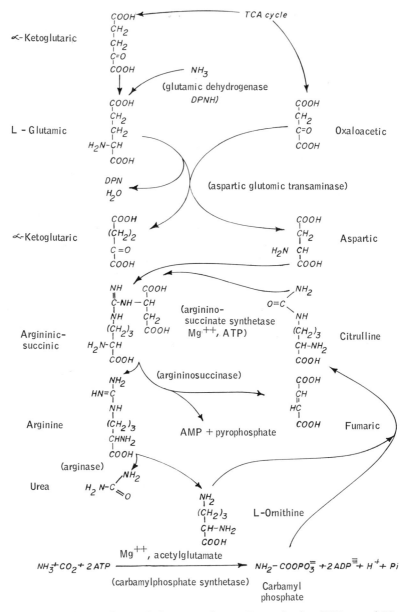

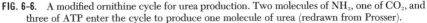

FIG. 6-6. A modified ornithine cycle for urea production. Two molecules of NH_3, one of CO_2, and three of ATP enter the cycle to produce one molecule of urea (redrawn from Prosser).

cultured these insects, and it is of some historical interest to note that ammonia along with allantoin, which is an oxidation product of uric acid, constituted the principal alkalizing and healing agent in the maggot therapy that was practiced around 1920–1930.

    Urea.   Urea, the principal nitrogenous end product in mammals, is formed characteristically through the ornithine cycle shown in Figure 6–6.

Two moles of ammonia enter the cycle, one from aspartic acid and the other from carbamyl phosphate. This reaction requires the expenditure of 3 moles of ATP for each molecule of urea produced. Urea is found in the excreta of many insects, but data to prove that it is formed through the ornithine cycle are still fragmentary.

Uric Acid. Uric acid is produced principally from the metabolism of nucleic acids in mammals, but this cannot account for the quantities excreted by insects. Most insects excrete uric acid, and the blood is nearly saturated at all times. There is also some evidence that uric acid may be stored, particularly in the fat body, and as a cheesy mass lining the integument, where it may stay in storage excretion or possibly may be in storage to serve as nitrogen reserve for further use by the insect. Data on the latter idea are still incomplete, but evidence is reasonably good that this may be the case.[13]

Anderson demonstrated that uric acid is synthesized principally in the fat body and that it is excreted by way of the Malpighian tubes.[1] Most available information on the formation of uric acid other than by nucleic acid metabolism has come from the study of its formation by birds. Introduction of isotope-tagged precursors has confirmed the hypotheses, and it is generally accepted that uric acid is formed according to the following reaction:

$3NH_3$ (from glutamic acid) $+ CO_2 + ATP +$ glycine $+ 2$ formate $\rightarrow$
hypoxanthine (ribose-1-phosphate required) $\rightarrow$ uric acid.

The sources of components of the uric acid structure as demonstrated by tagged molecules are shown in Figure 6–7. Carbon number 6 comes from carbon dioxide; carbon 2 and carbon 8 from formate; carbon 4 and carbon 5 from glycine; the nitrogens in the 7 position are from glycine; the nitrogen in the 1 position from aspartic acid; and the 3 and 9 nitrogens are from the amide of glutamine. Carbamyl phosphate is used, and glutamic acid is the direct source of ammonia. Of the known uricolytic enzymes, only xanthine oxidase has been demonstrated to be widely distributed in insects, but this does not preclude the possibility that others will be demonstrated when the number of species investigated is increased.

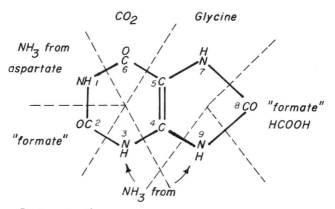

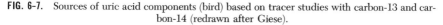

5-phosphoribosylamine formed from glutamate
and 5-phosphoribosylpyrophosphate

FIG. 6-7. Sources of uric acid components (bird) based on tracer studies with carbon-13 and carbon-14 (redrawn after Giese).

THE METABOLISM OF LIPIDS

Lipids include the neutral fats (triglycerides), phosphatides, cerebrosides, steroids, and the fat-soluble vitamins.[23] Lipids are the most concentrated source of energy available to an organism; when lipids are metabolized, they yield more than twice the energy per gram than either carbohydrates or proteins.

The neutral fats are esters of various fatty acids and glycerol. The differences in chemical makeup are due to the fatty acid composition, which may include several fatty acids in varying quantities and with different degrees of saturation. This fatty acid composition is more or less specific for animals, including insects. Alcohols other than glycerol also esterify with fatty acids, and the result is a series of compounds that enter into many metabolic systems. All of these compounds can be split by the hydrolytic activity of esterases, some of which are specific and some of which are more or less general.

The principal properties of fats and esters are associated with the degree of saturation of the fatty acid part of each system; indices such as the iodine number and the saponification number are used to characterize the compounds. The fatty acids released by the action of esterases are metabolized either to make new esters or to be degraded oxidatively, resulting in carbon dioxide, water, and energy. The fatty acids exist as long-chain carbon structures that cannot be broken down all at once, but they are degraded by successive desaturation and oxidation reactions that take place starting with the β carbon. These reactions cause successive two-carbon fragments to split off. If the carbon chain is relatively short, these reactions may be limited to the β carbon; or if the chain is long, these reactions can take place at both ends of the chain with the formation of a carboxyl group on each end of the molecule, which in effect creates two β carbons. Thus these reactions can start at both ends and work toward the middle. Regardless of the details of the degradation, the end result is a series of two-carbon fragments that can be fed into the Krebs cycle yielding energy.

Fatty acids and fats are also synthesized in animals from either carbohydrates or proteins. Synthesis of fatty acids is not just a reversal of the degradation process, although the first three steps appear to be similar. In the fourth step of a typical synthesis a TPNH-specific enzyme in the presence of acyl CoA is required. This enzyme apparently is a reductase. Details of this mechanism are discussed at length in various textbooks of biochemistry.

The steroids constitute a series of fatlike compounds that do not saponify and are not esters. The steroid molecule is characterized by a typical complex ring structure. These rings always have at least one OH group. The sterols differ from each other by the number and position of the C=C groups, the size and composition of the side chain, and the number and position of the OH groups. The steroid ring structure and the structures of several common sterols are shown in Figure 6–8.

Cholesterol is the most common sterol in higher animals, including insects (see Chapter 2). The ability of animals to utilize other sterols in metabolic processes is dependent upon the ability of the animal to convert these sterols to cholesterol.[12] Compounds derived from the metabolism of cholesterol are of great importance in the vital processes and the pathology of mammals.

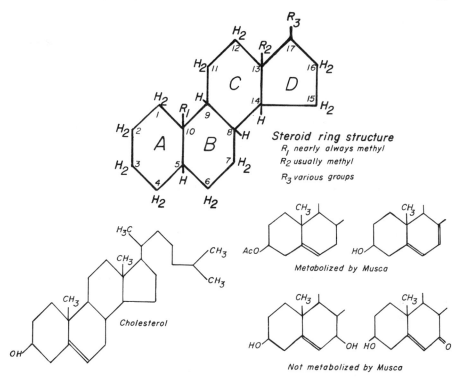

FIG. 6-8. The structure and nomenclature of the steroid ring; the structure of cholesterol, which is utilized by insects; and the structures of two sterols that are not utilized.

These compounds are the precursors for many of the hormones—vitamin D is a sterol—and they are the precursors of bile acids. Pathological accumulations of cholesterol derivatives in the principal arteries bring about arteriosclerosis and characteristic lesions of coronary occlusion and cerebral hemorrhage. In some cases, crystals are formed that build into concretions of cholesterol as is the case of gallstones.

Sterols are derived from dietary sources and from synthesis within the animal. Several factors affect the rate of sterol synthesis and some of these are important, particularly in the pathology of mammals. Similar concretions have been observed in insects.

Sterols in Insects

It is generally agreed that insects require a source of sterol in the diet. Insects require sterol for normal growth, normal reproduction, and metamorphosis, and as a precursor for hormones including neotinin, the juvenile hormone. In spite of these observations supported by good experimental backing, it is still not possible to define the physiological function of cholesterol in insects,[12] and this statement also applies to metabolism of all lipids in insects.[10]

The ability of insects to utilize sterols depends upon their ability to convert available (dietary) sterol to cholesterol.[12] Several insect species are able to convert plant sterols; the chemical changes necessary for such a conversion are known. Unfortunately, these chemical changes have not been demonstrated to take place in insects, although it seems apparent from the end results that conversion of plant sterol to cholesterol takes place.

Metabolism of Compound Lipids, Waxes, and Aliphatic Hydrocarbons

Compound lipids are esters of glycerol and other alcohols in which one fatty acid residue is replaced by a phosphoric or sulfuric acid radical in an ester linkage.[10] These compound lipids include the phosphatides, which are metabolically active forms of fats, as opposed to the true glycerides, which are principally stored fats.

Lecithin-type phosphatides have been identified from adults of the Colorado potato beetle (*Leptinotarsa decemlineata*), and other phosphatides have been found in blowflies and in the sugar beet webworm (*Loxostega stricticalis*). Insects also contain enzymes that split the ester linkages of the compound lipids, and some of these enzymes may be active components of defensive venoms.[10] Relatively little is really known about these compounds and their metabolism in mammals so that it is not entirely surprising that even less is known about them in insects.

Waxes are made up of a long-chain primary alcohol and long-chain fatty acids. Several of these waxes are produced by insects and are of commercial value (beeswax, shellac, etc.). Waxes are highly complex compounds, difficult to characterize precisely, and there are very few good studies that describe their formation or composition. Some insects are able to utilize waxes and even paraffins, and incorporation of these substances in the diet appears to improve growth.[24] Beyond this, relatively little is known.

Various derivatives of straight-chain fatty acids, alcohols, and paraffins are synthesized by insects for a definite function. Among these derivatives are the various odorous secretions used as sex attractants, trail markers, or in royal jelly, a food for larvae. These compounds are discussed further in the section concerning behavior.

METABOLISM OF HYDROCARBON INSECTICIDES

That some insects can convert DDT to the relatively nontoxic DDE, and phenothiazine (thiodiphenylamine) to a leucothionol before it becomes toxic has done a great deal to inspire the study of metabolic processes in insects. The knowledge of metabolism of insecticides has been summarized in several reviews.[7, 10, 15, 16] Most of the effort along this line has been slanted toward the understanding of problems of insect resistance to insecticides. This approach to the solution of these problems has been, for the most part, futile; however, the contributions to the knowledge of metabolic processes have been noteworthy. One of the more significant gains has been the definition of some of the detoxication mechanisms in insects. This subject has been reviewed at length by Smith.[21]

Detoxication Mechanisms in Insects

Some insect detoxication mechanisms convert organic compounds to innocuous metabolites that are usually excreted, but other mechanisms result in the production of compounds of greater activity than the starting material. These latter processes are nevertheless called detoxication mechanisms, although they represent a reversal in the meaning of the word from the standpoint of the insect. The author prefers to distinguish between these two types of reactions by calling reactions that result in compounds with greater toxicity than the starting material *reverse detoxication*. Reverse detoxication is an important factor in the action of several insecticides.

The detoxication mechanisms demonstrated to exist in insects include the following:[7, 21]

Glucoside Formation. This is a pathway analogous to the β-glucuronide pathway in vertebrates. By this reaction insects appear to conjugate phenols with glucose to form a β-glucoside in a manner more like plants than animals. By this pathway cockroaches can form a glucoside with both 2,4-dinitro-o-cresol and phenothiazine. β-Glucosidase is present in the gastric ceca of cockroaches, and the conjugation has been demonstrated from Orthoptera, Coleoptera, Lepidoptera, and Hemiptera.[7]

Ethereal Sulfate Conjugations. These have been demonstrated from the analysis of the excreta of several insects, and an arylsulfatase is present in the crop fluids of locusts. By this reaction, the phenolic OH group of a compound is esterified with sulfuric acid. The housefly converts naphthol to an ethereal sulfate through this process.[21]

Acetylation of Amino Groups. Insects, like mammals, acetylate amino acids to give corresponding acetamido compounds. These compounds have been found in Orthoptera and Coleoptera. Cockroaches have been shown to hydrolyze the acetamide bond in some of the compounds.[7]

Cysteine Conjugations. These reactions are associated particularly with the metabolism of halogen-substituted compounds. According to Smith,[21] there are two types of reactions. In the first, hydrogen in an aromatic ring is replaced by an acetylcysteine residue. In the second, a labile atom or group (e.g., Cl or NO_2) is replaced by the acetylcysteine residue. The details of these reactions as they take place in insects are not entirely clear, but as pointed out, some form of cysteine or glutathione conjugate is probably involved in the metabolism of lindane by houseflies, since alkaline hydrolysis of the excreta yields a mixture of dichlorbenzenethiols.

Hippuric Acid Formation. This conjugation of aromatic acids with glycine is known to exist in several insect species, and the methylation of heterocyclic nitrogen atoms has been demonstrated in Coleoptera.

Oxidations. These occur in detoxication processes of insects as follows. *Aliphatic oxidations* apparently take place in some Orthoptera and Coleoptera, but they appear to be less important in insects than in vertebrates. *Hydroxylation* of aromatic rings (as in phenothiazine) and hydroxylation in intermediary metabolism of aromatic amino acids appear to take place in the same manner in insects as in mammals. *Epoxidations* are rare in animals but must take place in the metabolism of cyclodiene insecticides.[7]

Reduction of organic compounds is a very rare detoxication mechanism in insects, but detoxications with compounds involving sulfur and heavy metals are relatively common. These compounds are rendered insoluble by their conversion to sulfides. The larvae of the horse botfly have been shown to contain rhodanase, an enzyme that converts cyanide to a thiocyanate and thus significantly reduces the toxicity.

These are the principal detoxication mechanisms as they are known and as they enter into the processes of intermediary metabolism. Further discussion of some of these is found in Chapter 12.

ELECTRON TRANSMITTER SYSTEMS

To return to the discussion of metabolic pathways, it has been stressed that energy is trapped through a series of chemical reactions, which were described as transactions involving an exchange of electrons. The pathways that have been defined indicate that certain compounds are essential for oxidations, reductions, and the splitting off of phosphate bonds, which act as donors, acceptors, and carriers of electrons from one molecule to another.

When electrons are split off from a substrate (a donor), they are accepted by a compound (an acceptor) and transferred through a series of oxidation and reduction steps producing a compound that can combine with atmospheric oxygen. The principal source of the energy trapped by the phosphate bonds comes from this interchange of electrons through a sort of "electron cascade." [22] This electron interchange has been so described because it may be pictured as a series of waterfalls over which electrons fall, driving a waterwheel (the enzyme reactions) by which electron energy is captured in a usable form. The electron cascade is outlined in Figure 6–9.

The processes in which electrons are removed from an atom constitute oxidations whether oxygen is directly involved or not, and conversely the addition of electrons is a reduction. One does not take place without the other (for every oxidation there has to be a corresponding reduction).

The compounds that have been studied most in the electron transmitter systems are the cytochromes. There are at least three types (A, B, and C) with subdivisions possible for each type. It is of some interest that Keilin, who is generally credited with their discovery (they had been observed earlier but not recognized), made his initial observations with preparations of insect muscle.

Cytochrome c is the member of the group that has received most attention. Cytochrome c is made up of a protein with an iron-containing prosthetic group, which is related to the heme of hemoglobin, but this prosthetic group is attached more firmly to the protein than in hemoglobin. Cytochrome c is reduced readily, but it cannot give up its electrons without the intervention of an oxidase, which is inhibited by cyanide but not by narcotics. Cytochrome B is also a conjugated protein with a prosthetic group similar to that of cytochrome c, but cytochrome B differs in that it is slowly auto-oxidizable. Because cytochrome B is auto-oxidizable, it is not completely inhibited by cyanide. Cytochrome A is subdivided into two components, A and A_3, both of which are hemochromogen compounds, but in these cytochrome compounds the heme resembles that of chlorocruorin, a respiratory pigment in some in-

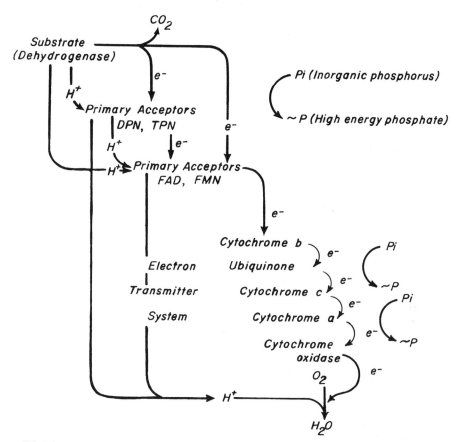

FIG. 6-9. The *electron cascade*, by which electrons are transferred through a series of metabolic steps ultimately to combine with oxygen, resulting in the production of usable energy in the form of phosphate bonds (redrawn after Villee).

vertebrates. Component A requires an oxidase to complete the electron transfer, but A_3 is auto-oxidizable. Cytochrome A_3 also differs in that it can form a compound with carbon monoxide. Some biochemists consider A_3 to be identical to cytochrome oxidase.[2]

A recently isolated component of the electron transmitter system is called *ubiquinone,* or CoQ. This compound has a benzoquinone ring that can readily take up and release electrons and a long side chain of 10 isoprenoid units with five carbons each. CoQ is found in all insect cells.

The operation of the cytochrome system is usually coincident with the Krebs cycle, and there is no evidence to indicate that its function in insects differs from that in other animals.

In the electron cascade system, it is understood that enzymes are present to catalyze the reactions. The enzymes and the accessory substances that serve as carriers have been reclassified by mutual agreement and are listed in the Report of the Commission on Enzymes of the International Union of Biochemistry (Pergamon, London, 1960). This report lists the enzymes involved in the electron cascade system as *oxidoreductases* and includes 13 categories with 37 divisions based on the groups that serve as donors and on the nature of the acceptors. Cognizance of the changing nomenclature and of the initial code used to designate various of the cofactors in coordinating results from the older literature with results from the more recent literature is important.

Conclusive data are not available, but it is relatively safe to conjecture that all systems that have been found in mammals for the production of energy are present and active to a greater or lesser extent in insects. The details of the reactions and the elucidation of the activity clearly belongs to the biochemists, but some knowledge of these reactions is vital to the study of physiology, since the prime vital function is the production of energy by the individual.

SUMMARY

Intermediary metabolism is a subject that should be treated through the discipline of biochemistry; however since all the vital functions of the living animal are in a way dependent upon production of energy, the processes that involve energy production must be considered in all but the most superficial physiological studies.

The principal product of metabolic activity is the energy released by the degradation of assimilated food and trapped by a series of chemical reactions. Exchanges of energy are made through the production of high energy phosphate bonds, and energy is converted to a usable form by the splitting of these bonds. All these processes involve electron transfers, which are brought about by enzymatic catalysis involving reaction chains that constitute the metabolic pathways.

Food categories can be interchanged through metabolic activity, and the anaerobic and aerobic pathways for metabolism of carbohydrate account for a large part of the energy produced. It is important to recognize that there are almost always multiple pathways through which an energy-producing reaction can proceed, so that if one pathway is blocked there is a strong tendency for the energy-producing reaction to spill over into another pathway.

The problems of intermediary metabolism hold the key to understanding many fundamental biological processes as well as to the mode of action of most biologically active chemicals, including those used as insecticides.

LITERATURE CITED

1. Anderson, A. D., and Patton, R. L. 1955. Uric acid synthesis in insects. J. exp. Zool., 128:443–451.
2. Baldwin, E. 1959, Dynamic Aspects of Biochemistry. 3rd ed., Cambridge University Press, Cambridge.
3. Barron, E. S. G., and Tahmisian, T. J. 1948. Metabolism of the cockroach muscle. J. cell. comp. Physiol., 32:57–76.
4. Bheemeswar, B. 1958. Amino acid metabolism in insects. Proc. 4th internat. Congress biochem. (Vienna), 12:78–89.

5. Candy, D. J., and Kilby, B. A. 1959. Site and synthesis of trehalose in the locust. Nature (London), *183*:1594–1595.
6. Cantarow, A., and Shepartz, B. 1962. Biochemistry. 3rd ed., W. B. Saunders, Philadelphia.
7. Casida, J. E. 1958. Metabolism of insecticides by insects. Proc. 4th internat. Congress biochem., (Vienna), *12*:216–238.
8. Chefurka, W. 1958. Glucose metabolism in insects. Proc. 4th internat. Congress biochem. (Vienna), *12*:115–137.
9. Giese, A. C. 1962. Cell Physiology. 2nd ed. W. B. Saunders, Philadelphia.
10. Gilmour, D. 1961. The Biochemistry of Insects. Academic Press, New York.
11. Kittsley, S. L. 1955. Physical Chemistry (College Outline Series). Barnes and Noble, New York.
12. Levinson, Z. H. 1960. Dietary sterols in insects *and* Evolution of insect sterol requirements (2 papers). Proc. XI internat. Congress ent. (Vienna), *3*:145–155.
13. Ludwig, D. 1954. Changes in the distribution of nitrogen in the blood of the Japanese beetle. Physiol. Zool., *27*:325–334.
14. Mehrotra, K. 1961. Carbohydrate metabolism in the 2-spotted mite. C. R. Biochem. Physiol., *3*:184–198.
15. Metcalf, R. L. 1955. Organic Insecticides. Interscience Publishers, New York.
16. O'Brien, R. D. 1960. Toxic Phosphorus Esters. Academic Press, New York.
17. Patton, A. R. 1962. Science for Non-scientists. Burgess, Minneapolis.
18. Pauling, L. 1960. The Nature of the Chemical Bond. 3rd ed. Cornell University Press, Ithaca, N. Y.
19. Rockstein, M. 1957. Intermediary metabolism of carbohydrates. Ann. Rev. Ent., *2*:19–36.
20. Sacktor, B. 1958. A biochemical basis of flight muscle activity. Proc. 4th internat. Congress biochem. (Vienna), *12*:138–150.
21. Smith, J. N. 1962. Detoxication mechanisms in insects. Ann. Rev. Ent., *7*:465–480.
22. Villee, C. A., 1962. Biology. 4th ed. W. B. Saunders, Philadelphia.
23. White, A., Handler, P., Smith, E. L., and Stetten DeW. 1959. Principles of Biochemistry. 2nd ed. Blakiston, New York.
24. Young, R. G. 1961. Effects of dietary beeswax and wax on larvae of *Galleria*. Ann. ent. Soc. Amer., *54*:657–659.

EXCRETION

7

Excretion is a regulatory process by which the internal environment of the animal is kept constant. In this process of regulation, excess materials are removed from the body fluids and eliminated with the solid excreta. The result of this regulation is the elimination of surpluses. This aspect of excretion has attracted the most attention so that the common meaning of the word often overshadows the precise scientific meaning.

In insects, the internal medum is the hemolymph. The physical and chemical properties of this fluid govern the environment of the cells and tissues that make up the organs, and the uniformity of the hemolymph is controlled by excretion.

All animals have some specialized organs that function as regulators. The contractile vacuoles of the protists are the organelles that probably control water—an excretory process. On the other extremity of the evolutionary scale are mammalian kidneys. Insects have specialized structures called the *Malpighian tubes,* which are the primary organs of excretion, but these are supplemented by other organs or parts of organs that have become specialized. Parts of the digestive tract have often been assigned excretory functions; in some specialized groups of insects other mechanisms have been discovered that serve the regulatory function. However, there has been a tendency to overemphasize the importance of such systems. An example of these other mechanisms is the presence of purines in the wing scales of the Pieridae, which serves as a type of storage excretion. This mechanism is mentioned often in dissertations on the excretory process in insects. Storage excretion is common in old imagos and as a temporary expedient during diapause and metamorphosis.

The literature on insect excretion is moderately extensive, but a large part of it consists of morphological descriptions of anatomical structures found in various of the insect groups. A number of reviews have been written on the subject. Among these is a comparative review of arthropod excretion by Maloeuf[9] and reviews of insect excretion by Wigglesworth,[23] Patton,[13] and Craig.[3]

GROSS STRUCTURE OF THE MALPIGHIAN TUBES

The Malpighian tubes were described in 1669 by the Italian scientist, Marcello Malpighi, who called them *vasa varicosa* and thought that they served a biliary function. In 1816, Herold observed that their function was excretory, and in 1820 Meckel gave them the name *Malpighian tubes*.

Malpighian tubes are found in all insects except the Collembola, and the family Aphididae (Homoptera). These structures are long slender tubes, which are often convoluted. Malpighian tubes attach to the digestive tract at a point that is by definition the junction of the midgut and the hindgut. Embryologically it is thought the tubes arise from evaginations of the hindgut tissue and that they must be ectodermal. However, according to Savage,[20] the Malpighian tubes of *Schistocerca gregaria* have an endodermal origin. In this species, six primary tubes develop, and from these tubes more arise until the average number is as great as 250. The primitive number is usually considered to be six, and they almost always exist in multiples of two. Mosquitoes are an exception to this in that they have five Malpighian tubes.

Regardless of the number, direct insertion of the tubes into the digestive tract is unusual. Instead, the tubes anastomose at the proximal end to form an ampullar structure that is usually bilaterally symmetrical and forms the connection between the Malpighian tubes and the digestive tract.

From the descriptive literature it is possible to construct schematic drawings that represent the common types of Malpighian tube systems.[23] These are shown in Figure 7–1 and consist of a basic type (A) with three variants (B), (C), and (D). While visualizing the anatomical structure it is important to remember the function. Regulation is the first consideration, so

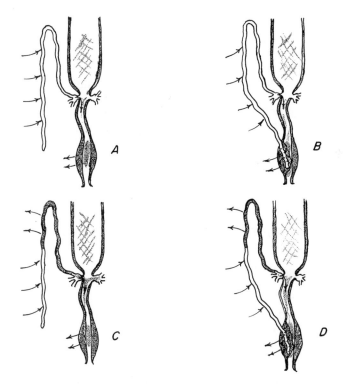

FIG. 7-1. Common Malpighian tube systems found in insects. **A**, Typical of Orthoptera. **B**, Typical of Coleoptera. **C**, Typical of Hemiptera. **D**, Typical of Lepidoptera.

that there must be provision for the filtration of the body fluid, the conversion of the filtrate into an excretable complex, and an arrangement for recovery of essential elements that have been absorbed along with the excess materials.

In the basic type of Malpighian tube system (A), the tubes are long and convoluted, and each tube is made up of walls one cell in thickness with four to six cells comprising the circumference. These tubes may lie more or less free in the body cavity, where they are bathed in the blood; however, some of the tubes are always closely associated with the fat body and digestive tract. Each tube is supplied with a fine trachea, and the cells of the Malpighian system are richly supplied with tracheoles, indicating that the tissues have high metabolic activity.

In the Orthoptera, there are a large number of tubes, and the arrangement may appear to be irregular; however, careful observation will show a repetition of the pattern. In these insects (type A), no visible difference exists in the appearance of the tubes over their entire length, but functional differences can be demonstrated.[6] The distal ends of the tubes may be simply closed with a terminal cell, or the ends may be attached to and imbedded in the tissues that surround the rectum on the hindgut.

Tubes with the distal attachment are described as *cryptosolenic* or *cryptonephridic*. According to Lison the latter term is the more descriptive.[8] Tubes of this type are typical of the Coleoptera, in which there is no visible differentiation over the entire length, and they are represented schematically by type B. The Lepidoptera (type D) also have cryptonephridic tubes, but these tubes are distinctly differentiated into two sections. The distal part is filled with a clear fluid, and the proximal part has solid particles that make it appear opaque. It is easy to demonstrate that the solid contents include purine base compounds by applying a simple murexide test.

Type C is typical of the Hemiptera, and through the extensive work of Wigglesworth with *Rhodnius*,[23] this type has been studied quite thoroughly. This type of tube is free at the distal end but shows a visible differentiation near the midpoint with the proximal half opaque and the distal half clear.

Wigglesworth also described two other tube types in which the granular material filled the entire length of the tube in one, and only the distal part in the other.[24] There is no logical way to explain these two types in terms of function as it is observed in the other types so that these must be considered to be either exotic or pathological.

HISTOLOGICAL STRUCTURE OF THE MALPIGHIAN TUBES

The histological structure of the Malpighian tubes of various insect species has been reported. The delicate nature of the tissues involved and the drastic treatment of fixation have produced some questionable results and conclusions. Nevertheless, generalizations that have validity can be drawn from this work. Very little in vivo work has been reported on the histology or microanatomy of the Malpighian tube system, but electron microscope studies of the tubes have helped to clarify some of the more obscure structures.

Beams et al. prepared sections of Malpighian tubes for electron microscope study by more or less standard methods.[2] They observed that in cross section, four to six large epithelial cells make up the tube wall. The cells are divided into three reasonably distinct regions.

From the outside of the tube (body cavity) toward the lumen these regions include: the basal zone, an intermediate zone with the nucleus, and an apical zone. The outer (basal) zone and the inner (apical) zone show the most interesting structures. The basal zone has an elaborate infolding of the cell membranes, which form intracellular compartments characteristically filled with vacuoles, mitochondria, and some sharply defined bodies that are otherwise unidentified. The apical zone has a brush border, which has been observed from normal histological study, and the filaments are made up of vertically arranged protoplasmic processes.

Sections taken from tubes in various stages of activity show that the mitochondria originate in the basal zone and migrate into the filamentous processes of the apical zone. In some cases the tips of these processes become swollen and bulbous from the contents. Thus it has been concluded that mitochondria actively transport materials from the basal part across the cytoplasm of the tube wall and into the processes where these materials can be discharged into the lumen by a pinching off of the end of the process. It is presumed that the mitochondria are replaced continuously in the basal zone.

Tubes of types C and D, in which there are obvious functional differences between the proximal and distal parts, also show differences in histological structure. The distal part, which normally contains a clear fluid, has a structure described as a honeycomb, made up of parallel filaments of protoplasm. The proximal part, which contains the granular material, has elongate extrusions of protoplasm that give the impression of cilia. There has been some speculation that these cilia-like extrusions may function to sweep the crystals in the lumen toward the junction with the digestive tract, but there are no authentic observations in which cilia-like movement has been proved. The lateral waving motion may be passive, and evidence that the processes can be extended or retracted into the cells of the tube wall is moderately good.

At the point of junction in the proximal-distal differentiated tubes a sharp change in the cell types is displayed. The cells of the distal part contain considerably more mitochondria and other cellular inclusions that are characteristic of actively secreting cells. It is quite common to observe cells of this region discharging materials into the lumen of the tube by either a merocrine or holocrine secretory process. Unfortunately, in vivo observations are rare or lacking, and most observations have come from the study of fixed tissue, which has introduced the possibility that the bursting cells are artifacts of fixation. To counter this criticism, however, cells of this type are not observed in the proximal part of tubes subjected to the same treatment.

Histological evidence indicates that the cells of the distal section of the differentiated tubes and the entire length of the nondifferentiated type are assigned a secretory function, by which they actively take up materials from outside the tube, pass them across the cell membrane, and discharge them into the lumen. The cells of the proximal part in those types where differentiation occurs are likewise given the function of reabsorption.

In types A and B, the reabsorption of essentials must take place entirely in some other part of the insect, the most likely site being the rectum of the hindgut. In cryptonephridic tubes reabsorption must be a function of the tubes associated with the wall of the rectum.

The histological structure of the tubes attached to the rectum has been given special attention. Ishimori suggested using their configuration as a taxonomic character to separate the immature forms of various Lepidoptera, and his work has a good description of the histological structures.[5]

From the inside of the gut toward the body cavity there are five layers of tissue. These include: a chitinous intima; an epithelial layer; a double, thin membrane; a single, thin membrane; and a layer of muscles. The Malpighian tubes lie in two levels with one level of tubes lying between the single and the double membrane and the other level lying between the double membrane and the epithelial cells. In this latter level, the cells that make up the tubes are large and thick. Usually these cells have a single nucleus, but binucleate cells have been observed. Most tubes are lined with an intima that is presumed to be chitin. No basement membrane is discernible.

The functional mechanism of the Malpighian tubes surrounding the rectum has not been entirely worked out, but it apparently is associated with the reabsorption of water and probably other essential materials from the hindgut. That substances other than water are reabsorbed and that these substances are liberated into the blood are strongly suggested by immersing the freshly dissected rectal structure from *Teneb rio molitor* larvae in dilute silver nitrate. Immediately, small round spots of white silver chloride appear at the apices of the convolutions of the tubes. Histological examination shows that at each of these locations is situated a specialized cell that has a form suggestive of a poppet valve in a gasoline engine, but it cannot function in this manner. Evidence of the circulation of essential salts, specifically sodium chloride, which appears in the excreta of most insects, was obtained by Patton and Craig,[15] who traced radioactive sodium-24 through the Malpighian tubes and into a saline surrounding the isolated rectum. Historically, this experiment may be of some interest, because it is believed to have been the first application of a man-made radioactive isotope as a tracer in insect physiology.

INTRINSIC MUSCLES AND MOVEMENT OF THE MALPIGHIAN TUBES

In vivo observations often reveal that the Malpighian tubes are in motion. The movement may be a springlike contraction or a peristaltic wave, and in each case the movement has been traced to the activity of intrinsic muscles intimately associated with the Malpighian tubes. Palm studied these structures extensively.[12] During the course of his work he examined over 3000 insects and described four types of contraction.

The Malpighian tubes of species of Orthoptera, Odonata, Hemiptera, Neuroptera, Tricoptera, Lepidoptera, Coleoptera, Diptera, and Hymenoptera were included in the survey, and all were found capable of movement. In Thysanura, Dermaptera, and Thysanoptera, there are no muscles, and the tubes are quiet. The muscular elements exist only in the proximal part of the tubes of Lepidoptera, Diptera, and Hemiptera, but they are present as strong bands along the entire length of the tubes of Odonata and Hymenoptera. In the Neuroptera and Coleoptera, and in the genus *Gryllotalpa* (Orthoptera), a network of fine muscle fibers are formed. In one genus Palm observed a well defined median band of muscles; this was the only part of the tube capable of contraction. In the cryptonephridic forms, the tubes surrounding the rectum are capable of contractions that are independent of those of the rest of the system.

In Orthoptera, the muscle system offers a special case. Careful observation of the tubes, as they lie in what appears superficially to be a tangled mass, reveals that they tend to form helical coils with a single strand of muscle fiber running through the center of the helix. As the muscle contracts, it causes the tube to compress in a motion resembling the action of a coil spring. Various parts of the tubes are supplied with separate fibers, which contract individually so that only sections of an individual tube may be active while the remainder may remain motionless.

Control of Contractions of the Malpighian Tubes

All of Palm's observations indicate that the muscle fibers involved in the contraction of the Malpighian tubes are striated, and temperature contraction response data indicates that the rates of contraction are too great to be attributed to smooth muscle. Further studies with the effects of combinations of temperature and humidity indicate the contractions are myogenic and probably are initiated by an intrinsic stimulation center somewhat like that already postulated for the heart. A change in the partial pressure of oxygen in the air surrounding the insect does not alter the rate of contractions, nor does HCN gas until its concentration reaches the point of asphyxiation. An increase in the carbon dioxide tension in the air decreases the amplitude of the contractions. Osmotic pressure and salt balance of the perfusion salines cause changes in the rates of contraction of dissected preparations, and the persistence of movement can be prolonged by the addition of glucose to the perfusion saline. The rate of contractions seems to be increased slightly by acid solutions, and slow changes in pH are tolerated. The addition of various common muscle stimulants has no appreciable effect upon the contractile process.

The Function of Tube Movement. It seems logical that any anatomical structure as well developed as the Malpighian tube muscles must serve a physiological function, but what the tube movement accomplishes is a matter of speculation. It has been suggested that these movements cause the contents of the tube to be propelled in a forward direction. It has also been suggested that these movements keep the contents mixed, which might enhance the penetration of materials through the walls of the tube and increase the efficiency of reclaiming essentials. Other possible functions remain obscure.

Mechanics of Malpighian Tube Function. Regardless of the histological structure, the physiological function of the Malpighian system is to regulate the concentrations of the various constituents and metabolites in the blood. In mammals, the kidney filters blood through a structure called the *glomerulus,* with blood pressure as the driving force. After the blood filters through the glomerulus, a tubular structure reabsorbs the essentials from the ultrafiltrate and returns them to the blood. In insects, the end result of the process is similar, but the mechanism must be different since the blood pressure of insects is negligible.

Perfusion experiments by Patton and Craig[15] showed that the rate of penetration of salt solutions through the Malpighian tubes of *Tenebrio molitor* could not be increased by adding hydrostatic pressure to the system, nor does a change in osmotic pressure of the perfusion saline alter the rate of absorption as related to a hyper- or hypo-osmotic system. Instead, these changes or forces tend to decrease the rate of absorption in all instances. The time during which filtration from a partially dissected system takes place can be increased by saturating the perfusing saline with oxygen. These observations seem to rule out osmotic pressure as a significant force in the filtering process.

Wigglesworth studied the excretory function of *Rhodnius*,[23] and the results of his work laid an excellent foundation for that of Ramsey,[18] which came later. Ramsey's experiments substantiated those of Wigglesworth and added data that show the existence of a physiological differentiation in the function of the proximal and distal sections of the tube. Since *Rhodnius* is a blood-sucking insect that engorges once between molts, it lends itself well to the type of experiments performed by Wigglesworth and Ramsey. It would be difficult to duplicate these experiments with other insects.

Among the early experiments of Wigglesworth was one in which he dissected the insects so as to expose the Malpighian tubes. Using a soft wax, he placed ligatures at various levels along the tube and observed the results.

If two ligatures were placed so that they were both in the proximal (opaque) part of the tube shortly after the insect had fed, the part of the tube between the ligatures would remain clear, while on each side the tube would fill with white granular material. If the ligatures were placed with one at the junction of the differentiated (proximal) section and the other proximal to this, the part of the tube between the ligatures remained clear but that part between the second ligature and the entrance into the digestive tract filled with crystalline material. In this experiment, the distal part of the tube became distended.

These observations indicated that there is a one-way penetration of the wall of the Malpighian tube at the distal part, and that there is a force developed sufficient to cause the distension of the tube. That the section of the tube between the ligatures in the proximal region is clear is interpreted to indicate that no penetration of the filtrate takes place in this region, but that the proximal part of the tube functions in the reclamation of water and other essential materials. It is a little difficult to rationalize the presence of crystalline material in the extreme proximal section, but until this material is otherwise explained, it may be considered the result of a back-up of the excretory effluent from an adjacent tube, probably by way of the ampulla. From his observations with *Rhodnius*, Wigglesworth proposed a scheme that could explain how the highly insoluble uric acid in solution in low concentration in the blood can be transported across the membranes into the tubes, converted to uric acid in an impure crystalline form, and eliminated. Wigglesworth's hypothesis lacks proof by demonstration, but it remains as a logical explanation of the observed phenomena. Wigglesworth's scheme is shown in Figure 7–2. In this scheme, uric acid in the blood is converted to a sodium or potassium urate by the reaction between uric acid and bicarbonate. The urate salts are relatively more soluble than uric acid itself and can cross the cell membrane in solution. Within the tube the urates are broken down to regenerate the bicarbonate, which is reabsorbed, and the uric acid is precipitated. It is necessary for the tissues of the Malpighian tubes to have carbonic anhydrase for this mechanism to work. This enzyme system has been demonstrated from insect tissue by Anderson et al.,[1] and it is likely that it exists in the Malpighian tissues; how-

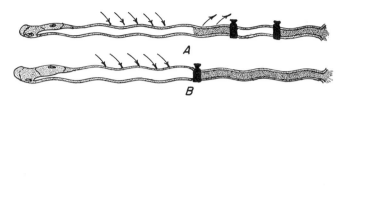

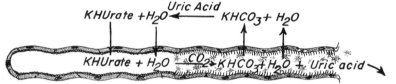

FIG. 7-2. *Top:* The effect of placing wax ligatures on the Malpighian tubes of *Rhodnius*. **A,** The effect of ligatures placed on a proximal (differentiated) section of tubule. **B,** The effect of a ligature at the distal-proximal junction. Note the swelling of the tubule, presumably caused by absorption of metabolites by the tubule.
Bottom: A hypothetical scheme to explain the penetration of insoluble uric acid through the Malpighian tube wall. The uric acid is converted to a relatively soluble potassium acid urate by the action of potassium bicarbonate. The bicarbonate is reclaimed in the tube and reabsorbed, leaving uric acid to be excreted. (Redrawn after Wigglesworth.)

ever, the same cycle could take place by substituting phosphate for bicarbonate, and the necessary enzymes for this reaction have been demonstrated from insect tissues.

Ramsey has contributed a number of details to elucidate the more obscure points regarding the mechanics of Malpighian tube function. His work includes studies with mosquito larvae,[17] *Rhodnius*,[18] and the isolated Malpighian tubes of the walking stick (*Dixippus morosus*).[19]

In mosquito larvae, osmoregulation is aided and partly controlled by the excretory system. When the external medium (water) is low in salts, the fluid excreta contains less sodium ion than the blood. It is not possible for Malpighian tubes to form urine higher in sodium content than the blood.

As a follow-up to this observation, Ramsey injected potassium (as KCl) into the blood of *Rhodnius* and checked the formation of urine and the concentrations of ions as the fluid passed along the length of the tube. He was able to show that this insect can remove potassium ion against a concentration gradient. Urine in the distal portion of the tube contains more potassium and less sodium than the blood. In the proximal region, the urine becomes more nearly like blood in its concentration of sodium and potassium. From these data, Ramsey concluded that sodium and water are reabsorbed from the region of the rectum (see also, Patton and Craig[15]).

By comparing studies of *Rhodnius* with studies of the mosquito, it is possible to substantiate the observations, using an intact insect. In this situation, concentrations of sodium and potassium in the blood can be altered physiologically. By increasing the concentration of salts in water surrounding the mosquito larvae, the concentration of salts in the blood can be altered by the absorption of salts through the anal gills. Concentrations of both sodium and potassium increase in the urine with increased concentration in the blood, and absorption in the rectum decreases. Circulation of potassium from the blood to the tube, to the gut, and back to the blood takes place. The concentration of potassium in the blood of the larvae is controlled by the rate of voiding, which also affects the amount of reabsorption; this rate is controlled by peristaltic movement of the gut.

Further studies with eight other insect species led Ramsey to conclude that the concentration of potassium is always greater in the urine than in the blood. Electrical potential measurements across the wall of the Malpighian tubes indicated an accumulation of positive charges in the lumen. Since sodium concentration is always lower in the tube than in the blood, it was concluded that while potassium is actively transported into the tube, sodium enters by simple diffusion.

With isolated Malpighian tubes of the walking stick, Ramsey observed that the urine (of this insect) is either isosmotic or slightly hypotonic to the blood. He measured the rate of urine formation and found that it would amount to about six microliters per hour, which in 24 hours would be equivalent to the total blood volume. The tubes of the walking stick actively secrete sodium, potassium, and water in all sections; but the sodium-to-potassium ratio of the contents is greater in the proximal part. Potassium acts as a diuretic, but sodium has little effect. The rate of secretion of potassium is more than 10 times that of sodium. The same observation also has been made in the larvae of *Sialus* (Sialidae, Neuroptera).

In addition to the behavior of sodium and potassium, Ramsey studied several divalent ions and some organic compounds. The results indicate that the concentration of a substance in the urine is nearly independent of the concentration of the same substance in the blood. There does not appear to be a maximum or minimum concentration for the removal of amino acids (for example) from the saline, although rates of penetration may be different for different amino acids.

The sum of these observations leads to the following conclusions:

1. The Malpighian tube is freely permeable, so that most metabolites of small molecules may pass through under the influence of a concentration gradient, if such exists.

2. Some salts and water are actively secreted, and it is not clear whether interaction between water and salts takes place.

3. This stream of saline passes rapidly down the tube and flushes out the diffusing substances.

4. Substances required by the insect are absorbed by the rectum and returned to the blood.

5. According to Ramsey, it is simpler for an organism to develop ways of absorbing needed substances than to develop ways of excreting all possible undesirable substances.

In considering these conclusions, the only question that arises is that of maintaining the favorable concentration gradient to cause continuous filtration of the protein-free fluid part of the hemolymph. Experiments in which the activity of the Malpighian tubes in excreting a dye (indigo carmine) is blocked by a chemical (ethylene glycol) show that the tubes also lose their ability to reduce blue tetrazolium, an indicator of oxidase activity.[14] The tubes also lose their fluorescence. These combined observations indicate existence of an active secretory mechanism that is driven by an enzyme reaction (or enzyme reactions). This conclusion is supported by the existence of a definite temperature maximum for excretory function (in the American roach), with a very sharp cut-off when this maximum is exceeded.[14]

A great deal is still to be learned about the mechanics of excretory function in insects. The whole process may be described as a filtration of the fluid portion of the hemolymph, excepting the protein that has molecules too large to pass through the membranes. The filtrate penetrates the wall of the tube either by diffusion (Ramsey) or by active secretion (Patton et al.), with the possibility that both processes are important. The essential substances are reabsorbed up to a threshold value, either in the proximal part of the tubes or in the rectal structures of the hindgut.

OSMOTIC BALANCE AND OSMOREGULATION IN INSECTS

The general subject of osmoregulation on a comparative basis has been thoroughly discussed by Prosser and Brown.[16]

Water is an essential constituent of all living things and is the continuous phase in which most metabolic reactions occur. It is of obvious importance that the animal be able to regulate the amount of water in the body fluid and tissues at just the right level; this is part of the regulatory function of the excretory system.

Through evolutionary development, insects are essentially terrestrial but members of several orders have returned to an aquatic habitat (both fresh and salt water) for at least part of their life cycle. The relationships between terrestrial and aquatic existence in some insects have already been discussed, for example, the work of Ramsey with mosquito larvae. Experiments with other aquatic insects indicate that osmotic concentration is maintained through compensatory regulation of nonprotein nitrogen (principally amino acids) if the salt content of the surrounding medium is reduced. These experiments also indicate that the nonprotein nitrogen (NPN) is correspondingly reduced if the osmotic concentration of the habitat is increased. In dipterous larvae (mosquitoes and midges) the anal papillae function in the process of osmoregulation. It has been demonstrated that isolated papillae swell in tap water and constrict in Ringer's solution. If a larva of *Aedes* sp. is ligated in front of the openings of the Malpighian tubes into the gut and then put into hyperosmotic glucose, the hind part shrinks, but without the ligature the whole larva shrinks. If the ligature is behind the opening of the Malpighian tubes and the larva is placed in fresh water, the posterior part becomes swollen while the anterior part does not. From such ligation experiments, Wigglesworth concluded that larvae normally swallow very little water, that the anal papillae are the organs most permeable to water, and that water is excreted by the Malpighian tubes.[24] He also found that it was possible to acclimate this species (*Aedes argenteus*) to habitats of different salinities and that when the osmoconcentration of the external medium is equal to or lower than 0.65 per cent NaCl, the internal osmoconcentration remains constant. When the concentration of the external medium is higher, the osmoconcentration of the internal fluid tends to follow. By a gradual process, it is possible to rear these larvae in sea water dilutions with an equivalent of up to 1.4 per cent NaCl.

In all aquatic insects, amino acids provide the principal osmotically active solutes with salts absorbed through specialized organs or through the gut. The external body wall is relatively impermeable. Water balance in the fluids is maintained principally through the activity of the Malpighian tubes.

Terrestrial insects have a severe water conservation problem and have developed various means for meeting it. Among these are the waxy covering on the integument, spiracle control, and the substitution of amino acids for salts as the principal osmotically active blood solutes. Insects with very rigorous economy also have developed to a high degree the ability to reclaim water from the excreta. This ability is easily observed by dissecting a larva of the yellow mealworm. The spent food bolus that traverses the hindgut is always soft and moist, but after passage through the rectum, it is eliminated as a powder-dry mass.

COMPONENTS OF INSECT URINE

The components of insect urine are primarily the end products of nitrogen metabolism plus excess salts and water that have been removed from the blood. This subject has already been discussed in part in Chapter 6.

Most of the data available on the components of insect urine have come from analysis of the solid excreta, a technique used because of the difficulty of collecting fluid urine free of fecal material. Most of the earlier work consisted of analysis of the meconia of *Lepidoptera,* analysis of fecal pellets, or in a few cases comparative analyses of the components of the food eaten and the excrement voided. These data do not yield an entirely conclusive picture of the processes that take place, but the problems of collecting urine directly from the Malpighian tubes have not been entirely solved.

One of the first analyses reported was the work of Siridot.[21] His analysis showed the following:

1. The main constituent of the sediment found in the Malpighian tubes of insects is a urate salt of various bases.
2. Uric acid always accompanies this urate.
3. Calcium oxalate is not found in these complex deposits.
4. Calcium urate in the excreta is usually colored a red-brown.
5. The complex deposits are not related to the urate crystals.

A more complete analysis was reported by Wigglesworth from his study of the excretory processes of *Rhodnius.* He arrived at the following conclusions: The adult *Rhodnius* engorges itself with two or three times its weight in blood at a single feeding. The fluid part of this blood is excreted during the first few hours as a clear urine—an alkaline fluid (pH = 7.8) more or less isosmotic with the blood. During this period, the urine carries most of the sodium and potassium chloride that was in the ingested blood. This urine also contains urea, bicarbonate, sulfate, and uric acid. After the first day the urine becomes acid (pH = 6.0 to 6.5) and is more concentrated. At this stage the urine contains a yellow pigment. Uratic spheres appear and increase in number in the urine until it is semisolid. Now the urine has only traces of sodium and potassium chloride and urea, but a small amount of sodium, magnesium, and phosphate is still present. Wigglesworth also recorded some creatine and amino acids. Almost all nitrogen is excreted as uric acid in the form of crystalline spheres with radial striations. About 80 per cent to 90 per cent of the uric acid present is in the free form. The remaining uric acid may be assumed to be either sodium or potassium urate.

These analyses and the conclusions drawn from them are typical of the many that exist in the literature. In addition to the nitrogenous excreta already discussed, other types are found in some species. Ammonia is excreted by many insects that inhabit a fluid or semifluid medium (Chapter 6); allantoin and in some cases xanthine and hypoxanthine have been detected (see Table 6-1). In regard to the data about the substance often reported as "creatine," this substance probably does not occur in the nitrogenous excreta of insects. Creatine is formed in vertebrate muscle from the metabolism of the phosphogen, phosphocreatine, and under abnormal conditions creatine may occur in vertebrate urine. The phosphogen found in insect muscle is probably phosphoarginine, so that data reported concerning "creatine" represents an unknown nitrogenous compound.

One of the more complete analyses of insect excreta from several divergent insect species was reported by Nation and Patton.[11] These data are summarized in Table 6-1. It is evident from these data that uric acid is the principal nitrogenous end product in all terrestrial insects. The existence of appreciable quantities of urea in the excreta of the yellow mealworm probably is the "exception that proves the rule."

ENZYMES OF THE MALPIGHIAN TUBES

The tissues of the Malpighian tubes have been described as active in several metabolic processes, and like the mammalian kidney, these tissues should be expected to contain enzymes with relatively high activity. A summary of some of the enzymes from Malpighian tubes was compiled by Craig.[3] These data are tabulated in Table 7-1.

In addition to the enzymes shown in Table 7-1, which is only a partial list of those enzymes that must exist in these tissues, several water-soluble vitamins associated with metabolic processes are found in high concentrations. Metcalf reported the concentrations of various of these water-soluble vitamins from bioassay of Malpighian tube tissue from the American cockroach.[10] The values are as follows: riboflavin, 840 to 1000 μg. per gram of fresh tissue, a value that is one of the highest ever recorded from an animal tissue; thiamin, 33 to 50 μg. per gram; niacin, 200 to 460 μg. per gram; pantothenic acid, 80 μg. per gram; and ascorbic acid, 600 to 1000 μg. per gram. Metcalf was unable to demonstrate the oxidative enzymes normally associated with riboflavin in highly active tissues, but the probability remains that riboflavin

TABLE 7-1. Distribution of Enzymes in the Malpighian Tubes

Enzyme	*Acrida bicolor*			*Mantis religiosa*			*Blaps gibba*			*Apis mellifera*		
	Proximal	*Intermediate*	*Distal*	*Proximal*	*Intermediate*	*Distal*	*Proximal*	*Intermediate*	*Distal*	*Proximal*	*Intermediate*	*Distal*
Alkaline phosphatase	+++				++		+++			+++		
Acid phosphatase	++	++			++		+++			++	++	++
Lipase		++			++			++	++	++		+++
Succinic dehydrogenase	+++	++	+	+	++	+	+	++		++	+	

Tabular material from Craig.[3]

is associated with and probably essential to an unidentified enzyme system that produces energy to drive the secretory processes necessary for the function of the Malpighian tubes.

EXCRETORY FUNCTION OF THE DIGESTIVE TRACT

Collembola and members of the family Aphididae are without Malpighian tubes, so that the regulatory function must be assumed for other organs. According to Waterhouse and Day, the midgut of the Collembola takes on the function,[22] and it has been suggested that loss of the midgut epithelia, which in this insect takes place just before a molt, is part of the process.

In aphids, the process was studied by Gersch, who used fluorescein dye to trace the process of elimination.[4] He found that this dye was picked up readily by parts of the digestive tract and eliminated, but it must be remembered that this group has a very highly specialized digestive system (see Figure 3–1, G).

Other examples cited by Waterhouse and Day include records of various dyes and iron salts that are absorbed by cells of various parts of the digestive tract and discharged into the lumen of the gut. They also point out that uric acid is present in the midgut of larval Hymenoptera, which has no through connection with the hindgut.

Undoubtedly the digestive tract, in addition to the rectal structure, functions as a regulatory organ in the excretory process. Regulation of water is probably the principal contribution of the digestive tract to the overall process; however, no good evidence exists that the digestive tract rivals the Malpighian tubes in the general excretory function.

STORAGE EXCRETION

In an animal, any pathway for the removal of a substance that controls the concentration of that dissolved substance in the blood is an excretory process. Thus, the deposits of uric acid and related purines often found in the fat body and lining the integument, particularly of old adult insects, can be considered a form of excretion, and the presence of these deposits represents failure of the normal organs of regulation. This deposition of excretory products is called *storage excretion*—a process by which excess products of metabolic activity are held in an inert form until they can be removed. At present, the technology of insect physiology has provided no reliable means of evaluating the well-being of insects exhibiting storage excretion, but appearance of uric acid crystals in the fat body or in the meconia of metamorphosing insects is usually only a temporary expedient used while the regular channels of elimination are inactive, which fact detracts from the importance of storage excretion as an excretory process. There are very few clear-cut examples of storage excretion or tissues that are specialized for this purpose; most evidence for its existence has come from the affinity of certain tissues for dyes taken from the blood (in some of the older literature the pericardial cells have been assigned this function). The possible presence of storage excretion must not be overlooked, but neither should its importance as a vital function be overemphasized.

ATHROCYTIC EXCRETION

In the normal course of living there are several possible sources of solid particulate material that appear in the blood of insects. This material may include fragments of cells, particles of melanin-like pigment, or foreign bodies. These particles are removed from the blood by specialized sessile phagocytes called *athrocytes*. The anatomical identity of the athrocytes has never been established, but they are described from observation of their function as associated with Malpighian tubes in some insects and with the digestive tract of others. It is easy to find examples of athrocytic activity in the Malpighian tubes of larvae of *Tenebrio molitor*. During the period between molts, dark granules of pigment presumed to be melanin appear in the blood. These granules are picked up by the cells of the Malpighian tubes, particularly near the proximal part, and some of the granules can be seen to enter the lumen of the tube. Most of the granules remain in the cells and are cleared during the molting process. It is easy to distinguish a recently molted larva from one that is preparing to molt by the presence of these dark granules in the tubes. Like storage excretion, athrocytic excretion should be recognized, but its importance may be minor.

SUMMARY

The primary function of the excretory system is to regulate the concentration of the constituents of hemolymph and to control the internal environment of the cells and tissues that comprise the animal. The result of this regulatory function is the elimination of excess materials.

Insects have as their primary organs of excretion specialized tubular organs called Malpighian tubes. These are roughly analogous to the vertebrate kidney in their function.

Practically all insects excrete some of their nitrogenous waste as uric acid. In some species, other nitrogenous compounds including ammonia, urea, allantoin, xanthine, hypoxanthine, and in a few cases, amino acids are present. The distribution of the various nitrogen end products in the excreta depends on the food, the type of excretory mechanism, and the habitat of the species.

The mechanical aspects of the excretory process in insects are described by a combination of several processes. Mineral salts, particularly those of potassium, and water are actively secreted; this process may be extended to other substances. There is some evidence that compounds penetrating the Malpighian tubes and eventually appearing in the urinary excreta may cross the walls by simple diffusion with a gradient.

LITERATURE CITED

1. Anderson, Am. D., and March, R. B. 1956. Inhibitors of carbonic anhydrase in the American cockroach. Canad. J. Zool., *34:*68–74.
2. Beams, H. W., Tahmisian, T. N., and Devine, C. L. 1955. Electron microscopy of malpighian tubule of grasshopper. Biophys. biochem. Cytol., *1:*197–202.
3. Craig, R. 1960. Physiology of insect excretion. Ann. Rev. Ent., *5:*53–68.
4. Gersch, M. 1941. The excretion of fluorescein by the aphid. Zeitschr. vergl. Physiol., *29:*506–531.
5. Ishimori, N. 1924. The relation of the malpighian tubes to the rectum in lepidopterous larvae. Ann. ent. Soc. Amer., *17:*75–86.
6. Lison, L. 1936. The excretion of acid dyes by the malpighian tubes of *Orthoptera.* Arch. Biol. Liege, *48:*321–360; 1938. Excretion of basic dyes by the malpighian tubes of *Orthoptera.* Zeitschr. fur Zellforschung mikros. Anat., *28:*179–209.
7. Lison, L. 1937. Athrocytosis in insect excretion. Ann. Soc. roy. Zool. Belg., *68:*41–48.
8. Lison, L. 1938. Cryptonephridic systems in insects. C. R. Soc. Biol., *128:*801–803.
9. Maloeuf, N. S. R. 1938. Physiology of excretion of arthropods. Physiol. Rev., *18:*29–58.
10. Metcalf, R. L., and Patton, R. L. 1942. Riboflavin metabolism in the American cockroach. Jour. cell. and comp. Physiol., *19:*373–376.
11. Nation, J. L., and Patton, R. L. 1961. Nitrogen partition in insect excreta. J. ins. Physiol., *6:*299–308.
12. Palm, N. B. 1946. Intrinsic muscles and movement of the malpighian tubes. Lunds. Univ. Arrskr., *42:*1–39.
13. Patton, R. L. 1953. Insect excretion. *In* Insect Physiology (K. D. Roeder, ed.). John Wiley, New York, Ch. 15.
14. Patton, R. L., Anderson, A. D., and Gardner, J. 1959. Rates of excretion of the American cockroach. J. Ins. Physiol., *2:*256–261.
15. Patton, R. L., and Craig, R. 1939. Excretion of various substances by larvae of *T. molitor.* J. exp. Zool., *81:*437–457.
16. Prosser, C. L., and Brown, F. A. 1961. Comparative Animal Physiology. 2nd ed., W. B. Saunders, Philadelphia, Ch. 2.
17. Ramsey, J. A. 1950. Osmoregulation in mosquito larvae. J. exp. Biol., *27:*145–157. See also: *28:* 62–73, 1951; *30:*79–89, 1953.
18. Ramsey, J. A. 1952. Excretion in *Rhodnius.* J. exp. Biol., *29:*110–126.
19. Ramsey, J. A. 1958. Excretion studies with the walking stick. J. exp. Biol., *30:*358–369, 1953; *31:*104–113, 1954; *32:*183–199, 200–216, 1955; *33:*697–708, 1956; *35:*871–891.
20. Savage, A. A. 1956. Origin and development of malpighian tubes in *Schistocerca.* Quart. J. microscop. Sci., *97:*599–615.
21. Siridot, S. 1958. Research on the secretions of insects. Ann. sci. nat. Zool., series 4, *10:*251–334.
22. Waterhouse, D., and Day, M. 1953. Functions of the gut in absorption, excretion, and intermediary metabolism. *In* Insect Physiology (K. D. Roeder, ed.). John Wiley, New York, Ch. 13.
23. Wigglesworth, V. B. 1931. Excretion in *Rhodnius.* J. exp. Biol., *8:*411–457.
24. Wigglesworth, V. B. 1939. Principles of Insect Physiology. Methuen, London.

8

MUSCLES AND NERVES

Muscles are the organs specialized to convert potential energy of food into the kinetic energy of heat and motion. They are associated with a triggering mechanism consisting of a more or less elaborate network of specialized tissues—the nervous system—arranged in various degrees of complication in animals and adapted to perceive environmental changes that are converted to impulses that stimulate the muscles. Depending upon the network involved, the nervous system can modulate or channel the flow of impulses and thus control the response of the muscles. This complex constitutes the neuromuscular system of animals.

The study of neuromuscular physiology is old. Modern technology has made it possible to verify some of the older observations, to correct some of the ideas that led to misinterpretations, and to add significantly to the knowledge of the very complex processes characteristic of higher animals. Neuromuscular physiology, like intermediary metabolism, is a field within the discipline of physiology that requires special consideration. It must be assumed for the purposes of this book that the student is familiar with the modern concepts of neuromuscular physiology, or that he will avail himself of the discussions in modern textbooks on the subject. A very much abridged outline is presented here mostly to acquaint the student with the specialized terminology so that he may better comprehend discussion of the special aspects of insect neuromuscular systems.

The tissues involved in the study of neuromuscular physiology are made of specialized cells arranged in definite patterns. The property of *irritability* has been developed to a high degree in both muscular and nervous tissues, and this factor differentiates these tissues from other tissues. The nerves are highly specialized for rapid transmission of stimuli, and the muscles are specialized to respond to these stimuli by contracting.

CHARACTERISTICS OF MUSCLES

Based on their appearance, structure, and microstructure, muscles can be classified as striated, smooth, or cardiac. All insect muscles are striated,[6] although they may vary appreciably in the appearance of the striations. Muscles can also be classified according to their gross function. On this basis, those muscles, with origins and insertions on skeletal structures, that usually function to move appendages, as in walking or flying, are called *phasic* muscles.

Those muscles that are arranged around hollow structures, with no strict origins and insertions except that they insert into and pull on another part of the same muscle, are called *tonic* muscles. Both muscle types are under reflex control, but many tonic muscles are capable of spontaneous and rhythmic contraction.

Phasic muscles are usually organized into motor units innervated in various ways. The possibilities include single or double innervation and polyneural innervation, which provides separate channels for fast contractions, slow contractions, and inhibition. All types are found in various insect muscles, but polyneural innervation seems to predominate in phasic systems.

Phasic muscles may be long or short. Long muscles are capable of producing a greater excursion of the appendage that they activate than are the short thick muscles; but the latter muscles produce the greater force.

The arrangement by which muscles can exert controlled force may follow one or more of the following mechanisms: (A) If a muscle is organized into many motor units regulated from the central nervous system, a gradation in response is possible by controlling the number of units activated. In skeletal muscles, the individual fibers exhibit an all-or-none response, so that each stimulated fiber contracts to its greatest extent and the over-all strength of the contraction is controlled by the number of individual fibers receiving the stimulation. (B) The second possibility is that the activity of the muscle units is controlled by frequency of stimulation of the individual units. High frequencies elicit a strong contraction and low-frequency stimuli give a lesser response. (C) In the third situation, multiple innervation occurs and different excitatory nerves cause contractions of different rates. The inhibitory axons can diminish the effect of the excitatory axons. (D) The fourth possibility is that the mechanical properties of the system can control the duration and magnitude of the contraction.[10]

THE STRUCTURE OF MUSCLES

Muscles (specifically striated skeletal muscles) are composed of bundles of *fibers* (fasciculi). Each bundle and each fasciculus is surrounded by a sheath of connective tissue, called the *epimysium* and *perimysium* respectively. The fibers are somewhat irregular in cross section and vary in size. Within each fiber are subunits called *fibrils*, or *fibrillae*, separated from each other by a relatively undifferentiated protoplasmic layer called the *sarcoplasm*. According to some histologists, the fibrillae are subdivided into *sarcostyles*, but this term is also used synonomously with fibrils.[8]

Muscles can be classified by their fibrillar structure utilizing the number and arrangement of the myofilaments, the nuclei, and the manner in which the fibers are imbedded in the connective tissue as the criteria. On this basis, four types of muscle have been described from insects. These are shown in Figure 8–1.

In the first muscle type, found principally in the larvae of certain Diptera, the fibrils are only slightly differentiated and are encased in a thick layer of superficial plasma that is devoid of fibrillae. The second type is nearly universally distributed among insects and is typical of skeletal muscles. The

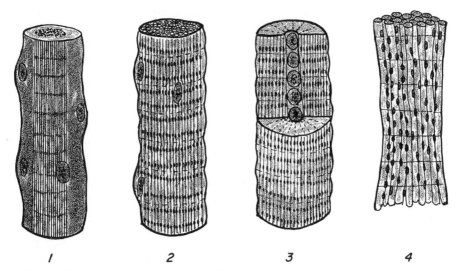

1   *2*   *3*   *4*

FIG. 8-1. The four common types of muscle fibers found in insects. 1, Typically found in honeybee larvae and in many dipterous larvae. It is characterized by fibrils resembling minute threads with no visible differentiation that are invested in a thick plasma. 2, Typically found in the skeletal muscles of most insects. 3, The tubular muscle found typically in adults of Hymenoptera and Diptera. 4, A fiber from a fibrillar muscle, typical of the indirect flight muscles of *Apis* and *Vespa*. (Redrawn after Wigglesworth.)

fibrillae occupy the entire structure and are arranged irregularly. Each fiber is sheathed in a tough *sarcolemma* with the nuclei of the sarcoplasm scattered throughout the substance of the plasma or disposed immediately beneath the sarcolemma. In the adults of many Hymenoptera, Coleoptera, and some Diptera, the nuclei of the fibers are arranged in flat bundles that radiate from the center. These are tubular muscles, which constitute the third type. In the fourth muscle type, there are individual bundles of fibrils, which are not imbedded in a matrix but are bound together with tracheoles. Between the bundles are discs thought to be either nuclei or stored food, presumably glycogen.[19]

Striated muscles evidently originated early in the evolution of animals since this type of muscle is found in nearly all phyla, including such primitive forms as the coelenterates. The ultrastructure of striated muscles has been visualized through electron microscopy and is the subject of lengthy discussion in specialized textbooks. A brief summary is all that is included here.[10]

The Ultrastructure of Striated Muscle

The cross striations consist of regions that are alternately strongly and weakly birefringent. These are called *anisotropic* (A) bands and *isotropic* (I) bands respectively. The I-bands are light when viewed by transmitted light and dark by polarized light and are divided by transverse boundaries called Z-lines. Between the Z-lines are structural units called *sarcomeres*. Each sarcomere has two light areas made from halves of the two I-bands, and an A-band lies between them. In the middle of the A-band is a lighter H-region, which may have an M-line in its center. Many of the fibrils are aligned with respect to the striations, and the space between the fibrils is filled with granular sarcoplasm, which often contains mitochondria. These relationships are shown diagrammatically in Figure 8–2.

In insect muscles, the fibers that are capable of high frequency contractions (the flight muscles) are characterized by a greater diameter of the fibers and larger sarcostyles, which are separated by a thicker sarcoplasm containing many mitochondria. The slower leg muscles have smaller fiber diameter, and the sarcostyles are narrow and close together with the mitochondria relatively scarce.[10]

The fibrillae of both vertebrate and insect muscles contain two types of filaments. One is thick, 110 Å to 140 Å in diameter, and the other type of filament, which is found in the A-band, is about 40 Å in diameter. The thin filaments are grouped around a thick filament in a hexagonal pattern (Fig. 8–3). The thin filaments run from a Z-line to the H-zone of the A-band extending through an I-band and part way through the A-band. The thick filaments extend principally through the A-band.[10] The microstructure of insect muscles has been reviewed in detail by Edwards.[6]

Various interpretations have been suggested for the cross striation pattern of muscles.[10] One suggestion relates the striation with contraction mechanics, a second relates striation to speed of movement, and a third states that striations are associated with the spread of excitation from the surface of a fiber inward to the contractile elements.[10]

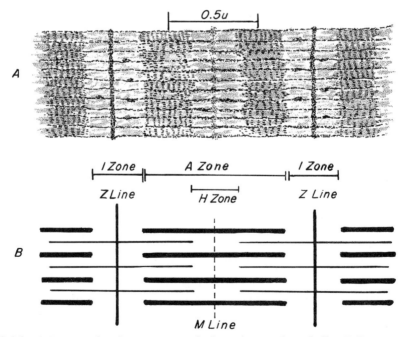

FIG. 8-2.   A, Drawing of an electron micrograph of a single striated muscle fiber. **B**, Diagrammatic arrangement of filaments. (Redrawn after Prosser.)

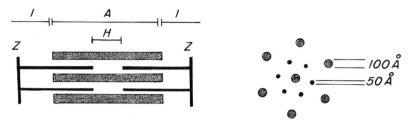

FIG. 8-3.   *Left:* The disposition of thick and thin filaments in longitudinal section through a single sarcomere. *Right:* Cross section through the A-band. (Redrawn after Giese.)

THE CHEMICAL BASIS OF THE CONTRACTILE PROCESS

The chemistry of the contractile process has been studied most extensively with vertebrate skeletal muscle. The procedure for study involves preparation of a press juice by the squeezing of minced muscle under high pressure and the extracting of fluid with salt solutions. By this process, soluble protein fractions (albumins, globulins) and soluble salts are removed, leaving two major proteins. These proteins are *myosin* and *actin*. In addition, there is a small amount of another component called *tropomyosin*, whose function is not entirely understood. These are the active components of the contractile process.

Myosin is an α-helical protein (see Giese for configurations of the α- and γ-helices[7]) composed of many dicarboxylic acids arranged in a helix around an axis and held in place by hydrogen bonds. The molecular weight of myosin is about 450,000. These molecules are long and thin (about 2000 Å by 50 Å), and because of this structure there are many ionizable residues. Near neutrality there is one free charge for every angstrom of length. This very high charge density explains why the molecule keeps its fibrous form and also, because of the linear form, its tendency to show a strong streaming birefringence (birefringence in a flowing solution).

Myosin appears to be present in the muscle fiber as a magnesium salt that binds monovalent ions readily. Most of the ATP (adenosine triphosphate) in the muscle fiber also appears to be bound to the magnesium myosinate. One mole of ATP is bound for each 18,000 gm. of myosin. Myosin can be fragmented further into two fractions, one light and one heavy, named *L*- and *H-meromyosin* respectively. These two fractions probably account for the angular deviations shown in the x-ray diffraction pattern for myosin.

Actin, which is less soluble in KCl than myosin, can be separated by increasing the concentration of the salt solution. Actin binds 4 equivalents of calcium per mole, and it is present normally as a calcium compound. In the absence of salts, actin behaves like a globular protein with a molecular weight of about 70,000. In the presence of ATP actin forms dimers, and in the presence of KCl and ATP in proper concentrations it polymerizes into long fibers. As polymerization takes place, ATP is split with the release of an inorganic phosphate and the production of ADP (adenosine diphosphate). In this state, the actin also assumes an α-helical pattern.

When actin and myosin are mixed in the presence of the salts that nor-

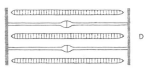

FIG. 8-4. Muscular contraction as envisaged from the contractile filament theory. Change in length of the muscle fiber changes the arrangement of the filaments. In A the muscle fiber is stretched; in B it is at its resting length; in C, D and E it is contracted. In C the thin filaments meet; in D and E they crumple up. In E the thick filament also meet adjacent thick filaments (not shown) and crumple. The crumpling gives rise to new band patterns. The central thick filaments are presumably myosin; the thin filaments, actin. (From Huxley, Nov., 1958: Sci. Am. 199:76.)

mally exist in muscle, the viscosity of the mixture becomes greater than the sum of the viscosities of the components; electron microscope studies indicate this is the result of an electrostatic association that gives rise to a complex called *actomyosin*. In resting muscle, the thick filaments are comprised primarily of myosin, and the thinner filaments of actin. As a result of stimulation, actomyosin is formed and in some way this complex is the active protein gel in the contractile process.

Theories of Muscle Contraction

Details of the contractile process are still uncertain, but by a combination of observation, models, and reasoning, several theories have been propounded to explain the contractile process. None of these theories has been proved as an exclusive explanation of the existing process.

Experiments with models produced by preparing filaments of actomyosin indicate that the synthetic fibers show tension (by contraction) when exposed to ATP in the presence of Mg^{++} and is accompanied by a breakdown of ATP. If more ATP is added, the actomyosin reverts to actin and myosin, and the tension decreases. Apparently this reaction is involved in some way with the contractile process. Two ideas of the mechanics of the process that approach an acceptable explanation of the result have been suggested.

One theory, suggested by Szent-Györgyi,[7] indicates that in the presence of Ca^{++}, actin and myosin combine to form a rigid molecule of actomyosin. The H-meromyosin, which has ATPase, splits ATP; the energy released is transferred to L-meromyosin, which loses an electrical charge, and as a result the molecule folds causing the contraction. The folding process can be superficially compared to the compression of a coil spring.

The other theory that seems to explain most observed phenomena is based upon studies by Huxley, and Hanson and Huxley (as cited by Giese[7]). This is the sliding filament theory, which can be summarized as follows:

During a muscular contraction, the A-band remains constant, but the I-band varies with the state of the contraction. If the A-band is assumed to be equal to the length of the thick filaments, the length of these filaments must be constant. The length of the H-zone in the middle of the A-band increases and decreases with the length of the I-band, so that the distance from the end of one H-zone to the beginning of the next remains nearly the same. This distance is equal to the length of the thin filament, so that these filaments must also remain nearly constant in length. The phenomenon that takes place can be explained by the idea that when a muscle fiber changes length, the two sets of filaments slide past one another (Fig. 8–4). When a fiber contracts to its fullest extent, the filaments meet and their ends may crumple, which produces a new band as shown in the electron micrograph, but this is the result of and not the cause of the contraction.[7]

From the combined observations, it is postulated that the motive power for muscular contraction is the formation of chemical couplings between the two proteins as they slide over each other. The couplings are made through bridges that are a permanent part of the myosin molecule with one coupling for each bridge, and contact is made with definite points on the actin. The cyclic opening and closing of the cross-links is believed to be coincident with the binding and dephosphorylation of ATP. The net result is that during a contraction, the I-band moves into the A-band by a sort of telescopic action.

The sliding filament theory explains such features of muscular contraction as the difference in force that is exerted by a rapidly contracting and a slowly contracting fiber. The basis for this feature is that a time factor is involved in the formation of bridges, and the fewer bridges that form, the less tension that is exerted. It is also possible to visualize by this theory why a muscle that carries a great load uses more energy than one that carries a

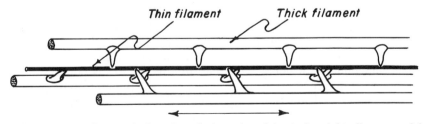

FIG. 8-5. Diagram showing the hypothetical relationship of the thick and thin filaments and the contact bridges according to the sliding filament hypothesis of muscle contraction (redrawn after Giese).

smaller load, because as more bridges are formed, more ATP is used. The possibility of continuing contraction (tension) can be explained on the basis of the breaking and the reforming of the bonds. So far, the bridges observed in electron photomicrographs that account for the sliding theory have been found only in striated muscle. A schematic representation of this is shown in Figure 8–5.

The Energy in Muscular Contraction

In the muscle, the sarcoplasm is the seat of the biochemical processes that result in the high energy used in the contractile process. The mitochondria have all the necessary oxidation-reduction and phosphorylation enzymes for the operation of the various glycolytic cycles.

Whole muscle contains about 1 per cent glycogen, about 0.5 per cent phosphogen (creatine phosphate in vertebrates and arginine phosphate in most invertebrates including insects), and about 0.025 per cent ATP. In vertebrate muscle, and to some extent in insect muscle, glycogen disappears during a contraction and pyruvic and lactic acids are produced. This reaction follows the Embden-Meyerhof pathway for muscle, and as was pointed out in Chapter 6, the Embden-Meyerhof pathway may be suppressed in favor of the pentose pathway and aerobic metabolism in insects. In any case, the energy is produced through normal glycolytic pathways with ATP as the medium of exchange. In the process, the ATP used is continuously replenished from the phosphogen as long as this is available.[7]

CHARACTERISTICS OF THE NERVE TISSUE

Just as the muscle tissue evolved to increased irritability, nerve tissue developed specialized characteristics to perceive and transmit *stimuli*. Stimuli are environmental changes, which may be mechanical, chemical, thermal, electrical, or the result of radiation. Magnetic fields may also exert a stimulating force as evidenced by some electromagnetic orientation experiments, although on isolated tissue magnetic fields appear to have no effect.[8]

Nerves of higher animals consist of cells with long fibrous processes specially constructed to conduct impulses. A nerve cell, called a *neuron*, is shown in diagrammatic form in Figure 8–6. Each cell has one *axon* and one or more *dendrites* attached to the cell body, which contains the nucleus. Individual neurons are capable of conducting impulses in both directions, but the anatomical arrangement is such that the dendrites are connected to the receiving structure and the axon conveys the impulse to the adjacent neuron. In general, the cell body is located within the ganglion of the central nervous system with bundles of fibers extending from it, but this is not true of the sensory nerves of insects, in which the cell body is peripheral. Neurons differ widely in shape, and functionally they may be divided into sensory, motor, and connector (association) neurons, depending upon their location and function in the nerve circuit.

The nerve trunks or nerve fibers are made up of large numbers of axons

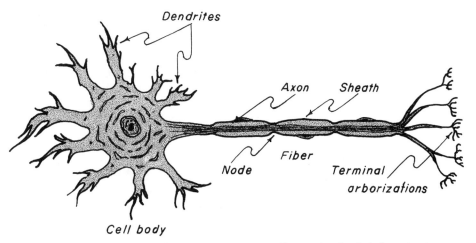

FIG. 8-6. Diagram of a nerve cell. Insect nerves are generally considered to lack the nodes shown in the diagram. (Redrawn after Giese.)

and dendrites, which are cabled together in a connective tissue sheath. In addition to the cell membrane that surrounds the axons and dendrites, there may be one or two outer sheaths. These are the outer *neurilemma* and the inner *myelin* sheath. The neurilemma is cellular, but the myelin sheath is made up of a noncellular material. The presence or absence of these sheaths is important in the effects of biologically active chemicals.

Synaptic Junctions Between Neurons

An impulse applied to a neuron is transmitted in all directions within the confines of the cell, but connection between the axon of one neuron and the dendrite of the next neuron is unidirectional. This connection is called a *synapse*. It consists of the interlacing of the processes of the axon and the dendrite in much the same relation as the plates of a variable capacitor, so that there is no actual contact and the impulse has to be transmitted across a finite space. This transfer can be accomplished in two ways.

Electrical transmission is known to occur at some synapses despite the morphological separation of the two neurons, which indicates existence of a sufficiently effective local circuit connection to permit the flow of electrons (current) to pass across the separation and propagate a stimulus. This implies that a distinctly different structure exists at the synapse than in the nerve fiber itself, since transmission at the synapse is unidirectional.

Most attention has been given to the presence of chemical mediators in synaptic transmission. These mediators are believed to be secreted by the terminal processes of the axon because of stimulation; when the mediators come in contact with the processes of the adjacent dendrites, that neuron is stimulated to transmit the impulse.

There are two principal types of mediation, but several additional compounds show a stimulatory effect. Acetylcholine, or a related derivative, is the best known mediator and has received most attention in insect studies; in fact its popularity has almost eclipsed the possibility of other mediators in insects.

Acetylcholine has a quaternary nitrogen atom at the choline end that bears a positive charge and a carbonyl group at the acetyl end that can be hydrogen bonded. Most of the specificity of blocking and potentiating drugs depends upon the charges and the dimensions of the acetyl choline molecule. A system depending upon acetyl choline or a related compound for mediation is called a *cholinergic* system.[10]

Another common system uses catechol amines of which noradrenaline is best known. These are *adrenergic* systems. Other compounds that have stimulatory effects and could serve as mediators include 5-hydroxy tyramine and γ-amino butyric acid.

The Chemistry of Nerve Impulse Transmission

When a nerve is stimulated, the metabolic rate increases, and chemical evidence indicates that carbohydrate is utilized in the central nervous system and in the nonmyelinated fibers. Metabolism must also take place in the myelinated parts, but the nutrients are unidentified.[7] The immediate source of energy is thought to come from the breakdown of a phosphogen, and RNA apparently serves in some capacity as a mediator in the synthesis of other materials. Some heat is produced during the transmission of stimuli, and oxygen is consumed. It is possible for a nerve to continue conducting in a nitrogen atmosphere, but an oxygen debt is incurred.

The best known physical or chemical factor that accompanies nerve transmission is the change in electrical potential. This change consists of a wave of negativity that traverses a nerve coincident with the impulse. The study of the electrical phenomena that accompany nerve transmission and muscle contraction constitutes a large part of electrophysiology. Knowledge of these electrical potentials combined with advances in electronic technology have made possible many of the recent advances in animal physiology.

Electrical Aspects of Neuromuscular Physiology

Electrophysiology was born when Galvani observed that if he connected two strips of dissimilar metal through a galvanometer and touched them to a wet animal muscle, a current would flow. He suggested that electrical energy was generated by the living muscle, but this idea was soon corrected, because it was pointed out that when contact was made with dissimilar electrodes, a battery was created. The salts and water associated with the muscle formed a *dielectric medium*, and the electrodes were *polarized*.

Following this primitive experiment, it was not long before it was shown that an electrical change is associated with both the transmission of an impulse by a nerve and the contraction of a muscle. The electrical change is caused by a wave of negative potential that moves along the tissue so that if two *nonpolarized* (similar metals) electrodes are placed at different points along the nerve (or muscle) and connected externally through a galvanometer, an electric *current* flows that causes the galvanometer to register in one direction and then in the other. If the excursion of the galvanometer is plotted, it displays a sine-wave type of curve called a *diphasic action current*. The current involved is very small, and in modern practice electronic devices are used to make the same measurement. These devices include amplifiers, and since voltage amplification is accomplished more easily than current amplification and oscilloscopes used for detection of results are voltage-measuring devices, results are expressed as *potentials*. Even though the terms are often incorrectly interchanged by physiologists, the effect of an impulse traversing a nerve should be expressed as an action *potential*. This potential is usually diphasic; it is important not to transliterate this into "two-phase," which has an entirely different meaning. Action potentials may be of the order of a few millivolts up to about 170 mv. in some giant fibers. The maximum potential recorded lasts a fraction of a millisecond and is called the *spike potential*.[7, 8]

In a single nerve, the magnitude of the impulse follows an *all-or-none* principle, so that once the threshold is exceeded the response is the same. The transmission of the impulse also remains at the same level of magnitude (occurs without *decrement*), if the action potential is measured in front of and behind a section whose excitability is decreased with cold or anesthesia.

When a nerve impulse has passed a given point on a neuron, a refractory period follows, during which no stimulus, regardless of its strength, will evoke a response. The changes in excitability are correlated with the phases of the action potential. The spike exists for a very brief time at constant magnitude, and no further activity can be induced until this period, called the *absolute refractory period*, has passed. For a short interval during the decrease of the spike, a strong stimulus can evoke a response. This is the *relative refractory period*, and is followed by a *negative after-potential*, which can be described as the broad base of the curve at the end of the descending spike. The negative after-potential period is followed by a *positive after-potential*, defined as a period of decreased excitability and thought to result from an excess positive charge.[7] These phenomena follow in very rapid sequence, and the neuron returns to normal excitability.

When electrodes are placed on the surface of a nerve fiber, electrotonic potentials develop at the point of contact and in the vicinity of the contact. The appearance of these potentials indicates that current is flowing along specific lines, but a propagated stimulus is produced only at the cathode $(-)$ after a stimulus has been applied at a minimum level for a minimum time. Anodic $(+)$ shocks are *accommodated,* and the nerve is in a state of *anelectrotonus.* Following a cathodal shock, the nerve is more excitable and is in a state of *catelectrotonus.* The reaction of the nerve depends upon its preceding experience, which alters the threshold of the neuron. This change in the threshold can be the result of either a subthreshold stimulation or an after-potential.[7]

The potential change in a nerve is greatest immediately under the electrode, and the change falls off exponentially at points further away. The best explantion for the observed phenomena is the theory that the nerve fiber acts as a core conductor—a cylinder of conducting fluid with a sheath of high electrical resistance surrounded by a layer of a conducting medium such as a salt solution. The polarization of the cell membranes is visualized as imposing

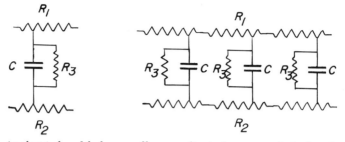

FIG. 8-7. An electrical model of a nerve fiber according to the core conductor hypothesis. R_1 and R_2 = longitudinal resistance, R_3 = the transverse (leak) resistance, and C = a capacitance between R_1 and R_2. (Redrawn after Giese.)

a capacity on the system, so that the nerve fiber is comparable to a condenser capable of being charged when a potential difference is applied across it. By using models and knowledge of modern electronics, it is possible to construct a system consisting of a series of capacitors that are by-passed by resistances of sufficient magnitude so that a slow flow of current is allowed to leak past the capacitance at all times. The circuitry of such a model is shown in Figure 8–7. This model functions *like* a nerve but not necessarily in a manner identical to it.

These are the most important points regarding the structure and the function of the nerves of animals in general. Details and further elucidation should be sought in the various textbooks and reference books on neurophysiology.

THE NEUROMUSCULAR JUNCTION

The medium of transmission of an impulse to a muscle, like the synaptic transmission, is not entirely resolved. The favored theory is that of chemical

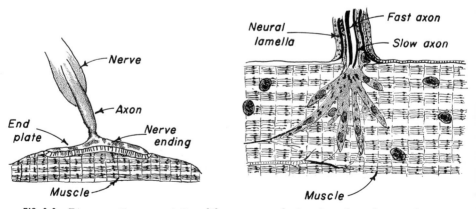

FIG. 8-8. Diagrammatic representation of the neuromuscular junctions of vertebrates and insects (redrawn from Giese and from Prosser).

transmission, although it has been demonstrated that an electrical transmission is possible and it is entirely reasonable to speculate that both types occur depending upon the animal and the anatomical situation.

Transmission from nerve to a muscle takes place through an end-plate. This is a structure in which the motor axon, with no myelin sheath, spreads over the muscle and branches into a number of end-feet, which penetrate the sarcoplasm (Fig. 8–8). Choline esterase is present in the structure, which suggests chemical mediation, and the production of vesicles that presumably carry acetyl choline has been observed. The motor end-plates for various animals probably function in a comparable manner but their morphology is more or less group specific.[7, 10]

TIME RELATIONS IN NEUROMUSCULAR PHENOMENA

When a muscle receives a stimulus, it either contracts in the sense that it shortens, or it increases the tension exerted on the body parts to which it is attached. A muscle in the first situation would be *isotonic* and in the second *isometric*. The effect of a stimulus depends more on the degree to which a living system responds to the stimulus than to the absolute physical or chemical magnitude of the stimulus. Discussion of these phenomena introduces a series of descriptive terms that lead to the time-duration concept of the stimulatory process.

If a stimulus is just strong enough to elicit a response, it is called a *threshold stimulus* (or *liminal stimulus*); a stimulus that is weaker is *subthreshold* (or *subliminal*). A stimulus just exceeding threshold is *minimal;* as the strength of the stimulus increases, indicated by the extent of the response, it reaches a point of *maximal* stimulation. Exceeding the maximal with a *supramaximal* stimulus causes injury or death of the tissue if it is continued.

The effect of a stimulus depends upon the duration as well as the inten-

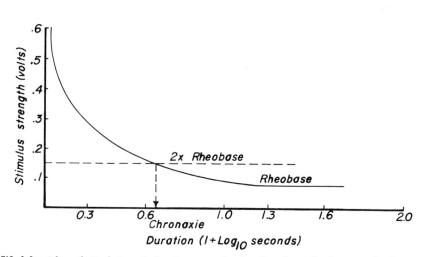

FIG. 8-9. A hypothetical strength-duration curve showing the relationship between the chronaxie and the rheobase.

sity. This time factor has been called the *chronaxie,* loosely defined as the time required for a stimulus double the threshold strength to become effective.[8] For every tissue there is a finite current strength below which no response occurs, regardless of the duration of the current flow. This lower limit is called the *rheobase.* It should be noted that this involves current and not potential.

It is assumed that currents in various circumstances are comparable when they are equal multiples of the rheobase in those circumstances. With this assumption and using twice the rheobase, chronaxies were determined for the neuromuscular systems of many animals. The basic relationship between chronaxies and twice the rheobase is expressed in Figure 8–9.[8] The importance of the chronaxie as a specific characteristic of a given animal has become of minor importance in physiological study, but the strength-duration concept remains. An elaboration of this concept can be found in textbooks of general or cell physiology.

PHYSICAL ASPECTS OF MUSCULAR RESPONSE

Neuromuscular studies are carried out by making trace recordings either mechanically or electronically. The complexity of the instrumentation can vary from a simple lever and a smoked drum kymograph to high-gain amplifiers and oscilloscopes, or as is an increasing practice, the recording of tracings by use of magnetic tapes to store the information for future study.

If a muscle is isolated so that it can be stimulated by a single electrical impulse, the result is a single contraction called a *simple twitch.* A muscle that responds in this way is *noniterative;* one that requires a series of shocks is *iterative.* The stimulus may be applied through a neuron or directly to the muscle tissue. If the response to the stimulus is converted to a graphic record, it would appear as in Figure 8–10. The sharpness of the peak is a function of the horizontal sweep frequency of the oscilloscope or the rate at which the kymograph revolved.

An appreciable period elapses between the application of the stimulus and the first noticeable indication of a response. This is called the *latent period.* Definitions of this term vary but as recording technology improves, duration of the latent period appears to be less and less, which indicates that it is due in part, at least, to a mechanical lag in the recording apparatus.

After a muscle has been stimulated, there is a definite refractory period just as in the case with nerves; if the stimulus is repeated over a long enough period, the tissue becomes insensitive to it unless the strength of the stimulus is increased. This insensitivity is called a state of *adaptation, acclimatization,* or *accommodation.*[8]

If a series of stimuli are applied to a muscle at a frequency that is less than the recovery period, a series of step-wise curves called a *summation* is produced. In this context a summation refers to muscle contractions; the same term in reference to nerve response means the additive effect of subthreshold stimuli applied at high frequency. If the frequency of a series of impulses is increased sufficiently, a state of continuous contraction called a *tetanus* results. Continued tetanic contraction or repeated stimulation at lower fre-

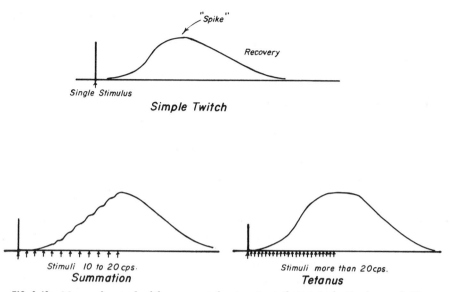

FIG. 8-10. Myograph records of the response of an insect muscle to a single stimulus, producing a simple twitch. Stimuli from 10 to 20 cps produce a summation, and stimuli at greater than 20 cps produce a tetanus.

quencies results in a gradual relaxation of the muscle without further contractions; this result is called *fatigue*.[8]

Active muscle in a normal animal is always in a state of partial contraction, which takes up the slack and produces a small amount of heat to help control the body temperature. This is a *tonic* contraction, which results from spontaneous impulses produced by the nerves.

PHYSIOLOGY OF INSECT MUSCLES

The microstructure of insect muscles and nerves has been reviewed by Edwards,[6] and the structure and physiology of the flight muscles have been discussed in reviews by Tiegs,[15] Pringle,[11] and Boettiger.[3] Aside from special adaptations peculiar to insects, there is no basic difference between the striated muscles of vertebrates and those of insects.

Nonresonating or Postural Insect Muscles

Nonresonating muscles include the locomotor muscles of the legs, abdominal muscles, and muscles not generally associated with flight. Polyneuronal innervation occurs in insects but in a simpler form than in crustaceans.[10] Double and triple innervation have been observed, and an entire muscle may receive just two axons. In other situations, a muscle may be divided into several motor units with two axons each and with a large number of end-plates distributed at intervals along single nerve fibers. The entire subject of the anatomical structure and innervation of locomotor muscles of insects was reviewed by Becht, and the review was followed by research leading to additional information.[2]

For his work, Becht used the myograph technique of Dresden,[5] and he concentrated on the action of the coxal muscles of the American cockroach. The second thoracic leg was severed at its junction with the thorax and cemented to a metal support. A fine straw carrying a writing stylus was inserted into the half-cut femur, which was arranged so that the stylus would bear on the strip of paper on a kymograph. Electrodes were placed at various sites on the efferent nerves supplying the coxal muscles, and the response was recorded according to the movement of the femur.

The coxal muscles involved are groups of extensors and flexors. The extensors include the posterior coxal extensor of the trochanter—a broad muscle that originates on the dorsal wall of the coxa near the rim—and an anterior coxal extensor of the trochanter, which arises from a mesoventral part of the coxa. These two muscles are separated by another group, the main extensor of the trochanter and its subdivisions. The main extensor is the most powerful muscle of the leg and originates on the mesothorax and the coxa. Its branches converge to a broad spoon shaped apodeme, and it is inserted with a tendon on the median apophysis of the trochanter.

There are three flexor muscles in the system. The anterior coxal flexor is a weak muscle that originates on the anterior wall of the coxa; the main coxal flexor of the trochanter has three branches that originate in the coxal rim and the ridge that limits the meron; and the posterior coxal flexor, which is a small muscle with four branches and originates on the posterior wall of the coxa. All of the flexors converge to apodemes attached to the lateral edge of the trochanter. Figure 8–11 shows the arrangement of the muscles in the leg of the cockroach.

By careful dissection, Becht was able to study the innervation and the responses of the anterior and posterior extensors without interference from the main extensor. He found that both muscles were innervated by bifurcations of the same axon and predicted correctly that these muscles would act as a single motor unit. Stimulation produced an all-or-none type of response, which did not increase in intensity when the stimulation was increased beyond the threshold level. The twitch produced was a typical reaction to stimulus at rates up to 6 cps and showed a gradual fusion of contractions, ending in a smooth tetanus at 30 cps. There was some summation and the height of the tetanic reaction on the kymograph was equal to or slightly higher than the simple twitch. During tetanic contraction, the muscles fatigue quickly, and continued response even at low frequencies could not be maintained. The coxal muscles are of the fast type; apparently the properties of rapid contraction with an inability to perform sustained work is a characteristic of this type.

When the main extensor is included in the preparation and appropriate dissection is made to isolate the system, it becomes apparent that this muscle must have two components. One component acts like a motor unit of the fast type, and the second is a slow type. Stimuli applied with increasing voltage to the nerve branch of the second (slow) component give three degrees of twitch contractions and three distinct tetanic contractions. Microscopic examination of the preparation showed that there are three axons on the smallest nerve

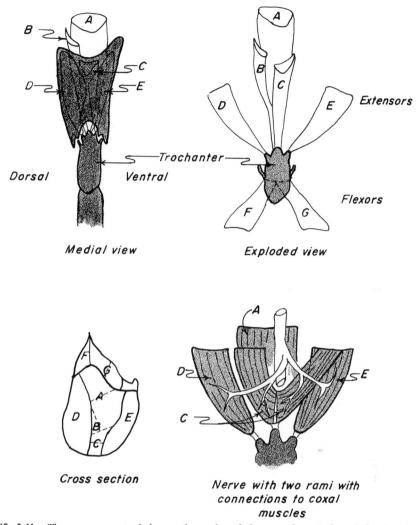

Medial view   Exploded view

Cross section   Nerve with two rami with
                     connections to coxal
                     muscles

FIG. 8-11.   The arrangement of the coxal muscles of the mesothoracic leg of the American
             cockroach (redrawn after Becht).

branches. Further experimentation revealed that this muscle, as well as other
muscles of the extensor system, is made of anatomically and physiologically
distinct muscle types in close association but capable of different types of
response.

The flexor muscles also showed differences in response and innervation.
From the experimental work of Becht, which supports the results of others,
in insects one muscle fiber apparently is capable of more than one type of
contraction, while in other anatomical arrangements the difference in the
response may be due to the functioning unit's being composed of more than
one muscle type. In some muscle preparations, responses appear that seem to
be indicative of the inhibitory activity of nerves, and evidence for the presence

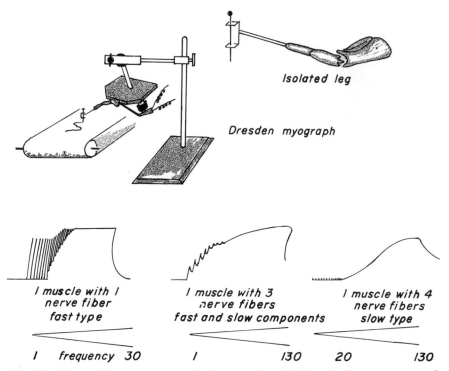

Isolated leg

Dresden myograph

I muscle with I
nerve fiber
fast type

I muscle with 3
nerve fibers
fast and slow components

I muscle with 4
nerve fibers
slow type

I   frequency 30   *I*   */30*   *20*   */30*

FIG. 8-12.   Myographic response curves for insect muscles with fast and slow components and
several degrees of innervation (redrawn after Becht).

of inhibitory nerves in insects is mounting although older work indicated their
absence. The number of stimulation thresholds that exist for a group of muscles is related to the number of axons with which that muscle group is supplied. The characteristic relationships found by Becht for various muscle types
are shown in Figure 8–12.

A reëxamination of the same system using the same muscles in isometric
arrangement and using an electrobiological pickup produced some conclusions that differ in detail from those of Becht. It was found that every muscle
or muscle group is innervated by a fast motor axon that gives a uniform type of
electrical response from the muscle associated with a uniform mechanical
response. The electrical responses are large postsynaptic potentials, which
bring about different degrees of electrical response from the muscle fiber
membrane. The mechanical response to low-frequency fast-axon stimulation
is composed of a twitch contraction of about 40 to 70 msec. in duration. The
rise time to peak tension is about 10 to 14 msec. and the half-decay time is 9
to 15 msec. At high frequencies of stimulation the fast axon gives a response
that causes the muscle to fatigue quickly.

Some muscles also have one or more slow motor axons, and the mechanical response to low-frequency stimulation gives small contractions of the
innervated muscle fibers. These muscles summate at higher frequencies to
give a smooth response, which shows less tendency to fatigue.[17]

Insect Flight Muscles

The muscles of flight in insects have properties and characteristics some-what different from locomotor and skeletal muscles. The flight muscles have been adapted to meet the requirements of a variety of wing forms.

Successful flight has as its first requirement the production of sufficient aerodynamic force to drive the wings through the complex beat cycle and to counter the force of gravity. The exoskeleton has special properties that help make this possible.

Flight muscles act in two ways—the contraction may be tonic, or it may be phasic. The tonic muscles hold the wing articulations in their proper position and insure the proper wing cycle—usually a figure eight with the long axis pitched to control the direction of flight. With the exception of insects that have a very low wing-beat frequency, the tonic muscles do not make adjustments in tension during the short duration of the wing beat. The phasic muscles act indirectly on the wing articulation and furnish power for the beat. These muscles have the most unusual ability to alter their length at frequencies as high as 1000 cps. It is not possible to distinguish a tonic muscle from a phasic muscle by simple morphological examination.[3]

Relatively little is known of the physiology of the tonic flight muscles, and it must be assumed that these muscles are similar to locomotor muscles. Phasic muscles have been studied extensively and their action described in detail.

THE MECHANICS OF FLIGHT

The flight path and the movement of the wings in the beat cycle are determined by the mechanical structure of the thorax, including the special features of wing articulation. The control of the complex relationships is an important function of both the tonic and phasic muscles. During flight, tension on the phasic flight muscles changes to achieve the aerodynamic force and probably never falls to zero. The wings must be moved through the beat cycle rapidly, and the shorter the wing, the higher the frequency must be to compensate for the decreased wing surface.

The rapid beat achieved in wing movement cannot be a direct function of a normal contractile process, which is relatively slow. Instead, the rapid wing beat must be explained on the basis of very short excursions that deliver maximum power. The mechanical properties of muscles can be represented by a model that consists of a contractile element in series with a series elastic element (Fig. 8–13). Both of these elements are in parallel with a parallel elastic element. To effect maximum power from short excursions the arrangement of the fibrils is important. The series elasticity must be reduced to a minimum, but parallel elasticity has an advantage.

The optimum arrangement for such a system indicates a short, thick muscle attached to the skeletal structure through a tonofibrilla with the system under load at all times. The loading of the muscle is important in the development of the rapid beat. At the beginning of the stroke, the loading of the muscle must be near a maximum; with the wing muscle connection arranged so

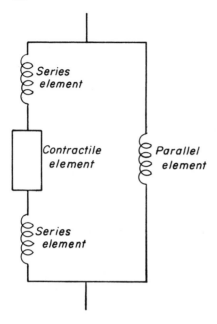

FIG. 8-13. Scheme for the mechanical arrangement of striated muscle (redrawn after Prosser).

that force is applied to the short end of the level, this is not difficult to visualize.

Several loading arrangements are utilized to accomplish three things. First, the inertia must be overcome at the beginning of the stroke; second, the damping effect of the air must be countered; and third, the aerodynamic force that counters gravity by producing maximum velocity at the midposition of the stroke must be achieved. In addition to loading caused by the resistance of the wing, the thorax produces some elastic loading because of the strain put on the structure by the application of the contractile force. Elastic loading is also produced by the action of antagonistic muscles, and changes in the loading result from changes in the mechanical advantage of the wing lever during the progress of the stroke. In some insects with a very high beat rate, there is a click mechanism in the wing articulation, which increases the loading at the beginning of the stroke.

To sum up the observations made concerning flight muscles and flight mechanisms in insects with very high wing-beat frequencies, it must be concluded that such frequencies cannot be achieved by a stimulation-contraction mechanism, but that such frequencies must be due to a resilient property of the muscle in isometric arrangement that is kept vibrating at high frequencies by successive stimulations. This is achieved by a stimulus of sufficiently high frequency that the muscle is held under constant tension during flight with an asynchronous beat superimposed.

The Structure of Insect Flight Muscles

Three types of flight muscles are recognized[3]—a microfibrillar type (type 2, Fig. 8–1), a lamellar muscle with ribbon-like fibrils arranged radially to form a tubular structure (type 3, Fig. 8–1), and a fibrillar type with large cylindrical fibrils bound loosely into a fiber (type 4, Fig. 8–1). The fibrillar muscle has large sarcomeres and a reddish color due to a high cytochrome content. Some of the nonfibrillar muscles are also so characterized, which distinguishes them from the white muscles.

The fibrillar muscle is the only oscillating type, and aside from moving the halteres of flies, it is exclusively a flight muscle. The lamellar type is found only in insects which have no longitudinal flight muscle (Odonata and some Orthoptera). The fibrillar type is found in insects that have one thoracic segment modified for flight, such as the Coleoptera, Diptera, Hymenoptera, and some Homoptera. The nonfibrillar muscles are synchronous with nerve stimulation while the fibrillar muscles are asynchronous.[6]

Insects with a slow wing beat (Orthoptera, Neuroptera, Ephemeroptera, and Lepidoptera) have phasic flight muscles that are nonfibrillar but of two types, which represent adaptations for flight. The locust (Schistocerca) appears to be the only insect in which this process has been studied in detail.[3] In Schistocerca, a system of parallel elastic elements in the form of twitch muscles are arranged so that one is active and one is passive. This arrangement offers an advantage over a strictly oscillating system in that energy is stored in the passive element during the stretch and can be recovered on the rebound. The resulting spring action reduces the amount of energy that otherwise would be lost at the beginning of each stroke to overcome wing inertia. This elasticity accounts for 50 per cent to 75 per cent of the total force. The parallel elastic elements are as rapid in their response as the contractile elements and dissipate only about 20 per cent as much energy. Under tetanic stimulation, the isolated locust muscle can be shortened to about 50 per cent of its rest length, and it can develop isometrically the same force per unit of cross section as a frog muscle; but at normal temperatures, a single tetanus induces irreversible changes in the locust muscle.

Under isometric conditions, the twitch tension of the system in the locust approaches the tetanus tension. This shows that a single nerve impulse can initiate a full active state of the muscle. The active state declines rapidly; if the muscle is allowed to shorten, the active state will be significantly reduced before the shortening process is complete. This rapid decline indicates the maximum isotonic twitch tension is lower than the isometric tetanus tension. Since the normal contraction that moves the wings is in the nature of a twitch, this type of muscle is always operating below its maximum tension.

The dorsal longitudinal muscle of the bumblebee is an example of a microfibrillar muscle, and the basalar muscle of beetles is an example of the type of muscle with large fibrils. The response of the microfibrillar type is a small twitch that summates with subsequent stimulation. The tetanus to twitch ratio is as high in this muscle as the ratio is in other arthropod muscles that are used to create a state of tension. One depolarization of the muscle junction does not fully activate the contractile mechanism, and the isometric tension-length relation is similar to that of vertebrate muscle. The muscle may shorten as much as 12 per cent, but the in situ shortening is limited to about 3 per cent. Following a stretch, the active state increases. If the length of a muscle is increased, a sharp rise in tension results; but if the length is decreased, the active state is increased following the stretch, and the tension increases.

The fundamental difference between the fibrillar muscles of the microfibrillar type and the large fibril type lies in the fact that in the first type, the full activation normal to any stimulation frequency is attained in response to stimulation no matter what the length of the muscle, while in the second the passive length of the muscle determines the degree of activation produced by a stimulus of given frequency. The tension and length relationship is only a little greater than that of nonstimulated muscle, and it more or less parallels this relationship without reaching a maximum. The muscle can shorten very little below the length at which its passive tension is zero.

THE STOMATOGASTRIC MUSCLES

The morphology of the musculature of the alimentary tract has been described for various species (see Jones for bibliography[9]), but very little true physiological work has been done on this muscle system. Day and Waterhouse summarized the knowledge of the stomatogastric muscles by pointing out that the gut is invested with layers of muscle consisting of an inner circular layer and an outer circular layer.[4] On the foregut, particularly, there may be longitudinal muscles that lie both outside and inside the circular layers. As far as has been observed, the muscles are striated, flattened, and anastomose frequently to form a network around the viscera. More recently, Beard[1] and Jones[9] reported on the rhythmical activities of the visceral muscles of *Galleria* and *Anopheles* larvae.

Beard used an electrographic recording technique and with the aid of various chemical agents studied muscle response. He found that there are three centers of activity in the foregut, which may be integrated or which may operate independently. The muscle movements are described as peristaltic and pulsatory contractions, and the peristalsis may move in either direction. If the anterior part of the foregut is considered to be the crop and the posterior part the ventriculus, the movement is pulsatory with a peristaltic wave of pulsation arising near the anterior, usually moving most strongly to the posterior. The contractions are rhythmic and give a strong diphasic electrical potential, which sometimes exceeds 10 mv.

Jones studied the action of the digestive tract of the mosquito, principally by observing the movement of food and dyes through the system. He points out that the contractions are independent in the parts of the system as a whole and that all evidence indicates that the contractions are of myogenic origin. Physiological data on the stomatogastric mechanism is such that no further conclusions can be offered.

STRUCTURE AND MICROSTRUCTURE OF THE INSECT NERVOUS SYSTEM

The nerves and their anatomical arrangement have been the subject of many morphological studies, and some of the principal nerve tracts have been worked out for some insect species. The modern literature has been reviewed by Schmitt,[14] and the insect nerve mechanism has been discussed from a physiological point of view by Roeder.[12, 13]

It is very difficult to separate the physiological function of nerves and muscles, since muscles depend on nerves for the stimulation that causes them to function. Physiological research on the nervous system has followed three general courses—application of electrophysiological methods to explore basic nerve phenomena, the study of the insect behavior that results from coordinated activity of the intact neuromuscular system, and the study of neurosecretions.

There are relatively few important differences between the basic structure of insect nerves and those of other invertebrates, and except for the degree of complexity, the systems in insects are similar or comparable to those of vertebrates. The central nervous system of insects lies along the ventral wall of the thorax and abdomen with segmental ganglia connected by double commissures. There is considerable morphological variation between different groups, and it is not uncommon to find fused ganglia.

The ganglia and the connectives are sheathed in a neural lamella of varying thickness, never more than a few per cent of the total diameter of the whole nerve. The sheath is formed of a layered fibrous network of lemnoblast cells, and the filaments that these cells form have properties suggesting that the sheath consists of collagen or a similar substance. According to Edwards,[6] it is probable that lemnoblast cells are derived from the basement membrane cells, but it has also been postulated that formation of the sheath is a function of the amebocytes of the hemolymph. Histochemical examination reveals that the neurolamellar sheath contains phosphatids, which suggest that the sheath may consist of a lipoprotein. This, and certain optical properties revealed under polarized light, suggests very strongly that the neurolamella of insects must be similar, if not identical, to the myelin covering of vertebrate nerves.

Electron microscope studies of the ganglia and the nerve cord connectives of the cockroach show that two types of cells exist in the ganglia. Dark cells present are characterized by a dense cytoplasm that results from an even distribution of large quantities of RNA, while the light cells have RNA in clumps with empty spaces between the organelles. The nucleus of these cells has a homogeneous granular matrix with a prominent nucleolus. Mitochondria, Golgi membranes, and lipochondria are distributed randomly. The processes of the neuroglial (sheath) cells often form indented pockets in the surface of the cells.

Neuroglial cells may be distinguished from other cell types by nuclei with peripheral clumps of chromatin and by long, membrane-enclosed cytoplasmic processes that form from 2 to 20 layers to cover the nerve cells and axons. The cytoplasm contains granules, vesicles, and Golgi membranes. The axons in the ganglia (internuncial or association neurons) are small, from 1 to 2 μ. in diameter. The larger axons are ensheathed singly; the smaller axons are sheathed in groups. The synapses are not between axon and cell body but are axo-axonal. Presynaptic axons are identified by their synaptic vesicles, but not all vesicle-filled axons come into direct contact with other axons. Postsynaptic vesicles have not been observed in the axoplasm.[6]

Three types of particles appear in the cells, and they are graded according to size. The particles from 30 to 50 mμ. in diameter are called granules,

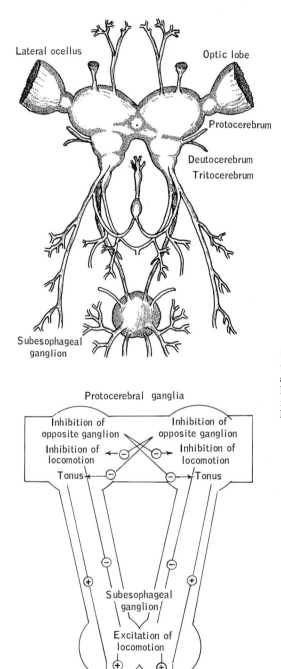

FIG. 8-14. *Above:* The anatomy of the brain of a grasshopper (redrawn after Snodgrass). *Below:* The modulation centers in the brain of a walking stick insect (redrawn after Roeder).

those from 100 to 150 mμ. are vesicles, and these intergrade with particles 120 mμ. and larger, which are called droplets. The deduction has been made that these particles contain the various mediator substances. The larger and more dense granules are considered to be neurosecretory.[6]

Arrangement of the cells of the nervous system in insects is much the same as in other animals. Differences that occur are usually details associated with specific systems.

Insect sensory organs perceive environmental stimuli and convert these stimuli to impulses because of *irritability*. In insects, the sensory neurons are peripheral instead of being located in the ganglion. An impulse goes through one or more internunctial neurons in the ganglion and is channeled through predetermined routes to effector neurons, which in turn activate the effector. This routing of an impulse describes a simple reflex arc, which exists only as a hypothetical scheme used for purposes of illustration. In the intact animal, the result of a stimulus may be modulated either by the intervention of systems in the ganglia of the head (Fig. 8–14) or possibly by a chopping effect that induces an on-off type of response in the sensory neuron.

Until relatively recently, the small size of insects discouraged attempts to solve many of the nerve transmission problems on an electrophysiological basis; however, improvements in technology are making it possible to sort out more and more details. There have been several investigations of the characteristics of transmission, synaptic junctions, and the effects of biologically active chemicals on the ventral nerve cords of large insects (American cockroach); and a good map of the nerve tracts,[12, 13] particularly in the giant fibers, has been prepared. More recently, electrophysiological methods have been applied to sensory receptors. The results of these methods are discussed in Chapter 9.

PERMEABILITY AND IONIC SALT BALANCE IN THE NERVES

It is well established that the outward gradient of potassium across the cell surface of the nerve is closely connected to irritability and to the transmission of impulses. The exchange of sodium and potassium ions in the ventral nerve cord of the American cockroach was studied by Treherne,[16] who used radioactive sodium-24 and potassium-42 in the form of chlorides to trace the exchange. These radioactive chlorides were incorporated into salines with levels the same as those in the hemolymph of insects. About 100 μl. of saline had to be injected into the body cavity of the insect to elicit a satisfactory level of nerve activity. This amount would be expected to increase the blood volume about two times; however, since the study was limited to adult males, the probability exists that the injected saline merely restored the level to approximately what it would have been in a nymph of the same weight. After injection, the levels of both sodium and potassium were checked using beta (radiation) counting and photometric analysis to determine the concentrations in the nerve and in the hemolymph.

The results of these experiments showed an influx of sodium per unit area of nerve cord at a rate of 13.9×10^{-12} moles per centimeter^{-2} per second^{-1}, and potassium at 13.5×10^{-12} moles per centimeter^{-2} per second^{-1}.

The results indicate that a rapid exchange of sodium and potassium takes place between the abdominal nerve cord and the blood. When the transfer constants for the entry of the ions into the nerve cord are compared, the K_{in} for sodium was 2.4 hour^{-1}, and for potassium, 33.9 hour^{-1}. It is apparent that the movement of potassium ions was about 14 times greater than for sodium.

These data are in some conflict with observations of Hoyle,[13] and those of Twarog and Roeder,[12] who proposed that the membrane surrounding the nerves acts as a protective mechanism for the underlying cells because of its impermeability. Treherne's observations lead him to conclude that the nerve sheath is in a dynamic steady state as regards the exchange of sodium and potassium and that the sheath is not a static barrier. Further experimental work by Treherne supports this idea and shows that the dynamic steady state of efflux of sodium and the influx of potassium is at least partially effected by

NEUROSECRETIONS

The existence of chemical mediators of transmission, and the possibilities for various types of mediators have already been discussed. The mediator is secreted by the axons and causes the regeneration of the impulse in adjacent dendrites; as soon as the mediator has accomplished this in the normal system, an enzyme is produced that inactivates the mediator.

With this idea as a starting point, it is not difficult to visualize the possibility that nerves may secrete other substances that, like hormones, control various responses in the body through chemical mediation. This idea also suggests that a link between the nerves and the endocrine system exists.

According to Scharrer, neurosecretory cells are nerve cells that show cytological structures characteristic of secretory activity.[18] Insect neurons that show this type of activity were observed first in the brain and ganglia of the honeybee;[18] since this observation was made, the technology for visualizing the granules that indicate secretory activity has improved sufficiently to trace the movement of the granules along the axons.

The secretory part of the axon is morphologically distinct from the rest of the tissue, which indicates a dual structure closely associated instead of a dual function of the same tissue.[18]

In the Apterygota, the neurosecretory cells are separated in a capsule of connective tissue located on the dorsal surface of the brain. In the Pterygota, medial neurosecretory cells are located on the dorsal surface of each hemisphere of the protocerebrum in the region known as the *pars intercerebralis*. Axons run from these neurosecretory cells to the *corpora cardiaca*, and some axons can be traced into the *corpora allata*. In some preparations, axons have been observed to lead to the dorsal vessel, where it is presumed they discharge secretions that are circulated in the blood. Neurosecretory cells have also been demonstrated in the subesophageal ganglion and in the ganglia of the ventral nerve cord.

The importance of the neurosecretions and the neuroendocrine mechanism is fairly obvious. They offer a new avenue for the approach and explanation of many phenomena that cannot be explained. Among these are the origin of the heartbeat, the contraction of the Malpighian tube muscles, and various observed behavior phenomena including periodicity and circadian rhythms.

SUMMARY

The nerves and muscles of insects operate as a unit, just as they do in other animals, to provide the necessary stimulus-response relationship that makes it possible for the insect to move about and react to favorable or adverse situations, and to provide some body heat. Except for degree of development, there are no major differences between these systems in insects and vertebrates. Minor differences that do exist bring about some unexpected responses, particularly to biologically active chemicals.

One of the more important adaptations in the insect neuromuscular system is the innervation of the flight muscles and the type of response that is produced. The very high wing-beat frequencies are attained by a mechanically resonant system, in which the muscles are held under isometric tension with an asynchronous stimulus superimposed. This system takes advantage of the elasticity of the muscle fibers and the skeletal structure of the thorax.

The basic structure of insect nerves is similar to that of other animals, and except for the fact that insects have peripheral sensory neurons, the general structural arrangement is similar. Insect nerves are covered with a lipoprotein-containing sheath that is similar if not identical to that of other animals except that it tends to be thinner. The rate of transmission of impulses through insect nerves is slower than that of vertebrates.

Recent developments in the study of nerve function and the tissues indicates that insect nerves are a source of secretions that exhibit a hormone-like activity. The importance of the neurosecretory mechanisms is still to be fully determined.

LITERATURE CITED

1. Beard, R. L. 1960. Foregut activity in larvae of *G. mellonella*. Ann. ent. Soc. Amer., 5:346–351.
2. Becht, G. 1959. Studies on insect muscles. Bijdr. Dierk., 29:1–40.
3. Boettiger, E. G. 1960. Physiology of insect flight muscles. Ann. Rev. Ent., 5:1–16.
4. Day, M. F., and Waterhouse, D. F. 1953. The structure of the alimentary system *in* Insect Physiology, K. D. Roeder, ed., John Wiley, New York. Ch. 10.
5. Dresden, D. 1956. A myographic technique for study of insect muscles. Nature (London), 177: 835–836.
6. Edwards, G. A. 1960. Insect micromorphology. Ann. Rev. Ent., 5:17–34.
7. Giese, A. C. 1962. Cell Physiology. 2nd ed., W. B. Saunders, Philadelphia.
8. Heilbrunn, L. V. 1952. An Outline of General Physiology. 3rd ed., W. B. Saunders, Philadelphia.
9. Jones, J. C. 1960. Anatomy and rhythmic activity of the alimentary canal of *Anopheles* larvae. Ann. ent. Soc. Amer., 53:459–474.
10. Prosser, C. L., and Brown, F. A. 1962. Comparative Animal Physiology. 2nd ed., W. B. Saunders, Philadelphia.
11. Pringle, J. W. S. 1957. Insect Flight. Cambridge University Press, Cambridge, England.
12. Roeder, K. D. 1953. Electric activity in nerves and ganglia *in* Insect Physiology, K. D. Roeder, ed. John Wiley, New York. Ch. 17.

13. Roeder, K. D. 1958. The (insect) nervous system. Ann. Rev. Ent., 3:1–18.
14. Schmitt, J. B. 1962. Comparative anatomy of insect nervous systems. Ann. Rev. Ent., 7:137–156.
15. Tiegs, O. W. 1955. Histology of insect flight muscle. Phil. Tr. roy. Soc. London (B), 238:221–359.
16. Treherne, J. 1961. Movements of sodium and potassium in the isolated nerve cord of *P. americana.* J. exp. Biol., 38:315–322; 629–636.
17. Usherwood, P. N. R. 1962. The nature of the slow and fast contractions in the coxal muscles of cockroaches. J. ins. Physiol., 8:31–52.
18. Van der Kloot, W. G. 1960. Neurosecretion in insects. Ann. Rev. Ent. 5:35–52.
19. Wigglesworth, V. B. 1939. Principles of Insect Physiology. Methuen, London.

9

SENSORY RESPONSE
AND BEHAVIOR

The sensory perceptors are the specialized parts of the nervous system that receive stimuli from external sources and transmit them to the neuromuscular system, and the result is manifested in the behavior of the individual. The morphology of individual sense organs has been the object of many investigations, some of which date back well into the Nineteenth Century. In some cases, very little has been added to the knowledge of anatomical structure; but the application of modern technology, particularly electron microscopy and electrobiology, has made it possible to extend knowledge and clarify observations.

In the study of sensory perception and behavior, it is very easy to make interpretations that border on the metaphysical. Anthropomorphic interpretations are not at all uncommon. In this type of work, great care must be taken to avoid this temptation.

In one way or another, animals perceive energy that emanates from external sources over a relatively broad part of the energy spectrum. The senses of insects are essentially of the same general types as those found in other animals, but they tend to differ in the type of external pickup structures.

Insects have the ability to detect radiant energy in the form of heat and light, mechanical vibrations including those of the substrate and the higher frequency vibrations in the air (sound), mechanical pressure including the force of gravity, the amount of water in the air, and the presence of volatile chemicals in the air (odors); and they can identify food with remarkable precision by a sense of taste. The perception of these stimuli singly or in combination results in responses that govern the behavior of the animal.

THE MORPHOLOGY OF SENSORY RECEPTORS

Snodgrass[41] and Dethier[10, 11] have presented effective reviews of the morphology of insect sensory organs, and discussion of the ultra-microstructure of some are available in the literature.[27]

The structural elements of insect sensory organs are usually one of two types. In the primary type (this includes most if not all of the sensory perceptors of insects), there are peripherally situated nerve cells (sensory neurons), which receive the stimulation either directly or through distal processes and transmit them to the ganglia of the central nervous system. In the secondary type, ectodermal cells are innervated by distal branches of a neuron located in the ganglion.

The primary receptors of insects are also of two types—receivers of specific stimuli, or the components of a sensory innervation of the epidermis that arises from a primary sense cell. Just how the latter type receives the stimulus is unknown, but apparently impulses are transmitted by some means from the epidermis.

The basal cell, or group of cells that make up the receptor complex, comprises the structure called the *sensillum*. The simplest type of sensillum is an innervated hair or seta that has a direct connection with the distal process of a sensory cell. The external part may be a spine, a scale, or a minute peg, and it is often observed that these external parts are sunk into pits or cavities in the integument (Fig. 9–1).

Organs that have typical setae are called *sensilla trichodea*. If the external process is spinelike, it is a *sensillum chaetica;* if scalelike, a *sensillum squamiformia*. If the external process is reduced to a peg or a cone, it is called a *sensillum basiconica* if the process is exposed; and if it is sunk into a pit, it is called a *sensillum coeliconica*. If the cavity is a deep pouch, it is a *sensillum ampulacia*.[41]

Sensilla with no external processes are probably derived from one of the aforementioned sensilla with the loss of the setae. Some of these sensilla are marked externally by a cuticular pit called a *sense pore*. Most sensilla of this type are dome or bell shaped in cross section with a thickening of the cuticula surrounding the distal process. These are known as *sensilla campaniformia*, and the perceptors that are covered by an elliptical plate surrounded by a narrow ring of membrane are called plate organs or *sensilla placodia*.

A third group of sensory receptors in insects have no external structure associated specifically with them. Each sense cell is connected in a special manner with two other cells, and the distal process has a characteristic rodlike structure, the *scolops* or *scolopale*. These are the *sensilla scolopophora*.

The light-detecting organs, the *sensilla optica*, or eyes, are a distinct group that have very little in common with other sense organs. The external cuticula forms a transparent lens structure that admits light to the receptive cells—the retina—that are specialized ectodermal nerve cells with centripetal axons that form the fibers of the optic nerve (Fig. 9–4).[41]

FUNCTIONS OF THE SENSORY RECEPTORS

The hair sensilla are located on various parts of the body; the external part is a single hair, spine, or a hair plate and as many as 100 fine hairs may be grouped together. These groups of fine hairs are usually located on leg joints or between intersegmental membranes. They function as perceptors of pressure and vibration. The finer hairs vibrate or become displaced by air movements and sounds of low frequency, and the stiffer hairs respond to contact displacement. The type of response resulting from stimulation de-

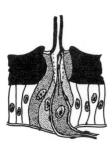

Hair sensillum

Peg sensillum

Campaniform sensillum

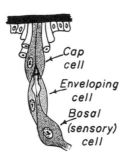

Plate sensillum

Cap
cell

Enveloping
cell

Basal
(sensory)
cell

Scolopophorous
sensillum

Simple Johnston
organ

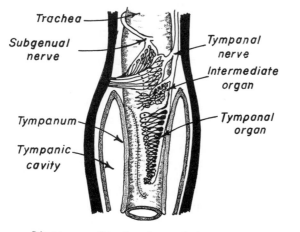

Trachea

Subgenual
nerve

Tympanum

Tympanic
cavity

Tympanal
nerve

Intermediate
organ

Tympanal
organ

Diagrammatic structure of the tympanal
organ on the foreleg of a katydid

FIG. 9-1. Diagrammatic representation of various types of sensory receptors found on insects.
(Redrawn after Snodgrass.)

pends upon the intensity of the stimulation. If a spine is deflected slightly and gently, the strength of stimulus is less than if it is deflected quickly and more acutely, and the response varies accordingly. This is not different from the response in vertebrate touch perception. The very fine hairs respond synchronously to stimulation applied by a rapidly vibrating needle, which indicates their sensitivity to low-frequency disturbances, either of the air or of the substrate.[10]

Some of the hair plates and sensory hairs located at strategic parts of the body, for example at the leg joints, have a definite effect on the stance and behavior of the insect. Dethier calls these sensory hairs *proprioreceptors*, and their position on flexing membranes on the body gives them a function in positioning the whole body.

The campaniform sensilla are more widely distributed on the insect body than other types of receptors. They exist in at least six morphological types,[41] and were shown by Pringle[33] to respond to mechanical strains in the cuticle. Campaniform sensilla can be stimulated by passive movements of the joints, by contraction of muscles, or by pressure on the cuticle. Their sensitivity to pressure is particularly great in the immediate vicinity of the joints on which they are located.

Pringle[33] used a model to demonstrate how this type of receptor can work. He stretched a rubber diaphragm that contained a circular hole over a frame; he cemented a paper strip over the opening in a slight arch to simulate the bell shaped cuticular dome; and he attached a vertical rod to the center of the paper strip. This model shows that all stresses can be resolved into shearing forces with extension and compression components. Any distortion of the diaphragm caused the hole to be shortened in one direction and widened in the other, which brought about a greater or lesser humping of the paper strip. The vertical rod, representing the distal process of the neuron, is raised and lowered (stretched or compressed) by distortion of the membrane in any direction. Distortion in any direction would lead to a stimulation, but from the model it is immediately apparent that there is a critical angle in the direction of the applied force below which doming increases and above which it decreases. Presumably, these would elicit different types of response.

The sensitivity of the sensillum depends upon factors such as the length of the cap and its elliptical or circular shape. Elongate sensilla arranged in parallel respond to the same direction of shear, so that it is entirely possible for a group to act as a unit. Circumstantial evidence points to the sensilla of this type actually acting on compression only, so that in order to respond to stresses in more than one direction, groups of receptors are oriented to accommodate stresses in different directions.

The nerve discharge from the campaniform sensilla is said to be always rhythmic with impulses of approximately equal amplitude,[34] which is a criterion often used to distinguish a single fiber discharge. Pringle has suggested that either the proximal processes of the individual bipolar sense cells have anastomosed, or development has been such that a single neurocyte has branched and sent a process to each sensillum, so that the functions of tropism have been taken over by secondary cells of the sensillum.[33] In either case, the production of synchronous, uniform discharges is complicated, and thus far it has been explained only on a theoretical basis.

On the legs, the campaniform sensilla are arranged so that they are compressed when the insect is standing in an upright position. Stimulation of these sensilla by the weight of the insect inhibits the righting reflex, but when the pressure is removed by taking the weight off the legs, the insect responds in a manner that restores the pressure to the leg sensilla. Restoration of the pressure is usually achieved by regaining a normal position, but in some cases it can be produced by placing the legs in contact with a solid object that supplies the pressure necessary to produce the stimulation. The flying reflex is also inhibited by stimulation of sensilla; it is easy to demonstrate that a fly suspended by the thorax does not attempt to fly if it has a ball of cotton or a fragment of pith in its feet. These receptors also play important roles in the normal walking movements and probably in the geotactic response that most insects exhibit.

The scolopophorous organs, otherwise known as *chordotonal sensilla*, also are widely distributed over the body of the insect. They usually are displayed in groups attached to the cuticle at some common point, and except for the tympanic organs, which are a special type, these sensilla have no external modification. The scolopophorous organs are characteristically made up of three distinct cells—a cap cell, an enveloping cell, and a sense cell (Fig. 9–1).

The cap cell is attached to the cuticula, and its inner part embraces the enveloping cell that surrounds the elongate distal process of the sense cell. The apex of the sense cell is connected to the cuticle by a terminal fiber that traverses the cap cell. The distinguishing characteristic of this type of receptor is the presence of a peg shaped sense rod at the apex of each sense cell. These sense rods vary in length from a few microns to as much as 25 microns. They may be cylindrical, or they may be bulb shaped. The typical rod is elongated and somewhat expanded at the distal end, but tapering to an acute point. The distal part of the sense rod always has a darkly staining body to which the axial fiber of the sense cell is attached.[41]

The function of the chordotonal sensilla has been proved in only a few cases. It is definite that these sensilla are the receptors associated with the tympanic organs, which function in the perception of sound, but other similar chordotonal organs are located in various parts of the body in situations where sound perception would be very unlikely. These other chordotonal organs are thought to respond to changes in pressure in much the same way that campaniform sensilla do. It has been suggested that while the campaniform sensilla respond to static changes in pressure, the sensilla scolopophora respond to pressure resulting from acceleration and deceleration when the insect is in motion.[10]

Phonoreceptors and the Auditory Sense

Sound vibrations are detected in insects by one of several receptors. The sound waves may cause the sympathetic vibration of the fine hairs of modified tactile sensilla, they may be received by the vibration pressure exerted on the tympanic membranes, which are innervated by chordotonal sensilla, or both types of receptors may be present to receive sound vibrations.

Hair sensilla as auditory perceptors are quite common in insects, and the frequencies that elicit a response cover a wide range, sometimes extending well into the ultrasonic; however, synchronous response may be limited. There is also the possibility that the hairs themselves are not the direct receptors, but as in the case of male mosquitoes, the hairs may cause the antennae to vibrate and stimulate the chordotonal sensilla of the Johnston's organ. In crickets and cockroaches, the anal cerci have long, innervated hairs that vibrate synchronously with sound waves of low frequency, and there appears to be no lower limit of perception. The upper limit of response is between 3000 and 4000 cps. On each end of the frequency range the response is not necessarily synchronous. There may be a doubling at very low frequencies and a halving or quartering of the response at higher frequencies.

The tympanic organs consist of a thin cuticular membrane associated with a tracheal sac that may decrease the damping and effective inertia of the membrane. Groups of chordotonal sensilla are attached either to the membranous drum or to the associated tracheal structure. Various methods have been used to prove that these chordotonal sensilla are auditory organs and that they respond over a frequency range lying between 250 cps and more than 45,000 cps. There is great variation of response in different insect species, and the thresholds of intensity vary at different levels of the frequency spectrum.

Even with the elaborate construction of the tympanic organ, insects do not always respond synchronously to sounds, particularly those of higher frequencies. With experience, insects can acquire the ability to distinguish between sound produced by another insect of the same species and an artificial sound produced with the same principal frequency. Pumphrey and Rawdon-Smith proposed a mechanism for this discrimination.[35] They concluded that higher frequencies are not perceived as such but act as a carrier wave with a modulation frequency impressed upon it. The modulated signal is perceived by the insect in a manner somewhat similar to the perception of a modulated audio signal that has been impressed on a radio carrier wave. While the human ear tends to respond principally to pure tone frequencies, the insect tympanum apparently tends to respond primarily to modulated frequencies (Fig. 9–2).

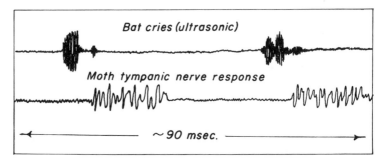

FIG. 9-2.   Response of the tympanum of a moth to ultrasonic cries of a bat (redrawn after Prosser).

CHEMORECEPTION, OLFACTION, GUSTATION, AND THE COMMON CHEMICAL SENSE

Chemoreception has been studied more avidly than other sensory reception in insects because of the economic importance of its function in the behavior of insects toward attractants and repellents. This subject has been reviewed by Dethier,[11] and by Hodgson[23] with much contributory work reported by Pumphrey and Rawdon-Smith.

Chemoreception can be divided into three categories, corresponding roughly to smell, taste, and the common chemical sense. The work that led to this breakdown into groups has been somewhat objective with insects and is based largely on behavior response. In insects electrophysiologic measurements have shown that the division of chemoreception into these three distinct categories is often impossible.

The olfactory and gustatory receptors may be divided into groups that respond to volatile chemicals in the gaseous state, to liquids or solutions of chemicals associated with food, and to chemicals such as acids, alkalies, and salts by the common chemical sense receptors. The level of response to chemicals by the common chemical sense is such that this sense requires a higher threshold of stimulation than the other receptors do.

The olfactory organs are most commonly located on the antennae, the maxillary palpi, or their homologues. There are three morphological types— pore plates, cones and pegs, and thin-walled cones and pegs set in pits. All these types have a thin cuticular covering innervated by a group of bipolar sense cells that have minute refringent bodies situated on the distal process of the neuron.

The measurement of stimulation thresholds and the acuity of the olfactory sense have been recorded for a number of insect species, but until the development of micro-electrodes (see Suckling for technology[42]) that allowed a direct pickup from the receptor, the evidence used to distinguish the levels of stimulation was based entirely upon the rejection or acceptance response of the insect for the material causing olfactory stimulation. This technique, using the behavior response, particularly in feeding, introduces a number of variables that cause problems difficult to resolve. The threshold values of a number of compounds for sense stimulation of several insect species have been tabulated by Dethier,[11] Chadwick and Dethier,[6] and others.

Variables that can alter the results from studies on the olfactory organs include temperature and humidity, singly or in combination; physiological state, hunger or satiation; sex and degree of sexual development; and the feeding habits of the different developmental stages of the same species. Hunger or satiation, or the related factor of conditioning, can bring about a complete reversal in the response. This reversal is usually transient, but it can produce confusing results.

The labellar chemoreceptors of *Phormia* were among the first to be studied by the electrophysiological method, which included use of micro-pipet-type electrodes with tips of the order of 0.5 μ. in diameter, or of such size that they could be placed over the external part of the receptor. These tips are filled with a solution of KCl, which forms a bridge to silver–silver-chloride electrodes; the impulse is picked up by making contact with a labellar hair. The usual impulse consists of a stimulus artifact followed by a spike potential from the receptor cell. The electrophysiological method of studying insect chemoreception has made it possible to visualize the electrical disturbance transmitted to the central nervous system by a single receptor and has revealed several characteristics of the chemoreceptors.

If the electrodes are arranged properly, it is possible to distinguish the spike potential from each of the two receptor cells that innervate the single hair. One receptor cell produces a response only when it is perceiving an acceptable food solution such as sugar; the other receptor cell responds to stimulation by nonfood materials such as salts, acids, and alcohols. Stimulation of the food receptor brings about a feeding reflex, and activation of the nonfood receptor either inhibits the feeding reflex or produces a rejection response. The magnitude of the potential is usually smaller from the food receptor than from the nonfood receptor. The thresholds of stimulation vary with the insect's condition and treatment. Generally, starved insects have a lower threshold than insects that have been fed; by stimulating two sets of chemoreceptors (a pair of bilaterally symmetrical receptors), it is possible to show summation (the additive effect of subthreshold concentrations) or inhibition brought about by central nerve activity. Data obtained by tapping nerves with micro-electrodes show that nerves produce large spikes when a normally rejected substance is offered and small spikes when an acceptable substance is offered (Fig. 9–3).

Sensory cells of the olfactory type also respond to changes in temperature and to flexing of the labellar hair. The magnitudes of the response to temperature change are within the normal physiological range, but the sites of excitation for these stimulations are different from those for olfactory stimulations. Chemicals stimulate by contact with the tips of the distal cells, and temperature effects are localized at or proximal to the cell bodies. There is similar localization of tactile stimulus.[23, 24]

The electrophysiological approach to the study of stimulation response phenomena in sensory organs emphasizes the difficulty in evaluating their function on a purely behavioral response basis because of the multiple sensitivity of the organs. For example, ganglia neurons in cockroaches respond to a common chemical stimulus with a threshold as low as or lower than the sensory organs. This response indicates that sensitivity to chemical environment is also a property of the neurons, as well as sense organs. Some neurons may function as chemoreceptors because of their location on the animal, not because they are specialized for this function.

The behavior of several insect species indicates they are able to detect

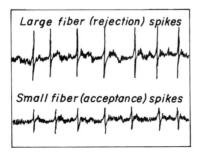

FIG. 9-3.   Acceptance and rejection spikes from contact chemoreceptors of *Phormia*. The large spikes indicate rejection and arise from a large nerve fiber, and the small spikes indicate acceptance and come from stimulation of the small fiber. (Redrawn after Prosser.)

and locate water by detecting differences in the amounts of water vapor in the air. This type of chemoreception enables the individual to orient itself to find an optimum environment or to locate a source of drinking water. Two physical principles have been suggested to explain the mechanism; both require further elucidation.

Culex and *Tenebrio* have sensory organs that act as hygrometers sensitive to relative humidity; wireworms have organs that act as evaporimeters and are sensitive to saturation deficiency. In the first type of sensory organ, the cuticle must have areas with hygroscopic properties that affect the intensity of the response. In the second type it is postulated that evaporation of water causes changes in ionic concentration, which alters the osmotic pressure of the tissue fluids. The pressure changes could cause mechanical stress and bring about stimulation. It is also possible that evaporation of water from the organ surfaces lowers the temperature enough to produce thermal stimulation. Other ideas proposed to explain the mechanics of this response have been listed by Dethier;[10] none of the suggested hypotheses is entirely satisfactory. Even identification of the humidity receptors has not helped to solve the problem, but it is possible to differentiate these receptors from olfactory receptors in some insects.

Dethier describes the sense of taste as contact chemoreception.[10] The methods used to investigate this process center around behavior and feeding response. The receptors typically are located on the antennae (bees and ants), on the legs (flies and butterflies), and on the mouthparts and adjacent surfaces of the pre-oral cavity of other species. In a few parasitic species, the contact chemoreceptors are found on the ovipositors. The location of the receptors has been determined by placing stimulants of increasing concentrations on various parts of the body; this technique has made it possible to locate the receptors and to correlate the expected response with the concentration thresholds for various materials.

THE LIGHT RECEPTORS

The physical structure of the insect eye was worked out in the early part of the Nineteenth Century largely by Johannes Mueller, who proposed the optical structure in 1829. He showed that images of objects are perceived by the juxtaposition of portions of the reflected light received from the object, so that the image formed is a mosaic. The degree of detail and the resolution of such a system depend on the number of facets in the eye and the type of eye.

Optically, the light reception system is composed of superimposed cylinders whose refringence is greatest at the central axis and least at the periphery. As a beam of light enters the cylinder, it is refracted in such a way that it reaches the receptor cell even though the angle of incidence is relatively small. The length of the cylinder of the eye may be of varying dimensions, depending upon which of two principal types is considered (Fig. 9–4).

In the apposition eye, which is found primarily in diurnal insects, the cylinder is relatively short, the principal focus lies at the posterior edge of

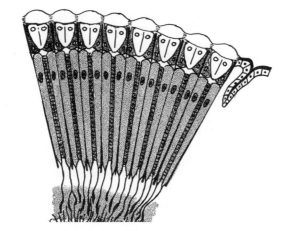

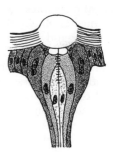

Diagram of the compound eye

Lateral ocellus of a
caterpillar

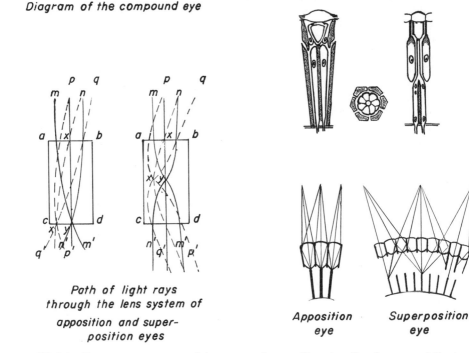

Path of light rays
through the lens system of
apposition and super-
position eyes

Apposition
eye

Superposition
eye

FIG. 9-4. Diagrammatic structure of the compound eye and lateral ocellus of a representative insect and the optics of the apposition and superposition eyes (redrawn after Snodgrass).

the cylinder, and the length of the cylinder is equal to the focal distance. The image is formed at the posterior surface, with the principal rays emerging parallel. In this type of eye, the retinulae (neural receptors) contact the lens cone. In most eyes of this type a dark pigment surrounds the cone and extends to the posterior extremity. This dark pigment curtain serves the same function as the iris of the human eye. Movements of the pigment compensate for changes in light intensity, making adaptation to light possible. Presence of this pigment also complicates the determination of the optical receptor pigments of insects, because it is very difficult to separate the two types of pigments and it appears that very few attempts have been made to do so.

The second type of eye, the superposition eye found mostly in the nocturnal forms, has the principal focus at a point half the length of the cylinder, so that the rays cross and come out the posterior surface at the same angle they entered. In this type, the ommatidium is greatly elongated and the retinulae do not contact the cone. In both eye types, the image is formed by the collective action of the light rays striking the sensitive ommatidium; in the apposition eye the image is made up of the sum of the points of light that strike the individual receptors, and in the superposition eye the mechanism more nearly approaches the type of perception found in the vertebrate eye.[34]

The resolving power of the eye depends upon the structure of the dioptric apparatus and the retina. Each ommatidium has two lenses—a cornea and a crystalline cone. The cornea is usually a biconvex area formed from three layers of cuticle. Each layer has a different refractive index. Beneath the cornea is the crystalline cone. The dioptric apparatus functions as though it might be formed from concentric layers with the refractive index greatest at the central axis and least at the periphery.

The lens system of the compound eyes of insects is capable of forming a fairly sharp image, and depending upon the number and the size of the ommatidia and the angle of incidence, the resolution may be moderately good. The visual acuity in arbitrary units is 0.017 for the honeybee and 0.0018 for *Drosophila*.[34] Using the same standards, the visual acuity for man lies between 2.0 and 2.5.[34]

Resolving power and the mechanism that controls acuity in flying insects are more complex in those that move rapidly than in the slower-moving species, and a theory of temporal resolution that distinguishes between the fast and the slow has been suggested. Modern electrophysiological technique makes it possible to study the potentials from the optic lobe;[1, 8] electroretinograms (ERG) are made from single units in the optic lobe[2, 4] and single ganglion cells.[23]

The insect eye falls far short of the vertebrate eye in intensity discrimination and acuity, but it is highly adapted to rapid resolution, particularly in the flying insects. Flicker fusion for the honeybee and the blowfly is of the order of 200 to 300 per second (the comparable figure for man is about 45 to 55 per second). Slow-moving insects do not have rapid resolution, which suggests the idea of fast and slow eyes; this idea is corroborated by quite different ERG measurements, which reflect a self-quenching system in the fast type of eye.

ERG measurements confirm the existence of slow and fast eye types in insects. The ERG of the slow eye type is usually monophasic, with the cornea negative and strongly affected by light and dark adaptation. The amplitude of the impulse varies with light intensity, the sensitivity to light is high, and flicker fusion occurs at a low rate. Records (ERG) with electrodes placed at various depths in the eye are shown in Figure 9–5. ERG records from insects with the fast type of eye are diphasic with large on- and off-waves. The ERG amplitude increases with increasing light intensity, and the flicker fusion frequency is high (Fig. 9–6). Specific differences in ERG response curves are common. An analysis of response curves for the eyes of various species has been summarized by Dethier.[9]

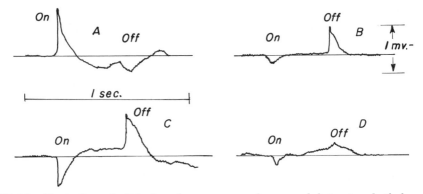

FIG. 9-5. Illumination potentials of grasshopper compound eye recorded at various depths by an intra-ocular electrode. A = 0.5 mm. B = 1.0 mm. C = 1.5 mm. D = 2.0 mm. This is a slow type of eye. (Redrawn after Prosser.)

The luminosity discrimination of the insect eye is moderately low. Measurements depending both on behavior and ERG records show that it is a general characteristic of insects to be sensitive to light waves over a wide band from about 2500 mμ. to about 7000 mμ. This is somewhat broader perception than is found in humans. In insects there is a tendency for greater perception on the short end of the wave length spectrum. There are many examples based upon behavior to show that insects generally respond more readily to short wave lengths than to long wave lengths, but there are no safe generalities that might be applicable to the development of truly attractive or repellent lights.

Color Sensitivity

The most dependable criterion that can be used to test insects for color sensitivity remains the behavioral response to conditioned reflexes. Observations of behavior toward colored objects suggests that insects do not possess true color vision in the sense that it is developed in man, but there is good evi-

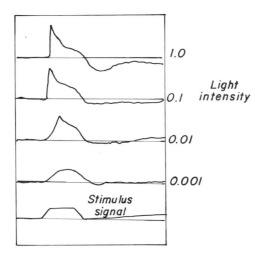

FIG. 9-6. Electroretinograms of the fast type of eye found in *Lucilia;* the electrode is placed at the retinal layer. This type of eye can follow flicker to frequencies as high as 200 or 300 per second. (Redrawn after Prosser.)

dence that many insects have the ability to distinguish between certain broad categories of color. Unfortunately, most of the data available have been based upon experiments in which light intensity was not controlled, and this factor could have a critical effect on the response. The subject of color perception in insects was reviewed by Weiss,[44] and more recently by Prosser.[34] Earlier work by von Frisch[15] indicates that honeybees have the ability to distinguish certain colors. It was demonstrated that bees could detect blue squares on a checkerboard when these were intermixed with gray squares. It was also shown that the bees could not distinguish red and that they confused yellow-orange and yellow-green. Bees conditioned to blue confused blue, violet, and purple. These results indicate that the light being perceived was reflected light and that those colors with a high ultraviolet component were perceived most readily.

Other evidence that insects are capable of perceiving color to a degree comes from the observation of optomotor reflexes and chromatophore responses; in many insects these observations indicate receptors for different sensitivity maxima. Flicker fusion frequency increases with increasing intensity of light, and a sudden shift of the resulting curve in some brightness range may correlate with a shift from rods to cones or the equivalent.[35] When the curve of relative spectral sensitivity is measured for different ranges of intensity, a shift (the Purkinje shift) of optimum wave length toward longer values in bright light may take place. This shift suggests different receptors for different parts of the color range and has been observed to take place in some insects.

Color vision in a number of species of insects has been studied, using a variety of methods. According to Schlegtendal,[39] many beetles, noctuid moths, and geometrids (Lepidoptera) can perceive color, but the nocturnal walking stick (*Dixippus*) is color insensitive.

Knowledge of color perception by insects is still confused by lack of sound data. When this problem is resolved, a wide variation in color sensitivity will very likely be evident in the various insect groups. The possibility is excellent that insects possess receptors, individually sensitive to different wave lengths of light. Such a system would result in the perception of as many colors as there are perceptors. This mechanism has been demonstrated to occur in *Limulus*, the horseshoe crab.[17]

Ocelli and Dermal Receptors

In addition to compound eyes, some insects have simple photoreceptors of at least three types, which include lateral ocelli, dorsal ocelli, and dermal receptors.

Lateral ocelli are similar to a single ommatidium in structure (Fig. 9–4). They are made up of a corneal lens and a crystalline cone that overlies a rhabdome-like structure.[9] The principal function of the ocelli is probably that of a perceptor of light and dark; any image perceived by ocelli probably is the sum of images from several units operating jointly. This would constitute a sort of compound eye.

The lateral ocelli typically are found on larvae, and the dorsal ocelli on adults where they augment the eyes. The lens of the dorsal ocellus is such that any image formed falls behind the retina, so that it is likely that these organs only perceive light and dark and add their stimulation to the effect of other receptors to facilitate reflex response. Observations of this effect indicate that when the ocellus of a grasshopper is darkened, there is a depolarization that spreads to the ganglion of the brain. This depolarization results in a discharge in the commissure, which facilitates some reflex responses. This is the *kinesis effect* in the terminology used by Wigglesworth.

The dermal receptors are not distinguished as morphological entities, but their presence is apparent in many larval forms that can orient themselves to a light source after all known receptors have been covered. The only organs described that are suspected of this function are a group of retinula-like cells located within the hypodermal tissue of the head region of blowfly larvae.

INSECT BEHAVIOR

Behavior results from the combination of all the responses of the sensory receptors, the nervous system, and the muscular system. When these systems act in a coordinated manner, the result is an activity that usually follows a fixed pattern. Behavior is a subject that approximates the study of human pyschology. It constitutes a field which has been the subject of book-length treatises. For general reference and bibliography, the student is referred to Fraenkel and Gunn,[13] Carthy,[5] Schnierla,[40] and to the many technical and semitechnical treatises on specific phases of the subject. The purpose of the following discussion is to provide necessary background for understanding the more complicated work, to outline the present status of the field, and possibly to create some interest for further investigations. Studies of behavior have a strong tendency toward anthropomorphism, a pitfall that must be carefully avoided.

Learning Capacity

The process of learning in insects has been studied to some extent, using more or less standard procedures; insect responses are more or less complex conditioned reflexes, rather than cognitative processes that allow them to solve problems. Cockroaches, for example, readily become conditioned to maze running, but if the direction of the maze is reversed, the insect cannot associate land marks with direction and reverse its response.[40] In this, the cockroach shows about one third the ability to complete the mission shown for the white rat. Rigidity of response to stimulation seems to be a characteristic of the insect reflex system.

The behavior patterns of insects fall into two rather broad categories. The first includes response patterns to external factors and are nonrhythmic; the second behavior pattern category includes response patterns that show rhythmic behavior patterns accompanied by internal control phenomena and metabolic changes. Into these categories can be fitted the various responses that enable insects to find and identify food and form the basis for sex behavior and the various patterns of behavior that have evolved for defense.

The Language of Behavior

As with every specialty, the field of behavior has special terminology, which has developed gradually. This terminology can be confusing because similar terms have been used with different meanings. Also, the close relationship of behavior to natural history has tended to produce an extensive literature, some of which is more philosophical than exact. The following is not intended as an argument on priority of terms but as a clarification of terminology that will surely confound students who consult various references.

Orientation. The study of orientation, particularly the sites of stimulation that control the behavior of individuals as regards environment, has enjoyed popularity for a long time. An early theory of the relationship of external factors and behavior was defended by Loeb, who postulated that organisms orient themselves in an environment so that bilaterally located receptors are positioned to adjust the intensity of stimulation to equality. This was the *tropism* theory, and except for its use in describing the movements of plants in response to light, it has been more or less abandoned. The various *kinesis* and *taxis* factors have supplanted the tropism theory to explain orientation.

Most modern behaviorists more or less follow the terminology proposed by Gunn,[13, 19] who defined *kinesis* as variations in generalized undirected locomotor activity due to variations in intensity of stimulation. Such variations may be changes in linear velocity or angular velocity (rate of change of direction); the first is called *orthokinesis* and the second *klinokinesis*. It is unfortunate the term kinesis was used by Wigglesworth in his widely used textbook according to the definition of Wolsky with the following meaning: "In addition to receiving specific stimuli, the majority of sense organs, when they are stimulated, have the effect of increasing reflex excitability of the nervous system. Their action seems to be necessary in order to open the nervous paths, to allow reflexes to take place, and to enable the nerve centers to carry out their normal function. Sense organs having this effect are called 'stimulatory organs'; and the increased activity due to their action is termed 'kinesis.' "[45] From this, one would expect the threshold of electrical stimulation required to produce a muscular response to be lowered when the eyes are stimulated by a light and raised when the eyes are blacked out. It is easy to demonstrate this phenomenon with cockroaches and other insects. The opposite of kinesis with this meaning is *akinesis* or *thanatosis*, a characteristic of many nocturnal insects that assume a rigid (death-feigning) position during the day, when they are stimulated by light.

By the accepted (i.e., currently used) terminology, both kinesis and akinesis as used by Wigglesworth are included in the Fraenkel and Gunn term, *orthokinesis*. *Klinokinesis* is approximately equivalent to the *phobotaxis* of Wigglesworth. The responses that Wigglesworth calls *topotactic* (truly oriented responses) are described simply as *taxes* and defined as directed responses to a single stimulation with the long axis of the body orientated in a line with the source. There are three kinds of taxes—klinotaxis, telotaxis, and menotaxis.

Klinotaxis is orientation indirectly attained by the interruption of regularly alternating lateral deviations of part or all of the body, accomplished by comparison of intensities of successive stimulations. This is a part of the *tropotactic* response of Wigglesworth, which he defines as orientation with regard to the source of a stimulus, so that bilaterally symmetrical receptors receive balanced stimulation. The definition of klinotaxis also includes avoiding reactions. Tropotaxis as used by Fraenkel and Gunn is orientation directly attained by turning to the greater or less stimulated side in response to the activity of bilaterally symmetrical receptors. This seems to equate the meaning of the two definitions, but Fraenkel and Gunn exclude description of a negative (*phobotactic*) response.

The *telotaxis* of Fraenkel and Gunn is an orientation that is direct and without deviation; it is identical to telotactic response as used by other authors except that it excludes cases in which response to two sources of stimulation bring about a line of approach between the sources with deviation toward one of the sources as the approach progresses.

When the response shows a temporarily fixed angle to the direction of external stimulation, or a fixed angle of 90° with locomotion not a prerequisite and seldom directed towards or away from the source, the reactions are grouped as *transverse orientation*. These reactions include the light-compass reactions used in direction-finding by some insects in which locomotion is at a temporarily fixed angle with the light rays, usually from one side. This is a *menotaxis* by Wigglesworth's terminology, which is defined as orientation to the dorsal or ventral light so that perpendicularity of the light to both the long and transverse axes of the body is maintained. The dorsal surface is usually kept up and locomotion need not occur. Menotaxis also includes the *geotactic* response.

The definitions summarized here are offered strictly for the purpose of clarification. It is most unfortunate that identical terms have been used for different meanings, since it unduly complicates a relatively simple series of responses, most of which result in change of direction of movement, stance, or position of the insect. Undoubtedly more types of stimuli and different degrees of response will be discovered as research in the field of behavior continues, and undoubtedly these will be couched in equally complicated terms.

Thus far, the discussion of behavior has considered the source and the end response of the insect to a stimulus. It is not difficult to manipulate these ideas mentally so that the possibilities for orientation, in regard to light sources, sounds, or other stimuli that bring about responses leading to the aggregation of a number of insects, can be determined. Probably more interesting and challenging from a physiological point of view are the problems of internal control systems in insects.

INSECT CONTROL SYSTEMS

The subject of insect control systems was reviewed by Mittelstaedt, who defines *active orientation* as the maintenance and control of the spatial relations of the animal.[30] Maintenance and control involve the systems by which the perceptors are connected with the effectors. The behavior of insects in achieving spatial relations with outside objects makes it evident that such a control exists. New developments in technology have partially removed this field from the observation-deduction methods of the naturalists and brought it into the realm of quantitative biology.

An analysis of insect behavior starts with a behavioral capability. A control pattern involves the connection of a series of subsystems. If subsystem A (the receptor) and subsystem B (the effector) are known, one method of connecting them would be as a direct chain so that the output of A would be the input of B. This pattern is the first of three basic control patterns.

A second type of pattern could include a situation wherein two subsystems have a common input and the outputs can be either subtracted or added; a third control pattern type might consist of a loop in which the output of A is the input of B, and the output of B feeds back to partially control the output of A. The first two patterns constitute open controls, since the output of the effector (B) never influences the final output. In the third system, which is a closed control pattern, this is a possibility. By analogy with electrical circuitry, in the first control pattern, subsystems A and B are in series; in the second, the arrangement is series-parallel; and in the third, A and B are a reflexed loop so that feedback from B will influence A. These three types of control patterns are diagrammed in Figure 9–7.

One of the key requirements of orientation is the ability of the organism to change its position to compensate for changes in the external environment. Such a situation arises when an insect is placed on its back, a situation that is compensated for by the institution of the righting reaction. The ability of an organism to change its position to compensate for changes in the external environment also can be illustrated by a group of male fireflies that are stimulated by a single flash of light. The duration of the flash in this case is too short to be within the limits of the reaction time of the insect, but the response observed is an orientation by which the insect turns accurately toward the direction of the flash. Since these fireflies complete the orientation while the stimulation signal is no longer present, any interference by the output system of the receptor on the input of the effector is precluded. This indicates an open control pattern.[30]

The case of the mantid that captures its prey by a quick movement of the forelegs shows a more complicated pattern. The eye of the mantid perceives the position of the object, and the forelegs strike. The direction of the strike is controlled by the angle of incidence of the object in relation to the eye. Any deviation in position of the prey during the strike period also appears in the visual field, so that a closed control might be possible to correct for the deviation. In this case, it is postulated that the deviation of position of the strike is altered when the output of the effector is fed back into the input of the perceptor and thus altered when the response to the deviation in position goes back to the effector. The time delay in this case must be less than the extension phase of the strike. The time delay has been measured for the mantid and found to be sufficiently greater than the time needed for extension of the foreleg so that a strictly closed system is precluded. Even with this complication, there remain three basic methods by which correction of the strike direction might be achieved.

The first possibility is that the position of the head is measured by a proprioreceptor, and the stimulus from this is added to the optic output.

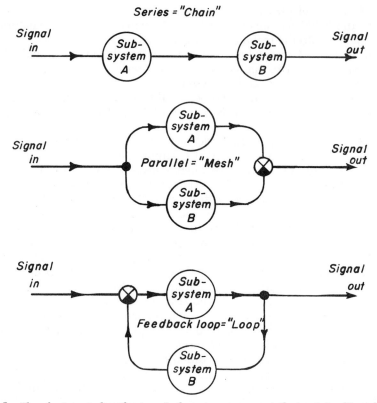

FIG. 9-7. Three basic control mechanisms. In the series arrangement, the input signal is modulated in subsystem A. The output from subsystem A is the input of subsystem B. The output of the entire system equals the modulating effect of subsystem A times the modulating effect of subsystem B times the input signal. (o = A × B × i). In the parallel arrangement, the input signal is fed directly to both the A and B subsystems. The outputs of these combine to either reinforce or cancel, so that the final output is equal to the output of A ± the output of B [o = (A ± B) × i].

In the loop arrangement, the output of subsystem A is fed back into the input signal through subsystem B. This alters the input signal reaching subsystem A and modulates the output accordingly $(o = \dfrac{1}{1 + \dfrac{B}{A}} \times i)$. (Redrawn after Mittelstaedt.)

The second possibility is that a copy of the output of the efferent subsystem may be added to the optic output. The third possibility is that the object output is fed back negatively into the afferent input, and if the loop that turns the head toward the prey is shown to operate during capture, a steady state of the optic reflex loop could be used to set the direction of the strike. The last possibility is the simplest and implies that the mantid must face the prey squarely before striking. It is a common observation that the mantid stalks and fixes its prey.[30]

Closed control orientation is common in insects, and very few seem to lack the facility for altering the response through some type of feedback loop. This type of orientation allows the insect to change its "mind" only when the variable is within the limited range of vision; beyond a finite velocity the eyes cease to respond to shifts in visual environment. This throws the optomotor reflex loop out of function. Since insects do continue to orient under such circumstances, another system is indicated that operates on a potentially unlimited range of finite values. This is possible only with a circular arragement described as a "course or gravity control" of animals.[30]

There are a number of possibilities for theoretical explanation of these phenomena based on experimental observation. These include the following:

Insects that orient themselves with a light source can maintain any angle between the light source and the body axis. If the angle is changed suddenly, the insect turns into the preshift relation but never more than 180°, so that to achieve the same angle the insect always chooses the least possible turn. When the phototactic response changes from positive to negative, the course of the insect changes 180° regardless of the previous angle between the light source and the body axis. If a change of brightness causes change of course, the animal turns in the same sense relative to the ground at light angles designated as $\beta \pm 180°$. If bees run a course on a horizontal, changes of height of the stimulating source above the plane do not change the course unless the height is 90°, but if the course is vertical there is a distinct influence of light source height. When forced to change quickly from a purely phototactic orientation on a horizontal to a purely geotactic orientation on a vertical surface, insects usually take a similar or identical angular position for both stimuli. Many species change their light course in nearly precise counteraction to the sun's azimuth position at the time of the observation, and they are thus able to keep a constant compass direction. Even the geotactic course shows a corresponding diurnal movement, which together with the other capabilities, enables bees to communicate by azimuth messages. The polarization pattern of the sky can be substituted for the sun in direction finding.[30] A culmination of these abilities is illustrated in bees, which are able to achieve azimuth communication under the sun at the equator as well as in the Northern and Southern Hemispheres. Bees and ants both can calculate their average compass bearing while moving on a winding path, being able to return to their colonies from excursions into unfamiliar and unmarked areas or to find their way by correcting for forced detours. These are observations that must be explained by systems of course control.

Two theories are considered basic to control patterns. The first is that light-course control requires that as soon as the image of the source deviates from a certain spot on the receptor, movements are elicited that correct the course with a return to normal. The visual spot shifts depending upon the inner state of the insect, so that each nerve unit representing such a spot would be the deviation of the image of the source from that spot.

A more likely alternative is that the afferent visual system measures one deviation of the image source from an anatomically fixed eye coordinate such as the median plane of the head. This deviation can be transformed into a single control variable of the type demonstrated for the afferent input of the mantid proprioreceptive loop. This control variable is added to the course order (nervous control variable), the value of which is determined by the inner state of the animal, which sets the reference point for this single loop.

The study of behavior on the basis of control systems is a fascinating approach that deserves greater attention.

Periodicity and Circadian Rhythms

It is well established that living organisms show differences in behavior at different times of the day, and a large amount of data has accumulated from field observations and laboratory study. Among the rhythms observed are synchronization of growth and reproduction with favorable seasons, and the daily activity rhythms associated with light and dark. Of all the environmental factors, the photoperiod is the only one that changes with mathematical precision during the course of the year; the importance of this factor in various phases of insect growth and development seems well established. This phase of control is usually treated under the discipline of ecology. Numerous examples and a general review of photoperiodism as it affects insects were presented by de Wilde.[46]

Of equal interest in physiology are the rhythms of approximately a 24-hour cycle; these rhythms have broader implications than does a direct response to an external stimulating factor. They are called *circadian rhythms,* a term introduced by Halberg[20] to describe those daily rhythms that persist under constant conditions of external stimulation (i.e., light or temperature) with a period approximating 24 hours. The period of the rhythm can be entrained to 24 hours by an environmental light-dark (LD) cycle of 24 hours, and the period of the rhythm can also be entrained to environmental LD cycles of periods close to 24 hours (i.e., 18 to 30 hours). Cycles that differ markedly from the 24-hour rhythm usually will not entrain.[31]

The phase of the circadian rhythm can be altered by changing the times of the L and D conditions. The period of the circadian rhythm is nearly independent of temperature over fairly wide temperature ranges, but in some cases the phase of the circadian rhythm can be reset by changing the phase of fluctuating temperature conditions.

That the period cannot be entrained to environmental cycles greatly different than 24 hours indicates the presence of some sort of intrinsic limitation of the insect's ability to respond to the period of the environmental cycle. It is also a characteristic of circadian rhythms that when free-running, the period usually only approximates a 24-hour cycle; thus, the organism tends to shift out of phase with the external environmental daily cycle. This tendency suggests that control of the rhythm is endogenous, although absolute proof is not available.

Whether the control is endogenous or exogenous, the organism apparently has some sort of timing device—an "internal clock." Most studies of circadian rhythms have been directed toward internal or external manifestations and not toward the actual control mechanisms. As Bünning states, it is the hands of the clock that are being watched.[3]

The importance of circadian rhythm phenomena in both fundamental and applied studies has been brought to the attention of physiologists in recent years, although it has been recognized and studied for a long time. Among observations related to this phenomenon are the time sense of bees and ants, rhythms of flight activity and feeding, rhythms in light-flashing of fireflies, and detailed studies of the eclosion rhythms of *Drosophila.* Most

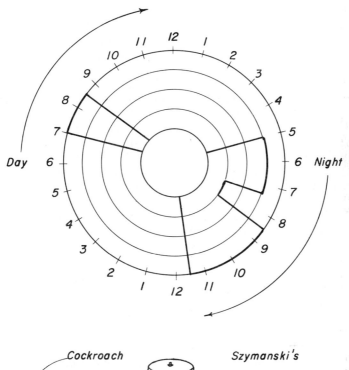

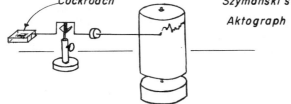

FIG. 9-8. Diurnal activity of a cockroach, derived from aktograph records (redrawn after Szymanski).

data have been collected by relating activity rhythms first with external stimulation and second with internal changes.

The first laboratory studies with insects were reported by Szymanski, who adapted an aktograph technique to the study of the activity of cockroaches.[43] He found that cockroaches were at rest, or at least quiescent, during most of the day and night, but that they displayed a period of high activity in the evening hours (Fig. 9–8). Later, it was shown that both the house cricket and the field cricket exhibited a definite daily activity rhythm that persisted in constant darkness, temperature, and humidity for at least several days.[28] It was also found that the phase of the rhythm could be changed by reversed illumination. Investigations of the oriental cockroach indicated that greatest activity occurred during the first half of the night and could be shifted by adjusting the time of onset of darkness.[18] Also, the activity persisted for several days in constant light or darkness, but eventually under these conditions, the activity of the cockroach spread evenly throughout the day. The American cockroach has also been studied and has yielded some interesting information. This is ordinarily a night-active species, but the activity that persists under changed conditions will eventually be lost. It was also observed that the circadian rhythm disappeared when the ocelli or the compound eyes were masked even though the LD cycle remained constant.[7] Later work indicated that only the ocelli are involved,[21] but this conflicts with data showing that the compound eyes are the principal receptors of the stimulation.[36] Still more recently it has been shown in the house cricket that either ocelli or the compound eyes can cause a change in rhythm if they are blacked out.[31]

That circadian rhythms are an intrinsic part of the behavior pattern of many insect species is well established, and entrainment caused by at least two external variables (light and temperature) has become routine laboratory experience (Fig. 9–9). The internal mechanism is not so well understood.

In an attempt to elucidate this problem, Harker devised a series of parabiotic and transplantation experiments, the results of which indicated that activity rhythm is regulated by an endocrine secretion of the subesophageal ganglion.[21] By means of a series of cautery experiments, she showed that a specific group of cells appeared to be responsible for the endocrine secretion. Further histological and histochemical observations indicate that there is also some involvement of the corpus cardiaca, which furnishes to the subesophageal ganglion a secretion that is important in maintaining the flow of the regulating substance. Although Harker's observations have not been confirmed,[36] they remain as a logical starting point for more advanced study that should lead to an understanding of the inner workings of the "biological clock" in insects.

Existence of circadian rhythms in insects and other animals has broad significance in the understanding of both fundamental and applied problems. Determination of various metabolites in the hemolymph of insects at various stages of the circadian cycle shows significant differences. This could be a very important factor in mode-of-action (of biologically active chemicals) studies, for example, since it implies that the internal physiology and biochemistry vary significantly with the time of day. This factor has not been

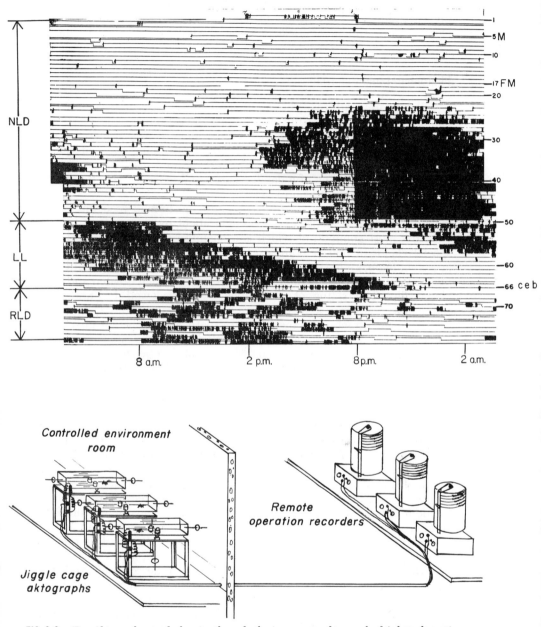

FIG. 9-9. *Top:* Aktograph records showing the arrhythmic response of a nymph of *Acheta domesticus* (lines 1–17; M = nymphal molt; FM = final molt). The normal circadian rhythm of the adult in a normal light-dark (NLD) cycle; the effect of a light-light (LL) cycle; and the response of the same cricket to a reversed light-dark (RLD) cycle when the compound eyes are blocked (ceb). *Bottom:* Diagram of the aktograph arrangement of Nowosielski with which the records (top) were obtained.

considered in studies not directly concerned with behavior. An example of the variability of hemolymph metabolites is the rhythmic fluctuation of blood sugar in the house cricket associated with the circadian rhythm.[32]

Pheromones and Behavior

Behavioral patterns other than those stimulated or triggered by environmental factors often involve sensory perception of the secretions of another insect. Among the responses particularly well developed in the social insects are those that enable recognition of members of the same colony, the directing of the sexes in courtship and mating, the blazing of trails to food, the giving of a danger alarm, and in some cases the provision for a last ditch defense against attack.

Sex Attractants.   The location and the mutual recognition of the male and female of a species are brought about by various sensory expedients, the most common of which is a chemical sex attractant secreted by special glands of one or both sexes. These secretions—called *pheromones,* or *ectohormones*—have been studied more thoroughly than many of the other secreted substances, and some of them have been isolated and defined chemically. The status of this subject was reviewed by Karlson and Butenandt.[26]

The sex attractant of the silkworm moth has received a great deal of attention. It comes from the paired lateral glands of the last abdominal segment and has been identified as an ester of *p*-nitroazobenzenecarboxylic acid and a polyunsaturated primary alcohol with more than 10 carbons. The attractant is extruded from the glands of the receptive female. When fertilized, the female no longer produces the substance. Extracts of the secretions of other Lepidoptera indicate that the sex attraction mechanism is similar, but the chemical structure of the attractants has not been determined.

In the mealworm, *Tenebrio molitor,* both sexes produce a sex pheromone, but the secretion of the female is more potent than that of the male. In Hymenoptera, the sex pheromones of the bumblebee have been shown to exist, but they have not been identified. A number of substances, including farnesol, citronellal, and hydroxycitronellal, show varying degrees of attraction, and the odor of these substances indicate that they are similar in chemical structure. In the Hemiptera a Δ-hexenal acetate has been identified as a constituent of an attractant secretion (presumably a sex attractant) of one of the tropical giant water bugs (*Belostoma* sp.).

Roth[38] described in two species of cockroach the courtship and mating behavior, which indicates the importance of the pheromones. In the German cockroach, the individuals meet more or less by accident and apparently identify the opposite sex by the presence of a secreted pheromone. The male courts the female by raising his wings to expose tergal glands that emit the attractant. The female feeds upon this secretion and is maneuvered into the position for the copulation that follows. In the case of the American cockroach, a male that comes into the proximity of a virgin female, or a female that has produced an ootheca and is ready for further impregnation, perceives an odor from the female sex glands. The male follows the scent until the female is overtaken, and courtship begins. Finally, the female is maneuvered into a proper mating position, and the male clasps the female genitalia. After a successful impregnation, the female ceases secretion of the attractant until the ootheca has matured and has been dropped. The chemical purification of the female attractant has been achieved by collecting the substance from a cold finger under which large numbers of virgin females have been allowed to run; the substance has been tentatively identified as 2,2-dimethyl-3-isopropylidene cyclopropyl propionate.[25] This is subject to confirmation.

The use of sex attractants to lure males or females to destruction is certainly not new, and the isolation of the specific attractants has made the idea attractive in the applied fields of insect control. The use of sex attractants offers a means of striking at a prime function (reproduction) and, if successful, should make it possible to control the biotic potential of relatively restricted groups of insects. It has been reported in the popular literature that some of the attractants are effective over a radius of approximately one mile, but this seems doubtful. Insects are not super-animals, and powerful as the attractant may be, this must be proved conclusively or else it should be relegated to the collection of super-phenomena (nearly supersonic flight velocities, for example) reported to be within the capabilities of insects.

Trailblazing Secretions.   Many social insects can blaze a trail that can be followed by others from the same colony to food or to their home community. For a good many years it has been known that the blazes or signposts that guide individual insects are chemical secretions. The chemical identity of many of these materials is unknown; however, because of their odor and reaction they must be either related to or identical with compounds such as the citronellals and the citrals, with the latter group predominating.[26]

Defensive Secretions.   The defensive behavior of insects includes the strictly behavioral characteristics by which some insects hide from enemies, employing some type of mimicry including the akinesis reaction described by Wigglesworth.[45] In addition, many species produce poisonous or repellent secretions that can be set free with explosive force. Interest in insect defensive secretions is very old, and it is surprising how accurately some of the early investigators identified some of the chemical constituents by the simple expedient of comparing odors of the secretions with known chemicals. Recently interest in chemical defense mechanisms has been renewed along with the study of other glandular secretions of insects; with modern chemical technology it has been possible to achieve positive identification of some defensive chemicals. The recent progress in this field has been reviewed by Roth and Eisner[37] and was the subject of a symposium reported in the Proceedings of the 11th International Congress of Entomology (Vienna, 1960).

Roth and Eisner list 31 chemicals that have been positively identified from the defensive secretions of insects and related forms. The most common compounds found are benzoquinones, and 2-methyl-1,4-benzoquinone was found in 27 of the secretions of species reported. The second most common compound found in these secretions is the ethyl derivative of 2-methyl-1,-4-benzoquinone; there are also impure mixtures including some unidentified compounds.

Apparently benzoquinones are the most common irritants in the defensive secretions. These compounds have a penetrating odor that resembles chlorine, and they are very irritating to the skin of humans. Contact causes severe dermatitis, and the vapor causes skin irritation and lacrimation.[29] Other irritating chemicals in defensive secretions include formic acid and acetic acid, and in some insects the secretion includes a wetting and penetrating agent, such as caprylic acid and the aldehydes of six- and ten-carbon alcohols, which presumably increase the effectiveness of the irritant.[37]

Methods of expulsion of the secretions and the structural mechanisms of the organs that expel the materials are, as might be expected, quite variable and more or less group specific. The glands usually have a saclike cuticular reservoir for collection and storage of the secretion, and the principal variation is in the mechanics of delivery.

Expulsion can be achieved by muscular contraction at the site of the storage sac; it may be brought about by the application of pressure through the distortion of the body; or it may be the result of hydraulic pressure exerted in the hemocoel through the body fluid. Tracheal pressure has also been suggested as a source of the expulsion force. In the bombardier beetles (*Brachynus* sp., Carabidae), which are well known for their ability to expel a protective secretion both with force and an audible report, an oxygen-producing chemical is present that is activated within the reservoir. The activation of this chemical has been described as the source of the pressure in the firing mechanism.[37]

COMMUNICATION AMONG INSECTS

That there is a purposeful means of communication between animals other than humans has been intriguing scientists for many years. The presence of this ability in insects, particularly the social forms, has been proved beyond reasonable doubt. The most complete study of insect communication has been the work of von Frisch and his associates, who have worked principally with the honeybee.[16] Because descriptions of this work have been so widely disseminated in the scientific literature, in semipopular releases, and in the popular press, it is only briefly outlined here.

Honeybees have been proved capable of communicating information on the source of food, the direction of the source, the distance from the colony, and the richness of the strike by a combination of codes that center around a series of purposeful movements called a *dance*. The forage scout bee that has been successful returns to the hive laden with nectar and pollen, which it shares with the other forage bees in the hive. This sharing communicates the type and amount of food to be found at the source. The direction and distance are imparted by a dance, which consists of more or less contiguous circular movements and a "waggle" of the abdomen. The orientation of the circular movements gives the compass direction, and the "waggle" gives the distance. An internal correcting mechanism compensates for the passage of time between discovery and the communication of instructions, so that the information is accurate despite the fact that the sun, which is the primary reference point, has moved during the interval. On cloudy days when the sun may be obscured, the sky polarization pattern can act as a secondary reference for direction finding. It is of interest that bees from different localities may communicate in different "dialects," so that a colony of German bees might not be able to "understand" the directions given by an Italian bee.

Communication of simple messages is not restricted to social insects. Orthoptera, for example, produce sounds that, on the basis of behavioral response, indicate a communicative function. There are other examples of sound communication in insects. As modern technique for sound analysis is more widely used in the study of insects, it is probable that a number of new discoveries in this field of investigation will be forthcoming. The subject of insect sounds has been reviewed by Frings and Frings,[14] and by Haskell.[22] These authors have cited many references pertinent to the subject.

Faber classified the sounds produced by various insects into 28 categories with subdivisions of each.[12] These categories can be reduced in number to about six general types of sound that appear to be used for communication. The simplest category includes the "ordinary" sounds of insects, which appear to be used to let other insects of the same species know of the presence of the insect making the sound. Four of the six types include the sounds emitted during courtship and mating. Among these are: the "rival song," a duet used as a challenge between males about to fight over a single female; a "courtship song" or serenade; a "nuptial song," which is a sort of triumphal sound produced by the successful suitor; and a "mating song," which is used by the copulating male presumably to quiet a restless female. The sixth category includes the alarm cry or the sound emitted by many insect species when disturbed; it is thought to be either a warning of impending danger or a protective measure to scare off aggressors. The other categories are derived from combinations of these.

A few minutes of listening on a warm summer night is all that is necessary to reach the conclusion that insects produce sounds, and it is assumed that these sounds are purposeful. The recording of these sounds, decoding the characteristics of the sounds and associating them with behavior, and the analysis of structural mechanisms for sound production offer many possibilities for ingenious research.

SUMMARY

It is evident that insects have highly complicated behavior patterns that result from the action of the receptor-effector mechanisms. Much of the literature is based on observation of behavior in response to stimulation, and it is a relatively recent development to analyze the mechanisms on the basis of quantitative biology.

Insects respond to sensory stimulation primarily through a series of ordered reactions between the receptor and the effector mechanisms. Available evidence suggests that these reactions are reflexes that follow a predetermined pattern, and that these reactions lack the flexibility of response exhibited by the higher vertebrates. No thought process, in the anthropomorphic sense, appears to exist.

Insect behavior is governed by external stimulation, which triggers a series of reactions in the internal control system. There is excellent evidence that some characteristic behavior patterns are rhythmic and are controlled by an endogenous "biological clock" mechanism.

Secretions play an important role in locating food and home, attracting mates, keeping the population of a social colony satisfied, and in defense. In these activities the pheromones, or ectohormones, are an essential part of the control system.

Communication of information between members of a colony or intra-specifically has been suspected by naturalists for many years, and recent technological developments and perseverance of those who have studied the subject have yielded interesting results. Further investigation is almost sure to be fruitful.

LITERATURE CITED

1. Adrian, E. D. 1937. Synchronized reaction in the optic ganglion of *Dytiscus*. J. Physiol., *91*: 66–89.
2. Autrum, H. 1949. Experimentia, *5*:271–277. See also: 1953. The electrophysiology of insect eyes. Klin. Wchnschr., *31*:241–245.
3. Bünning, E. 1960. Biological clocks. Cold Spr. Harb. Symp. quant. Biol., *25*:1–9.
4. Burtt, E. T., and Catton, W. T. 1956. Responses of optic lobe of locust and other insects to il-lumination. J. Physiol., *133*:68–88; 1959. *146*:492–515.
5. Carthy, J. 1958. Behavior of Invertebrates. Allen and Unwin, London.
6. Chadwick, L., and Dethier, V. G. 1949. Stimulation of blowfly by aliphatic aldehydes and ketones. J. gen. Physiol., *32*:445–452.
7. Cloudsley-Thompson, J. L. 1953. Studies in diurnal rhythms. III. Photoperiodism in the cock-roach. Ann. Mag. nat. Hist. Series XII, *6*:705–712.
8. Crescitelli, F., and Jahn, T. L. 1939. Electrical responses of insect eyes. J. cell. comp. Physiol., *13*:105–112; 1942. *19*:47–66.
9. Dethier, V. G. 1942. Optical and visual properties of insect ocelli. J. cell. comp. Physiol., *19*: 301–303; 1943. *22*:115–126.
10. Dethier, V. G. 1953. Chemoreception. *In* Insect Physiology (K. D. Roeder, ed.). John Wiley, New York, Ch. 21.
11. Dethier, V. G. 1956. Chemoreceptor mechanisms. *In* Molecular Structure and Functional Ac-tivity of Nerve Cells (R. G. Grenell and L. J. Mullins, eds.). Amer. Inst. biol. Sci. pub., *1*:1–30.
12. Faber, A. 1953. Sounds and communication in insects. *Orthoptera*. Staatl. Mus. Naturkde., Stuttgart, Part 1.
13. Fraenkel, G., and Gunn, D. L. 1961. Orientation of Animals. Dover, New York.
14. Frings, H., and Frings, M. 1958. Uses of sounds by insects. Ann. Rev. Ent., *3*:87–106.
15. Frisch, K. von. 1914. Color discrimination by the honey bee. Zool. Jahr. Physiol., *35*:1–182.
16. Frisch, K. von, and Lindauer, M. 1956. The language of bees. Ann. Rev. Ent., *1*:45–58.
17. Graham, C. H., and Hartline, H. K. 1935. Spectral response of single visual sense cells (*Limu-lus*). J. gen. Physiol., *18*:917–931.
18. Gunn, D. L. 1940. The daily rhythm of activity of the cockroach, *Blatta orientalis*. J. exp. Biol., *17*:267–277.
19. Gunn, D. L., Kennedy, J. S., and Pielou, D. P. 1937. Classification of taxes and kinesis. Nature (London), *140*:1064–1065.
20. Halberg, F. 1960. Temporal coordination of physiological function. Cold Spr. Harb. Symp. quant. Biol., *25*:289–310.
21. Harker, J. E. 1961. Diurnal rhythms. Ann. Rev. Ent., *6*:131–146.
22. Haskell, P. T. 1962. Insect Sounds. Quadrangle Books, Chicago.
23. Hodgson, E. S. 1958. Chemoreception in arthropods. Ann. Rev. Ent., *3*:19–36.
24. Ishikawa, S. 1962. Visual response of cells of the optic lobe of the silkworm moth. J. ins. Physiol., *8*:485–491.
25. Jacobson, M., Beroza, M., and Yamamoto, R. T., 1963. Isolation and identification of the sex attractant of the American cockroach. Science, *139*:48–49.
26. Karlson, P., and Butenandt, A. 1959. Pheromones in insects. Ann. Rev. Ent., *4*:39–58.

27. Larson, J. R. 1962. Fine structure of labellar hairs. J. ins. Physiol., *8:*683–692.
28. Lutz, F. E. 1932. Diurnal rhythm, *Orthoptera.* Amer. Mus. Novit., *550:*1–34.
29. Merck Index. 1960. 7th ed., Merck & Co., Rahway, N. J.
30. Mittelstaedt, H. 1962. Control systems in insects. Ann. Rev. Ent., *7:*177–198.
31. Nowosielski, J. 1961. Studies on circadian rhythm of the house cricket, *Gryllus domesticus.* Thesis for the doctorate, Cornell University library.
32. Nowosielski, J., and Patton, R. L. 1963. Circadian rhythms in crickets. J. ins. Physiol, Vol. 9.
33. Pringle, J. W. S. 1938. Mechanoreceptors on the palps and campaniform sensilla on the legs of cockroaches. J. exp. Biol., *15:*101–138.
34. Prosser, A. L., and Brown, F. A. 1962. Comparative Animal Physiology. 2nd Ed., W. B. Saunders, Philadelphia.
35. Pumphrey, R. J., and Rawdon-Smith, A. F. 1939. Frequency discrimination by insects. Nature (London), *143:*806.
36. Roberts, S. K. 1960. Circadian activity rhythms in cockroaches. J. cell. comp. Physiol., *55:*99–110.
37. Roth, L. M., and Eisner, T. 1962. Chemical defenses of arthropods. Ann. Rev. Ent., *7:*107–134.
38. Roth, L. M., and Willis, E. R. 1960. The biotic associations of cockroaches. Smithsonian misc. Coll., *141:*1–470.
39. Schlegtendal, A. 1934. Color vision in arthropods. Z. verg. Physiol., *20:*545–581.
40. Schnierla, T. C. 1953. Insect behavior. *In* Insect Physiology (K. D. Roeder, ed.). John Wiley, New York, Ch. 26, 27, and 28.
41. Snodgrass, R. E. 1935. Principles of Insect Morphology. McGraw-Hill, New York.
42. Suckling, E. E. 1961. Bioelectricity. McGraw-Hill, New York.
43. Szymanski, J. S., 1914. A method for measuring the quiet and active period of animals. Pflug. Arch. ges. Physiol., *158:*343–385.
44. Weiss, H. B. 1943. Color perception by insects. J. econ. Ent., *36:*1–17.
45. Wigglesworth, V. B. 1939. Principles of Insect Physiology. Methuen, London, Ch. 8.
46. de Wilde, J. 1962. Photoperiodism in insects and mites. Ann. Rev. Ent., *7:*1–26.

10

REPRODUCTION, GROWTH,
AND DEVELOPMENT

Insect reproduction has received relatively little direct attention in physiological studies, because the processes involved are so intimately associated with other systems and controlled by factors treated in other categories that the over-all reproductive process is studied only piecemeal.

There is nothing particularly outstanding about normal insect reproductive processes, although some exotic situations have been described in specialized insects. For the most part, insects reproduce bisexually; the differences that exist are in the details of mating behavior, impregnation of the ovum, and the deposition of the mature egg. From the standpoint of the propagation of insect species the reproductive process is highly successful. The high biotic potential of insects makes the reproductive process a subject of importance in applied entomology.

As soon as the egg is fertilized, the processes of growth and development begin. Growth is an increase in size and mass, and development is the change in structure and function that goes along with growth.

References on the physiology of insect reproduction per se are difficult to find, but there is a wealth of literature to describe the morphology of the reproductive organs, particularly the genitalia. Also many studies have been made on the factors that control the rates of reproduction, on the peculiarities and adaptations of various species, on endocrine control, and on insect genetics. No other animal has been given as complete a genetic study as the fruitfly, *Drosophila melanogaster*.

THE MORPHOLOGY OF INSECT REPRODUCTIVE SYSTEMS

Snodgrass has provided a detailed review of the morphology of insect reproductive systems.[11]

The reproductive system is derived from two germ layers and morphologically from three sources. The internal structures comprising the ovaries and testes are mesodermal; the ducts and external genitalia are ectodermal. The latter are modified from the cuticle. In many ways, the genital organs of the two sexes are similar.

The Female Reproductive System

The female reproductive system (Fig. 10–1) has a pair of ovaries and two lateral oviducts, which converge to form a median oviduct. The median oviduct opens posteriorly through a gonopore. Somewhere between the gonopore and the ovipositor, there are paired accessory glands and a pouchlike structure—the spermatheca—which receives and stores the spermatozoa during the interval between copulation and impregnation of the mature egg. Impregnation takes place as the egg passes through the duct just before it is deposited.

The ovaries consist of a series of tapering units called ovarioles. The ovarioles converge at the anterior end to form filaments that unite to make a suspensory ligament, which is anchored in the fat body or to the body wall. The posterior end of the ovariole is a narrow stalklike duct that connects to the lateral duct.

There are two types of ovarioles in insects, and the second can be divided into two subtypes. These types of ovarioles differ in the mechanics of providing nutritive elements to the developing germ cells. The first, or *panoistic,* type has no special nutritive cells, and nutrients for the developing eggs apparently are absorbed from the hemolymph. In the second, or *polytrophic,* ovariole the eggs alternate with nutritive cells called *trophocytes,* or nurse cells. The trophocytes appear to be derived from oogonia just as the egg cells are. In the second subdivision of polytrophic ovarioles, the nurse cells remain in the upper part of the egg tube (*vitellarium*) but maintain a protoplasmic connection that may become an elongated strand leading to the eggs they nourish. This is the *acrotrophic* type of ovariole. In each type, the food elements must ultimately come from the hemolymph.[11] In the terminology used by Wigglesworth,[15] the ovarioles are classified as *panoistic* and

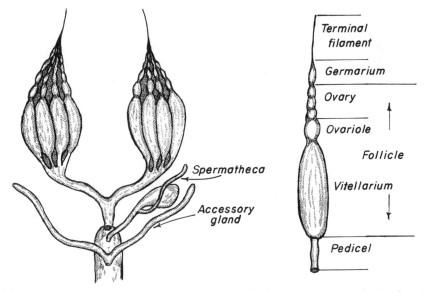

Terminal
filament

Germarium

Ovary

Ovariole

Follicle

Spermatheca

Vitellarium

Accessory
gland

Pedicel

FIG. 10–1.   Diagram of the structure of the female reproductive organs (redrawn after Snodgrass).

meroistic, and the latter is divided into a *polytrophic* type and an *acrotrophic,* or *telotrophic,* type.

In the early stages of insect development, the ovaries are incased in a peritoneal sheath that, with the exception of certain Diptera, is lost in the adult stage. The number of ovarioles varies with insects, but four, six, or eight are typical. In some of the Hymenoptera and Diptera, the number of ovarioles may be increased vastly, but in the viviparous flies they number two.

Structure of the Ovariole.   Considering a single ovariole from the anterior to the posterior, it is formed of a solid strand of cells. The middle section is the egg tube, which contains the germ cells. In the adult, the egg tube is an elongate sac filled with cells, some of which develop into ova. The wall of the tube consists of a *tunica propria,* which may be overlain by an epithelial sheath. Most of the egg tube has a follicular epithelium lining. Each egg tube has two principal divisions. The anterior part has germ cells in an active state of division and incipient differentiation, and is called the end chamber, or *germarium.* The middle section is the vitellarium, or zone of growth, in which the egg cells grow and attain mature size.

The germarium is the primary ovarium of the young ovary, and the cells that it contains soon develop into oogonia and then into oocytes with accompanying nutritive cells. The germarium also contains smaller cells, which develop into follicle cells. According to Snodgrass, these follicle cells may be either *cystocytes* or *trophocytes,* both of which accompany the developing ova.

The vitellarium is an extension of the egg tube beyond the germarium. As the oocytes multiply, their mass and volume increase causing the vitellarium to enlarge. At the anterior end the follicle cells have an apical position in the tube and begin to exhibit a definite epithelial arrangement while the nurse cells assume an axial position. The growth of the oocytes divides the vitellarium into egg chambers, which become successively larger toward the posterior end of the tube. Beyond the last egg chamber, a mass of follicle cells forms a plug that closes the end of the tube.

The oocytes are produced continuously from the oogonia, so that the first oocyte encysted becomes the lower egg and is the first to mature. The tube is lengthened with each additional oocyte by the rapid multiplication of the follicle cells.

During the early adult life of the insect, the ovarioles grow; when the last egg in each tube is fully formed, it is enclosed in a *chorion.* However, this fully formed egg is still in the oocyte stage, because maturation does not take place until the egg has been deposited. Mature oocytes should not be considered to be ripe eggs. If there is one mature oocyte in each ovariole, the insect may deposit as many eggs at one laying as there are ovarioles; however, some insects oviposit single eggs and in noncontinuous succession. A few insects alternate production of full grown oocytes so that a large number of eggs may accumulate in the discharge passages. This makes the production of egg masses possible.

The pedicels, or stalks, of the ovarioles are short tubes that connect the posterior part of the ovariole with the lateral duct. Each pedicel has a lumen that communicates with the end of the duct, but the lumen is closed at the upper end by the epithelial plug of the egg tube. When the first egg is ready to be deposited, the cells of the epithelial plug and the cells of the retaining walls are dissolved, and the egg passes into the oviduct. The walls of the pedicel may be made of a simple elastic sheath, or they may be covered by an extension of the muscular sheath of the oviduct.

When the oocytes are fully developed, a chorion that resembles the cuticular structure of the body wall but containing no chitin, forms over the entire surface of the oocyte, except for one or more small points through which the sperm cells gain entrance. As the egg passes through the oviduct, it is fertilized by sperm cells from the spermatheca, which enter through the micropyle opening in the chorion. Usually the egg is deposited externally, but in a few species it is retained within the body until it is ready to hatch. This results in the production of viviparous larvae.

The Male Reproductive Organs

In many ways the male reproductive organs are similar to those of the female. They arise from the same germ layers and have essentially the same parts. The male system consists of a pair of testes opening into lateral ducts, called the *vasa deferentia*, and a median ectodermal tube, the *ductus ejaculatorius*. The latter is comparable to the median oviduct of the female. Various accessory glands are associated with these parts, and it is not unusual for part of a *vas deferens* to be enlarged to form a storage chamber, or *vesicula seminalis*. The male gonopore, located on a median intermittent organ, is called the *penis*, or *thalis*.[11]

The typical testes consist of a group of sperm tubes with male germ cells in successive stages of development, as well as other cells that have various functions (Fig. 10–2). The sperm tubes, comparable to the ovarioles, are called testicular follicles. In the more typical insects, the testes resemble the ovaries in that the sperm tubes arise serially from the distal part of the exit duct. Each sperm tube is attached to a *vas deferens* by a thin tube, the *vas*

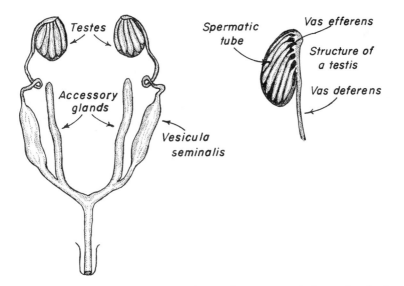

FIG. 10-2. Diagram of the structure of the male reproductive organs (redrawn after Snodgrass).

efferens, but there are no terminal filaments on the anterior part of the testicular tubes. Many variations have been observed. In higher insects, the testes usually show a more compact structure because of the incomplete separation of the sperm tubes within the peritoneal sheath.

Each sperm tube is divided into regions according to the state of development of the germ cells. The upper part, containing the primary spermatogonia, is called the *germarium*. Beyond this is the *zone of growth*, in which the spermatogonia begin a multiplication stage and often are encysted. Beyond this is the *maturation zone*, and still further along the tube is the *zone of transformation*, where the spermatocytes develop first as *spermatids* and finally into mature *spermatozoa*. The entire process of spermatogenesis normally takes place within the tubes of the testes. During their development, the sperm cells are fed by the dissolution of some of the spermatogonia that lie in the neighborhood of the apical cell, but as was observed with the egg, the ultimate source of nutrient is the hemolymph.

External Genitalia

The organs concerned with the mating process and the deposition of eggs are usually modified from cuticular structure. These organs are so varied in different species that they have a specific taxonomic character.

The copulatory apparatus of the male usually includes an organ for conveying spermatozoa into the spermatheca of the female. This apparatus is very often associated with paired grasping appendages that hold the female during copulation. The receiving organ of the female is called the *copulatory pouch*. The external genitalia of the female show great modification for the deposition of eggs, depending upon the habitat of the insect and the substrate on which the eggs are normally deposited.

FACTORS IN FECUNDITY

Insects are poikilothermic animals so that their rate of metabolism and activity are functions of temperature. Egg production, a metabolic process, is also a function of the ambient temperature. An increase in the rate of egg production may be accounted for by an increased metabolic rate or increased activity that makes the possible contact between sexes more frequent. When the ambient temperature reaches either a maximum or a minimum, the rate of egg production drops off, although a female may continue to lay eggs under adverse temperature conditions if the pressure of fully developed oocytes in the ovarioles is sufficiently great. Under both high and low temperature situations, the eggs deposited usually are sterile, probably because spermatozoa are inactivated at low temperatures and cannot move into the micropyle of the eggs and at high temperatures spermatozoa are more readily killed than are eggs.

Any factor that tends to increase metabolic rate, if that factor is not carried to an extreme or if it does not destroy some part of the reproductive system, can be expected to increase egg production. Sublethal doses of several insecticidal chemicals have been suspected of producing this effect.

Nutrition affects the fertility of females more than that of males. This might be expected, because demands are greater in terms of nutrients for egg production than for production of spermatozoa. A great deal of study has been done on nutrition, but still no single factor or no group of factors has been found that controls egg production. Insects that have both reproductive and sterile castes apparently control sex development by feeding their larvae pheromones secreted by the nurses. If these are considered food materials, this might be interpreted as sex control by nutrition. In holometabolic insects, food reserves are acquired in the immature stages. Thus, larval nutrition is important, and underfeeding of the larvae can affect the fecundity of the adults.

Impregnation stimulates egg laying rather than egg development,[15] probably because a chain of events is triggered by the copulatory act and storage of spermatozoa in the spermathecae.

Reproductive cycles are internally controlled by hormones, but sex hormones and their activity in insects have not been studied adequately. In many insects, mating activity approximates a circadian rhythm.

Various miscellaneous observations have been recorded or passed by personal communication among people who are fostering insect populations for laboratory study. Some of these may have basis in empirical fact, while others may be merely subjective observations. Examples of these observations include the following: Blowflies copulate and produce more eggs if they are kept under nearly continuous illumination; some Lepidoptera only mate in sunlight or a very bright artificial light; wax moths do not produce eggs readily when the humidity of the rearing chamber is low.

The possibility of controlling fecundity so as to limit insect populations has been suggested and applied with reasonable success in limited infestations. Fecundity control may be practical, but we must await critical evaluation of the factors involved.

OTHER REPRODUCTIVE PROCESSES

Polyembryony, parthenogenesis, hermaphroditism, and neoteny have been described from the reproductive repertoire of insects. It is well known that aphids are parthenogenic during part of their normal life cycle,[12] and certain scale insects have been shown to be truly hermaphroditic. These are among the exceptions to the general rule, and because of the exotic nature of their processes they have been widely discussed in general entomology courses. Knowledge of the existence of these types of reproduction is important but deserves little more attention until critical studies of the physiology of the processes have been completed.

GROWTH AND DEVELOPMENT

Processes that attend increases in size and mass and those that bring about changes in form and function are complex, and the literature is extensive. Monograph type reviews have been presented in the work of Wigglesworth, [16, 17] and diapause, a special aspect important in many insects, was studied and reported by Lees.[8] The metabolic aspects of diapause have been reviewed by Harvey.[5]

The processes of growth and development begin with the first cleavage of the egg and end when the individual has completed its life cycle. Each insect group shows specific differences, but some general patterns are followed by all insects to a greater or lesser extent.

The Growth Laws

As a matter of convenience it is important in experimental study to be able to determine the stage of development of immature forms by some means other than counting the molts as they take place. In many species, physical measurements of a part or the ratio of measurements of two parts can be related to development. The most common formulas are presented in the form of rules based on the observations of Dyar and Pzibram.[15]

Dyar demonstrated that the head capsule of caterpillars increases in width with each molt by a geometrical progression, and once the factor is established for a species, this can be used as a criterion to determine larval instars. Numerical factors for the linear growth of the head capsule for the silkworm (*Bombyx mori*) and for the related *Philosamia ricini* are 1.91 mm. and 1.52 mm. respectively. It is quite important to emphasize that the factors used in Dyar's rule are valid only under controlled conditions. Various environmental factors can alter both the linear dimensions and the number of molts in many species.

Pzibram formulated a rule somewhat like that of Dyar except that he used weight instead of linear dimension as a criterion. He postulated that with each instar, each cell in the animal would divide, and the weight would double. Under this system, the linear dimensions should increase by a factor equal to the cube root of two (1.26) because of the surface-volume ratio. If this factor is applied properly, Pzibram's rule is as readily applicable as Dyar's. It is easy to show that stepwise increases in weight attend development.

Neither the rules of Dyar or Pzibram should be considered to be laws, because they both imply that all parts of the body increase in size at a uniform and homogeneous rate. This is not the case. Different parts of the body grow at different rates during the developmental stages of the life cycle. Dyar and Pzibram assumed harmonic growth; this concept is called *heterogonic* or *allometric* growth. The principles that govern the growth process have been discussed at length by Huxley[6] and by Needham.[9]

Some of the complicated processes attending the growth of animals can be defined on a mathematical basis by use of the principles set forth by Huxley.[6] For purposes of illustration, the simplest expression is satisfactory.

If the character X represents the linear dimension of a part of the insect, and Y represents the dimension of a differentially growing part, the mathematical relationship is expressed by the equation $Y = bX^k$. The terms b and k are constants, and b is numerically equal to the value of Y when $X = 1$. This is a fractional coefficient and for the present has no further use. The constant k indicates that for the range over which the expression holds true, the ratio of the relative growth of the part to the relative growth of the first dimension is a constant, and the reference is to the absolute growth rate at a given instant divided by the actual size of the differentially growing part at the same instant.

The principles of heterogonic growth are complicated, but they have important implications, among which is use of a linear measurement of body parts as a taxonomic character, particularly in heterometabolic insects. When the constant k changes in value, the heterogonic growth curve will show a change in slope in accordance to the differential rate of growth of the two measured parts.

Growth in the Embryo

As soon as spermatozoa enter the micropyle of the egg, growth begins. During maturation of the egg the female nucleus migrates to the surface of the egg and throws off several polar bodies which are lost. The female nucleus then returns to the center of the egg and combines with the sperm nucleus, cell division takes place, and embryonic development begins. The cleavage nuclei disperse in the yolk and eventually migrate toward the surface where they are oriented to form a single cell layer of the blastoderm. This migration starts at a definable part of the egg called the cleavage center, which is always found at the site of the presumptive head of the embryo.[1]

The next step in the embryonic development of the egg is the aggregation of the blastoderm cells ventrally in the region of the future prothorax to form the germ band. The germ band spreads in both an anterior and a posterior direction. The median cells of the band turn inward in gastrulation and form a groove, which finally closes. The in-turned cells divide to form a thickened layer between the ventral and dorsal walls of the blastoderm, and these become the mesodermal layer. At the anterior and posterior ends of the germ band invagination takes place to form the precursors of the stomodeum and the proctodeum; soon after this the invaginations are connected by a band of endodermal cells that arise from the inner layer of the mesoderm. This completes the three embryonic layers from which all the organs are derived.

The first segments to be differentiated in the germ band are the second maxillary and the first thoracic segments. From this point the segmentation proceeds both anteriorly and posteriorly. The extremities appear first in the second maxillary and the first thoracic segments. All major developmental processes take place in a definite order in a time and space relation, from the first visible differentiation of the egg to the first aggregation of the blastoderm cells in the germ band. The migration of the cleavage nuclei and the importance of each nucleus have been determined by experiments involving spot irradiation treatments, in which individual nuclei were killed selectively. These experiments demonstrated the totipotent powers of the cleavage nuclei in the production of normal embryos up to the 128-cell stage.[1]

Control of Embryonic Organization

Insect embryogenesis has been analyzed in a review by Counce, who indicates that many problems remain to be resolved.[4]

Initial organization of the development of the germ band is controlled by two different centers—the activation center and the differentiation center. These two centers interact and set into motion the processes that direct future development. In principle, this development takes place in the same manner in all groups of insects, but details vary widely. Various ligaturing and cauterizing experiments have demonstrated that if the activation center of insect eggs can be isolated, this center is located at the posterior pole of the egg. Destruction or isolation of the activation center by any means results in failure of the embryonic germ band to form, if the injury takes place at an early enough stage. This shows that the activation center depends on the interaction of the cleavage nuclei with some factor in the region of the center. The product of this interaction is a specific substance that diffuses into the yolk and provides the stimulation for the development of the embryo.

The differentiation center has a midpoint in the anterior half of the prothorax and extends in an anterior direction to the second maxillary segment; in a posterior direction it extends to the second thoracic segment. If a ligature is placed at the midpoint of the differentiation center, a germ band will form on both sides; however, if the ligature is placed on either side of the differentiation center, the germ band will form only on the side that contains the differentiation center.

Part of the process of control exerted by the differentiation center is physical. The yolk contracts away from the chorion to provide a space into which the blastoderm cells migrate and aggregate, and the differentiation center is a focal point of morphodynamic movement. Experimental work has shown that the function of the differentiation center is partly to initiate the physical changes in the yolk structure that force the migration of the blastoderm cells into definite patterns.[1]

Organ Formation.   As the differentiation of the embryo proceeds, the *anlage* of each organ appears, usually more or less in the order of arrangement of each organ from anterior to posterior in the mature animal. From anterior to posterior, the embryo develops the anlage of the eye, the anterior and first maxillary segments, the first, second, and third thoracic segments, and finally the abdomen.[1]

Hormones in Growth and Development

Knowledge of essential processes in animals indicates that growth and development in insects must be controlled by hormones. The endocrinology of insects, particularly as regards growth and development, has been a subject of great interest. The work of Butenandt and Karlson, who were the first to isolate the metamorphic hormone in pure crystalline form, is of historic interest.[2] Insect endocrinology has been studied and reviewed by Bodenstein[1] and by Wigglesworth,[17] and contributory work by many other workers has added appreciably to the understanding of growth and development processes and their sequence.

As insects grow, they must molt in order to produce a new skeleton that can accommodate the increased volume of the body. In the Holometabola a marked change in body form takes place as growth proceeds. The timing of all growth and development processes is controlled by a series of hormones that are secreted in a predetermined sequence. In functional plan, the endocrine system of insects is remarkably like that of vertebrates.[10]

Centers of Hormone Production in Insects. The principal centers of hormone production are associated with the central nervous system. In the brain are specialized neurosecretory cells (identified principally by histophysiological observation) that comprise the *pars intercerebralis*. These cells secrete hormones that are liberated into the blood by way of the *corpora cardiaca*—a secretory complex comparable to the hypothalamic-neurohypophyseal system of vertebrates.[10] The corpora cardiaca regulates the activity of the prothoracic gland. Associated with, and morphologically close to, the *corpora cardiaca* are paired structures—the *corpora allata*—which have endocrine function. The subesophageal ganglion also has neurosecretory cells, but the function of these has not been proved.

Identified Insect Hormones and Their Functions. Most data on insect hormones have been accumulated from studies of the control of molting, pupation, and metamorphosis. The existence of the hormones involved was first proved by Kopec[7] and substantiated by Wigglesworth.[14]

Postembryonic development follows an orderly series of stages through the larval stages to the adult, and a common plan appears to exist for all insects.[10] This may be summarized as follows:

A stimulus, which may be entirely different from species to species, is transported by nerve axons to the corpora cardiaca, from which the stimulus causes the brain hormone to be liberated. The brain hormone activates the prothoracic glands, and they produce the growth and differentiation (molting) hormone. The active principle of this hormone has been found to be a 2-β-unsaturated ketone containing 18 carbons, and the hormone has been named *ecdysone*. Actually, there are two ecdysones (α and β) identified so far, and these stimulate the molting process and immediately effect an epidermal increase in protein, ribonucleic acid, the mitochondria, and the endoplasmic reticulum. These changes take place regardless of whether the molt results in another larval instar, a pupa, or an imago.

In larval molts, an additional hormone is secreted by the corpora allata, which is also controlled by part of the brain. This is the juvenile hormone, which suppresses the activity of the molting hormone. The juvenile hormone has been identified as existing in all animals. It is secreted in progressively smaller quantities as the insect develops; when development of the insect reaches the final molt stage, this hormone is not secreted at all. A schematic of growth and development hormone relationships is shown in Figure 10–3. The corpora allata do not degenerate in the adult stage but become reactivated to secrete a hormone involved in vitellogenesis, at least in some species.

DIAPAUSE. Diapause is an indefinite term used both quite loosely to describe any state of arrested activity (such as inanition brought about by low temperature), or with tight restriction of definition to describe a predetermined stage of development in which both growth and development are suspended. Diapause may be facultative or obligatory, and according to Lees,[8] control over development in either case is endocrine. A fine line of distinction seems to exist in the case of a facultative diapause and hibernation. A number of insect species overwinter in adult form (ladybird beetles, Coccinellidae, Coleoptera, and some hemipterans of the family Pentatomidae, for example), and these insects can be revived to normal activity

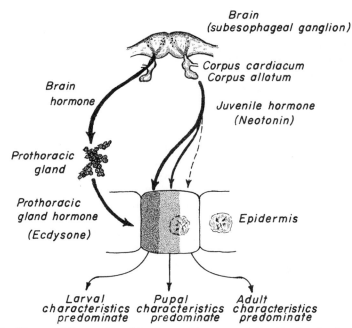

Brain
(subesophageal ganglion)

Corpus cardiacum
Corpus allatum

Brain
hormone

Juvenile hormone
(Neotonin)

Prothoracic
gland

Prothoracic
gland hormone   Epidermis

(Ecdysone)

Larval   Pupal   Adult
characteristics   characteristics   characteristics
predominate   predominate   predominate

FIG. 10-3. Diagram of the growth and development hormone relationships in a developing insect. Relative concentrations of hormone are indicated by the thickness of the arrows. (Redrawn from Prosser after Schneiderman and Gilbert.)

simply by warming them. Whether this is a true diapause and whether the arrested activity is the result of hormone control or the reflection of the effect of reduced temperature on metabolic activity are questionable. It appears reasonable that the latter situation cannot be considered a true diapause.

The recent literature on the physiology of insect diapause has been reviewed by Harvey[5] who states that arrest of development is characterized by minima in both endergonic biosynthesis including such processes as protein synthesis, and exergonic energy-trapping activities such as respiration. Wigglesworth[16] suggests the former and Williams[18] the latter, and alternatively it might be considered that the minimum in biosynthesis is a biochemical expression of the arrested development and the energy-trapping minimum a feedback compensation for the diminished demand for energy.[5]

Diapause is stimulated through environmental factors, principally the photoperiod and temperature. These environmental factors are perceived and effect the stimulation of the neurosecretory cells that regulate development. The neurosecretion can also be stimulated directly without perception of a nerve stimulus in the usual sense. The most likely environmental factor responsible for triggering the onset of diapause is the photoperiod. Other such factors may be involved; these have been studied and reviewed in ecological studies.

Termination of an obligatory diapause is often a problem in laboratory study of insects. According to Van der Kloot,[13] during the diapause period acetylcholine accumulates in the brain until it reaches such a concentration that acetylcholine esterase is synthesized. The reactions that follow cause the brain to regain its electrical properties, which were suspended during dia-pause, and make it capable of secreting its hormone. What happens follow-ing this is still a matter for speculation. Ecdysone appears to be involved, and the most recent hypothesis proposed by Clever and Karlson[3] indicates that the ecdysone acts on chromosomes to activate specific genes, outwardly manifested by the formation of chromosome "puffs." So far this explanation is morphogenetic. It is often possible to break an obligatory diapause after a minimum time by exposing the insects (eggs, pupae, etc.) to sharp and rather sudden chilling, followed by a return to normal temperature. Like those of many other physiological phenomena, the factors are being worked out slowly and the information fitted together like the components of a jig-saw puzzle. It may well be some time before all of the components have been described.

The Action of Hormones. According to Prosser,[10] endocrinologists are not in general agreement on how broadly the definition of a hormone should be interpreted, and it is impossible to draw a sharp line of distinction between true hormones and chemical coordinators. Present knowledge of modes of action of either category is such that it is impossible to classify these substances precisely.

According to the hypothesis that has the best supporting evidence, the principal characteristic that distinguishes insects between successive growth periods is rate of protein synthesis. This hypothesis opens a number of lines of speculation on the role of the hormones and the role of nucleoproteins in the increased rate of protein synthesis accompanying growth.

The energy for protein synthesis is provided by the splitting of the terminal phosphate from ATP produced by cyclic oxidative phosphorylation in the mitochondria of the cells. The enzymes specific for each amino acid are presumed to be activated by the transfer of the phosphoryl group from the ATP, and the enzymes activate the substrates by exchange of the phos-phoryl group for the carbonyl group of the amino acid. The activated amino acids then link together to form the characteristic polypeptides. The en-zymes involved are intracellular peptidases. Another possible source of energy for protein synthesis is the oxidative process in the mitochondria; this process may be activated by an electron transfer through a series of fixed cytochromes, which are components of the enzyme surface and pro-vide the appropriate spatial relations. This possibility leads to the concept that the amino-acid–specific activation centers may be assembled in the required sequence so that the activated carboxyl of one amino acid can react with the amino group of a second amino acid to form a peptide. This chain of events would leave the enzyme surface free, and the production of specific protein would be made possible.

Peptidases in cells appear to be polynucleotides, and nucleic acids are known to be essential for the synthesis of proteins by microorganisms. In this way, the process of incorporation of amino acids into proteins may be associated with the microsome fraction of the cell, which fraction is richest in ribonucleoprotein. Thus, ribonucleic acid produced in the nucleolus is discharged into the cytoplasm and is intimately associated with the produc-tion of proteins. Microsome granules can be distinguished by electron micros-copy and presumably carry the enzymes responsible for protein synthesis.[16]

MORPHOGENIC CHANGES PRODUCED BY HORMONES. Activity of the

juvenile hormone provides an example of the type of morphogenic change
that can be brought about by a chemical substance, and the classic example
is the change that takes place in the formation of a butterfly from a caterpillar. These changes are brought about by varying the concentrations of
the juvenile hormone. According to current ideas, the form of the organism
is the product of the action of nuclear genes, and these genes are dependent
for their activity on the presence of relatively simple chemicals. Some of
these chemicals have been isolated, and it has been proved that they produce
changes in the development of genetic characters. The juvenile hormone
acts by controlling the development of alternative genetically controlled
forms. There are various ways of looking at this activity, but permeability
control within the cell, which control activates or suppresses the activity of
the gene-controlled enzyme system, explains the observed phenomena as
well as any of the existing hypotheses.[16]

THE DIFFERENTIAL SENSITIVITY OF ORGANS TO HORMONES.   The direction of development that is followed in a given insect species is determined
by the hormones present, but fulfillment of development depends upon the
organ systems themselves. Experimental evidence indicates that the response to hormones of the various organ systems varies both with the system and the physiological age. These variations can be explained on the
basis of nucleoprotein metabolism, but this metabolism exists in all living
systems. Therefore, the threshold of stimulation for a given hormone must
differ for different tissues, even those tissues comprising a single organ.[1]

The concentration of a hormone in an animal tends to increase during
the period of release, and assuming differential sensitivity of the organ systems, it follows that development in a predetermined sequence will take
place. The difference in response capacity of a tissue to a hormone is as important as the hormone itself in the control of the ultimate development. This
concept also helps explain the development of abnormal forms and the production of freaks. These may arise because of aberrations in the normal
sensitivity of the tissues to hormones.

Genetic Control of Development

It is well established that the pattern of growth and development is controlled by a genetic pattern that is peculiar to the species. The chromosomes
and genes that control the characters of insects have been studied extensively, particularly those of *Drosophila*.

Genes are chemical entities that control the development of specific
characteristics, and certain chemical substances sometimes called gene
hormones can alter the genetic pattern of an individual. Implantation experiments have demonstrated, for example, that in the meal moth, *Ephestia*
(in which exists a red-eyed mutant of the black-eyed race), the testes of a
larva from the wild black-eyed type grafted into a red-eyed mutant produces a black-eyed individual. This aberration is attributed to the presence
of a diffusible substance produced by the testicular tissue that overrides the
character for red eyes and thus changes the genetic pattern. The gene hormones that have been demonstrated are neither species nor genus specific.[1]

These observations coupled with recent developments in the study of insect hormones form a basis for very interesting speculation. The genes that control the characteristics of the individual insect are chemical substances, probably polynucleotides, and a chemical process involving these compounds exerts the force that controls these characteristics. It has also been shown that the influence of the genes can be altered by the gene hormones.

SUMMARY

Most insects reproduce bisexually, and except for specialization in detail peculiar to the species, nothing about the process is unusual except storage of the spermatozoa in the spermatheca of the female. The spermatheca is a pouch located near the posterior end of the genital tract, and the egg is not fertilized until it is on its way to oviposition. There are examples of types of nonsexual reproduction in various species, and parthenogenesis is important in the propagation of some species. This is best known in the aphids.

Embryological development follows a predetermined specific pattern with both secretory activity and morphogenic movement influencing the arrangement of cells. Some insect types have the ability to readjust the development to nearly normal, even after moderately drastic interference, but other species lack this ability. Interference with normal development must occur before diffusible factors have been elaborated in order to have any effect.

The development of insects and the growth that attends development are controlled by a number of factors, some of which may be environmental. Development is controlled primarily by a system of regulatory hormones, which interact to produce an orderly sequence of events that result in the normal number of instars and finally maturity.

LITERATURE CITED

1. Bodenstein, D. 1953. *In* Insect Physiology (K. D. Roeder, ed.). John Wiley, New York, Ch. 29–32.
2. Butenandt, A., and Karlson, P. 1954. Crystallization of insect molting hormone. Z. Naturf., 93:389–391.
3. Clever, U., and Karlson, P. 1960. Production of chromosome puffs in *Drosophila* with ecdysone. Exp. cell Res., 20:623–626.
4. Counce, S. J., 1961. Insect embryogenesis. Ann. Rev. Ent., 6:295–312.
5. Harvey, W. R. 1962. Metabolic aspects of diapause. Ann. Rev. Ent., 7:57–80.
6. Huxley, J. S. 1932. Problems of Relative Growth. Methuen, London.
7. Kopec, S. 1922. Endocrine control of insect development. Biol. Bull., 42:324–342.
8. Lees, A. D. 1956. Physiology and biochemistry of diapause. Ann. Rev. Ent., 1:1–16.
9. Needham, J. 1931. Chemical Embryology. Cambridge Univ. Press, London.
10. Prosser, C. L., and Brown, F. A. 1961. Comparative Animal Physiology. W. B. Saunders, Philadelphia, Ch. 20.
11. Snodgrass, R. E. 1935. Principles of Insect Morphology. McGraw-Hill, New York.
12. Suomalainen, E. 1962. Significance of parthenogenesis in insect evolution. Ann. Rev. Ent., 7:349–368.

13. Van der Kloot, W. G. 1960. Neurosecretions in insects. Ann. Rev. Ent., *5*:35–52.
14. Wigglesworth, V. B. 1933. Hormones controlling molting and metamorphosis (*Rhodnius*). Quart. J. micr. Sci., *76*:269–318.
15. Wigglesworth, V. B. 1939. Principles of Insect Physiology. Methuen, London, Ch. 1 and 3.
16. Wigglesworth, V. B. 1957. The action of hormones on insect growth and development. Symp. Soc. exp. Biol., *11*:204–227.
17. Wigglesworth, V. B. 1959. The Control of Growth and Form. Cornell Univ. Press, Ithaca, New York.
18. Williams, C. M. 1951. Biochemical mechanisms in growth and metamorphosis. Fed. Proc., *10*:546–552.

THE INTEGUMENT
OF INSECTS

The integument of insects serves as a protective barrier between the outside environment and the internal organ systems and as a skeleton that holds the parts together, and it provides the physical external structures of the sensory perceptors. The integument is composed of a material with remarkable properties providing hardness and rigidity at some places and fatigue-free flexibility at others. It also has important permeability characteristics.

For many years, the integument of insects was described by merely stating that it was chitinous, and beyond morphological descriptions very little was known about its physical and chemical properties. In 1939, when Wigglesworth's textbook on insect physiology appeared, the section on integument showed the fewest references—indicative of the lack of attention this important system had received. During the years that followed, however, this deficiency was corrected. In 1952 Richards[15] presented a book-length description of the integument of arthropods, the subject was brought up to date in 1957 by a review by Wigglesworth,[23] and a large volume of literature has accumulated on special aspects of insect integument physiology.

MORPHOLOGY OF THE INTEGUMENT

That the cuticle of insects is composed of three distinct layers has been recognized for many years. These layers have been studied in detail, and many of the individual properties of the layers have been established. The classic picture as presented by Richards is shown in Figure 11–1. In descriptive terms, there is a *basement membrane*, which lines the integument and separates the body cavity from the cellular *epidermis* (or *hypodermis*). The epidermis provides the cellular structure and the glands associated with the integument. The middle layer is relatively thick and is called the *procuticle*. It gives bulk to the skeleton and contributes to its rigidity.

The procuticle is divided into two layers called the *endodermis* and the *exodermis*. These layers may be distinct or fused, depending upon the insect species.

On the outside of the insect covering the procuticle is a very thin layer

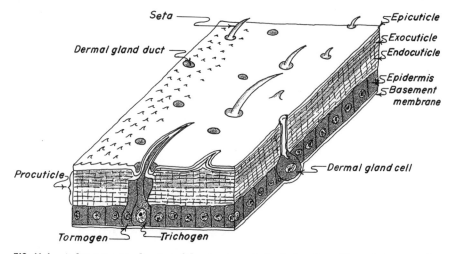

FIG. 11-1. A diagrammatic drawing of the structure of a typical section of insect integument (redrawn after Richards).

known almost universally as the *epicuticle*. This layer contributes most of the protective qualities, and it is made up of very complex materials that are continuously renewed, so that the entire system must be considered to be an actively living system.

The Terminology and Synonomy of Cuticular Structures

Just as with the other physiological systems, the terminology used by various people to describe the same layers of the integument has been variable. This is especially true of the epicuticular layers. To help integrate the observations, Lower[10] made a comparison of the terminology as it had appeared in the published literature. His data are summarized in Tables 11–1 and 11–2.

The term *cuticulin*, which was originally used to describe the epicuticular layer, has lost most of its meaning in light of more recent discoveries, and it has been supplanted by terms that are both more descriptive and definitive.

The Epicuticle

The epicuticular layer varies in thickness from one to several microns. Superficially, it is divided into at least two zones, and at least five layers have been described using various special techniques. Work describing this layer and its physical and chemical properties has been extensive.

Early in the Nineteenth Century, Odier recognized the existence of the epicuticle as a distinct part of the insect integument. Very few additional contributions were made until 1928 when Kuhnelt demonstrated that the epicuticle was a thin nonchitinous layer that contained fatty acids and cholesterol.[9] He likened it to the cuticle of plants. His observations were

TABLE 11-1. The Four Cuticulins

Type	Author and Year	Anatomical Position	Chemical Composition
Cuticulin I	Wigglesworth, 1933	The epicuticle as it was known in 1933.	"A complex mixture of fatty or waxy substances without protein."
Cuticulin II	Wigglesworth, 1947	That part of the epicuticle internal to the polyphenol layer.	"A polymerized lipoprotein subsequently tanned with quinones" (Pryor's sclerotin).
Cuticulin III	Dennell and Malek, 1955	The inner part of the cuticulin II layer.	"Protein impregnated with lipoid and an additional protein with an aromatic group" (tanned).
Cuticulin IV	Dennell and Malek, 1955	Similar to cuticulin III but confined to arthrodial membranes.	"A simple protein having an isoelectric point of about pH 2.8" (untanned).

Slightly modified after Lower. [10]

substantiated by Wigglesworth, who found that the integument of *Rhodnius* is composed of a complex of fatty acids and waxy substances. Wigglesworth named this material *cuticulin,* and defined it as a highly polymerized non-proteinaceous lipoid material.[21] A few years later, Ramsay observed that there was a thin surface film on the integument of *Periplaneta* that was different from the other materials that had been described.[14] Bergmann analyzed the exuviae of insects to try to define the chemical structure.[3] By various extraction procedures, he found residues composed of a mixture of paraffins, alcohols, and fatty acids with 25 to 30 carbons. In light of present knowledge this work is not definitive, but it does indicate the general nature of the components and it explains the highly refractory properties exhibited by the epicuticle. Subsequent work mostly defined small differences, which in some cases left the situation confused. This confusion is avoided by considering the probable formation of the epicuticular layer.

When the epicuticle is formed, the layer closest to the procuticle is the first to be laid down after a molt. This layer is composed of the substance that Wigglesworth described originally as cuticulin; it is now known to consist of a polymerized lipoprotein that has been tanned by quinones secreted by the cells of the epidermis. Next is a polyphenol layer made of proteins rich in dihydroxyphenol. This second layer is secreted by the epidermal cells, and it flows in liquid form over the insect and hardens. The phenols in this layer are loosely bound to the proteins when in the liquid state, and tightly bound after solidification. This polyphenol layer is also tanned by the quinones, after which it becomes highly refractory (resistant to ordinary methods of disruption).

The third layer is deposited on top of the polyphenol layer in the form

TABLE 11-2. Synonomy of the Nonchitinous Layers of Insect Epicuticle

Wigglesworth, 1947	Richards, 1952	Dennell and Malek, 1955	Lower, 1959
Cement layer	Tectocuticle	Cement layer	Cement layer
Wax layer	Lipid epicuticle	Wax layer	Wax layer
Polyphenol layer	Questionable	Not recognized } Amphion	Polyphenol layer if permanent. } Amphion
Outer resistant zone	Lipoprotein layer	Paraffin layer	Outer zone
Inner less resistant layer } Cuticulin layer	Basal protein layer } Cuticulin layer	Cuticulin layer } Epicuticle	Inner zone } Epicuticle

Slightly modified from Lower.[10]

of an emulsion secreted by the epidermal cells. The emulsion contains a series of waxes that harden after they are spread over the surface. The fourth layer is a cement that flows through the openings of the dermal glands and covers the wax layer.

Thus, from the inside toward the outside, the layers of the epicuticle consist of a polymerized lipoprotein, a polyphenol layer, a wax layer, and a cement layer. The different observations reported usually can be resolved in approximately the same way when differences in terminology are considered.

Wigglesworth pointed out that the supposed laminar structure may be an oversimplification of the fact, and that this type of structure does not necessarily represent a true picture of the epicuticle.[23] Since it can be demonstrated that wax can pass through the unbroken integument of insects (the honeybee, for example), it is reasoned that the epicuticle may be impregnated to varying degrees by the diffusing waxes. All four layers of the epicuticle are not always present, and epicuticle of the sensory structures often has just two layers. When part of the structure is missing, it is almost always one of the two inner layers.

The cement layer is not more than 0.10 μ. in thickness. In some areas, the cement layer forms a continuous sheet, while in others it is penetrated by the tubercles of the integument. The cement is produced by the Verson glands of the epidermal layer, consists of protein and lipoid material, and has been assumed to be a lipoprotein. When the Verson glands complete cement production, the duct from the glands is sealed with a phenolic compound, possibly a tanned protein. There is evidence that in some insects the lipid component of the cement layer is a highly saturated fatty acid that has a very strong reducing action. This suggests a hydroxycarboxylic acid that, according to Beament,[1] is similar to shellac, which is produced in quantity by the lac insect.

The wax secretion provides the waterproofing layer of the cuticle. There is an inverse relation between the thickness of this layer and its melting point. The thickness and other properties of this layer appear to be related to the environment and the developmental stage of the insect at the time the layer is produced. How these waxes are secreted and are able to permeate the integumental membranes is not fully understood, but there are several plausible hypotheses.[2]

In the newly molted pupae of *Tenebrio*, the cuticle is smooth and glossy, and it is covered by a primary wax layer that may be as much as 0.25 μ. thick. Four to twelve hours after molting, the cement layer flows over the primary wax layer, and within thirty hours, the surface becomes dull. The dulling process is caused by the separation of the surface wax into fine filaments. If smoothed out these filaments would form a layer about 0.15 μ. thick. The filaments show the same molecular and crystalline structure as the primary wax.

These observations were interpreted by Holdgate and Seal as follows:[8] The cement layer is a shellac-like material. Shellac has a wax as a constituent, and if the *Tenebrio* pupal cement is similar to shellac, the appearance of the surface wax filaments in the pupal cement could be attributed to crystallization of the excess waxes on the surface of the cement layer. This explanation obviates the necessity for explaining the secretion of surface wax filaments through the primary wax and cement layers. In elaborating on this hypothesis, Holdgate and Seal suggest that the cement layer may be more nearly a single outer epicuticle, the main component of which is wax rather than a laminated structure with a central zone of bound carbohydrate and shellac.

Thus far, transport of the wax has been considered to take place with the wax in the form of an emulsion or a solution associated through solubilization with another material that is probably a protein. This may not be true in some species.

The cockroach (*Periplaneta*) is coated with a grease that has a melting point of 34° C. when it is first secreted. As this grease is exposed to air, it hardens, forming a waxy material with a melting point of 55° C. This change does not take place if the grease is sealed in a tube, even when it is exposed to oxygen and light, but the change can be brought about in less than an hour if the grease is heated *in vacuo* at 100° C. This behavior suggests a relatively hard wax dissolved in a solvent; the solvent isolated has the properties of an eight- to ten-carbon alcohol. Eight- to ten-carbon alcohols are miscible in all proportions with insect waxes, and it is possible to form a synthetic grease that has all the properties of the natural covering by dissolving beeswax in the solvent.[2]

If intact waxes of insects are exposed to fat solvents such as chloroform, the waxes are removed from the insect. This is evidenced by the fact that the permeability of the integument to water increases. There is no increase in permeability of the integument to water when octane or decane are used as solvents. When these are used, the wax appears to be dispersed in such a way that the water repellent properties are improved rather than diminished. From these observations it may be assumed that similar compounds exist as wax solvents in all insects. Eisner et al.[6] demonstrated that eight- to ten-carbon compounds of a nature similar to these alcohols are included in the defensive secretions of insects, presumably to improve the spreading power of these secretions and to potentiate their effectiveness as irritants.

The Permeability of the Epicuticle.   It is well established that the waterproofing of the integument is a function of the wax layer of the epicuticle. The changes that take place in the wax layer may be associated with changes in environmental conditions, including such factors as temperature and dryness.

There is a critical maximum temperature for insects that if exceeded will cause a transition in the wax layer from nonpermeability to permeability. The most likely explanation for this is that the critical temperature is the melting point of the wax. Two different processes related to the hardness of the wax may occur. At transition temperature an organized monolayer of hard wax becomes permanently disorganized, but a grease undergoes changes in the packing of the molecules without displacement of the polar groups from their substrates.

Because insects are a very diverse group, it is not surprising that aquatic and terrestrial forms are different. This difference is obvious when a comparison is made between the integument permeability of the aquatic larva of *Sialis* (Neuroptera) and the terrestrial *Tenebrio* (Coleoptera). The wax cover has about the same thickness in both insects, but *Sialis* exhibits no sudden change in the rate of transpiration when a rise in temperature occurs. It is possible that in this type of insect, the wax layer of the integument is permeated with pores, thus overriding the other permeability effects and that the insect is able to live only because of its aquatic environment. The same structure would certainly be lethal to *Tenebrio*.

Wetting Properties of the Epicuticle

Wetting and resistance to wetting are important properties of the epicuticle. This characteristic is controlled by a combination of physical and chemical properties of the surface. Roughness of the cuticular surface tends to exaggerate resistance to wetting, particularly if the angle of contact with the wetting agent is small and is partially due to the trapping of air by the rough surface, which causes an increase in the angle of contact. According to Beament, areas that are more readily wettable are proteinaceous and lack the usual wax layers.[2]

The continuing secretion of wax also affects the wetting properties, because a reorientation of the polar molecules takes place owing to the attraction of liquid water in the cuticle. As the wax layer crystallizes, the angle of contact with water increases because of the roughness of the wax filaments.

Some General Aspects of Epicuticle Permeability

Beament has pointed out several factors that have caused confusion in the study of permeability,[2] among which is the terminology, which has been inadequate to describe the subject.

There is a distinct difference between the term *transpiration*, meaning the evaporation of water from the surface, and *permeability*, which means the penetration of water through the membranes. The difference in meaning between these two terms must be recognized, and any critical evaluation of permeability must allow for a rate of transpiration above the minimum so that saturation deficiency at the surface is more or less constant.

As a generality, terrestrial insects have an epicuticle almost impermeable to water because of the wax layer, but in some insects evidence exists of a secondary layer at lower levels that also has permeability control. There is no argument that the epicuticle is an active, living system that is continuously renewed by the insect and that the cuticle is the first line of defense against invasion of foreign materials from the outside as well as protection against water loss from the inside. The remainder of the integument, although not highly permeable to water, is sufficiently permeable so that without the external wax layer a terrestrial insect could not survive.

The Procuticle

The procuticle lies directly beneath the epicuticular layer. It is composed of an exocuticle and an endocuticle, both of which have as a constituent the glucosamine called chitin, which is always associated with protein and other complex materials. These materials are polymerized into a plastic substance possessing a relatively high water content. The chitin and the protein are intimately linked so that chitin as such is nonexistent in the integument of insects except in the mucoprotein complex.

The two layers of the procuticle usually display laminations, the significance and source of which remain a matter of speculation. It can be visualized that the laminae arise as a result of strains brought about by the hardening process, and the result is a very remarkable material. The two procuticular layers are chemically similar, differing quantitatively in the relative amounts of chitin and protein in the complex; the layers are often physically distinct. The procuticle ranges in thickness from 0.2 μ. to about 10 μ., and in some insects the exocuticle and the endocuticle can be pealed apart. In most insects, the two layers appear to be intimately fused.

Permeability of the Procuticle. The degree of permeability of the procuticle is a function of its water content. As dehydration of the layer progresses, the permeability of the procuticle decreases. Many insects exhibit asymmetric permeability to water through the procuticle, with the gradient being inward in direction. This type of asymmetry has been described in terms of a molecular valve structure, such as is demonstrable in the skin of the frog.

Pore Canals in the Procuticle. The procuticular pore canals are minute ducts that penetrate from the epidermis through all but the thinnest of cuticles. These canals arise from the epidermal cells. Electron microscope studies by Richards and Anderson[16] showed that the canals are actually helical rather than straight tubes as described by Leydig, but the helical structure has no known physiological significance. Further examination reported by Way indicates that the outer ends of the canals are often branched like a tree with each branch extending to a tubercle on the epicuticle.[20]

The contents of the pore canals and their possible functions have been a subject of interest for many years, and the presence of these structures has been rediscovered many times. Leydig treated integument with silver nitrate and noted that the canals filled with a black residue that he assumed to be protoplasm. This observation led to the conjecture that the canals contain protoplasmic processes from the cells of the epidermis and that the canals function in the formation of the procuticle in a manner comparable to the function of the Haversian canals of vertebrate bone. Although this conjecture seems logical, the validity of this function is severely weakened by the observation that very thin cuticular areas of some insects do not have pore canals.

Immediately following a molt, the pore canals of the outer endocuticle remain, but those of the inner endocuticle become filled with a chitinous material. Even though the canals are blocked, the outer layers of the endocuticle continue to be deposited, so that the materials from which these layers are formed must reach the surface of the endocuticle by a diffusion process through the matrix itself. This process was called *intersusception* by Wigglesworth. If the cuticle is treated with diaphanol, weak potassium hydroxide, or pepsin, the aperture of the pore canal at the outer end is opened. In the mature cuticle, the blocking material of the pore canal is moderately soluble.[23]

From these observations, it seems reasonable to conclude that the pore canals provide a channel for molting fluid, and that they probably transport the protein and the dihydroxyphenol hardening agent, but that they are not involved in the secretion of the waxes.

The Crystalline Structure of the Procuticle. An x-ray diffraction study reported by Fraenkel and Rudall[7] has offered some explanation both of the physical processes that take place during the hardening of the procuticle, and of the origin of some of the laminations.

Fraenkel and Rudall used sarcophagid flies in a prepupal stage and compared the diffraction patterns of the soft integument at this stage with the hardened pupal integument. In the species they used, the integument of the last instar larva hardens to become the pupal skin. In the larval state, it is soft and translucent.

Small sections of the integument were examined during the various stages of transition, and the results inspired the following hypothesis: When the insect reaches a critical stage in its development, and pupation is imminent, the integument contracts. This is an irreversible process and is initiated by a hormone. The length of the insect decreases by 40 per cent, and the circumference increases by 12 per cent. These dimensional changes result in a surface area decrease of 36 per cent. The x-ray diffraction patterns made at the different stages revealed both that the molecular structure of the procuticle changed during the transition by becoming more compact and that the molecules were rearranged in a plane parallel to the transverse axis of the body. Before pupation, the crystallites were movable and were approximately parallel to the surface. The ability of the integument to swell by absorbing water is reduced greatly in the hardened state. The stepwise process of hardening is as follows:

1. The crystallites of chitin become more highly oriented in the hardening process.

2. Dehydration takes place, causing the crystallites and molecules to become more closely packed.

3. The solubility of the proteins decreases.

4. The dispersal phase of the chitin-protein association changes from a dispersal of chitin in protein to a dispersal protein in chitin.

Composition of the Procuticle. It has already been established that the procuticle, which makes up the bulk of insect integument, is a complex that contains chitin but is not made exclusively of this material. Chitin is a compound that resembles cellulose in its chemical structure. The principal difference between the two compounds lies in the substitution on the chitin molecule of an acetylamine in place of the hydroxyl group on the number two carbon of the molecule. Chitin forms chains of molecular elements linked by carbon molecules, which explains the orientation possibilities demonstrated by x-rays.

The precursors of the procuticle are secreted in liquid form by the epidermal cells. As the liquid is secreted, it forms a uniform layer, which is subsequently hardened by a tanning process that is probably the same as that described for the epicuticle.

The Epidermal Layer

The epidermal layer contains the cellular components of the integument that are responsible for formation of the outer parts. The epidermal layer also contains the dermal glands, enocytes, and other specialized tissues that function in the organization of the living skeletal structure. At the time of a molt, the cells of the epidermis become active and produce both the enzymes that digest the parts of the old integument, and the material that forms the new skin.

Activity of the Epidermis at Molting.   In the growth and development of the insect when an increase in the size of the skeleton is essential, a definite sequence of events takes place that, among other things, results in the production of the molting fluid. This fluid is secreted by the cells of the epidermis and contains a protease. It has also been assumed to contain a chitinase. According to Passonneau and Williams,[13] the fluid is secreted first as a dilute aqueous protein gel that has no action on the pupal cuticle. A little later, it is converted to a sol, and the chitinase action increases. At about the same time the proteinase activity appears. It takes about 20 days for the old endocuticle to disappear entirely.

As the old cuticle is removed, a thin, white pellicle, which lies beneath the old skin and the new skin, becomes visible. Wigglesworth called this pellicle the ecdysial membrane and considered it to be one or more laminae of the old endocuticle. The origin, other than this, and the function of the membrane are obscure.

During the general activity of the epidermis that accompanies a molt, the enocytes show definite secretory activity. The best evidence of the nature of these secretions, although circumstantial, indicates that enocytes contribute the lipoprotein for the formation of the procuticle and the epicuticle. The activity of the enocytes reaches a peak just before the lipoprotein layer of the epicuticle is deposited; when the lipoprotein layer is first laid down, it gives staining reactions that are identical to the reactions of the enocyte contents.

PERMEABILITY OF THE INTEGUMENT AS A WHOLE

In addition to water, other molecular substances and some ionized electrolytes penetrate the integument of insects, and some data are available to explain the observed phenomena.

Richards and Fan[17] studied the diffusion of electrolytes by means of a diffusion cell technique and concluded that while penetration definitely does take place, the rates are very slow. They also showed that in the rates of diffusion great variation exists. They could offer no logical explanation on which to base a prediction of the variation. When considering the processes of permeability, it is very important to distinguish between the penetration of ionized substances and the penetration of molecular substances. Very little definitive work has been reported on the former.

Treherne reported on the diffusion of several nonelectrolytes through the cuticle of the migratory locust (*Schistocerca gregaria*).[19] In his tests, he included ethanol, phenol, phenyl thiourea, *m*-toluyl urea, diethyl thiourea, dimethyl thiourea, and urea. He found that the permeability of the whole cuticle is related to the solubility of the material of the wax layer in the nonelectrolyte being tested. He also found that the deviation from a linear relationship with solubility, as observed in the rapidly penetrating compounds, results from the resistance offered by the structures beneath the wax layer. More than half this resistance to diffusion came from the lower layers of the epicuticle.

The diffusion of compounds through the procuticle was essentially the same as expected if one assumed that the procuticle was comprised of liquid-filled spaces larger than the diameter of the diffusing molecules. The measured rate of diffusion of molecules was about one fourth the rate expected for an undisturbed water layer.

COLORS IN INSECT INTEGUMENT

Many insects are brightly or even brilliantly colored, and a discussion of the origin of these colors is necessary to round out any dissertation on the integumental structure. Colors arise either from incorporated pigments or because of physical phenomena. Both aspects have received appreciable attention.

Studies on the pigments of insect integument were reviewed by Chromartie.[4] Many papers exist in the older literature on this subject, and recent advances in chemical separation and analysis techniques have made it possible to confirm some of the earlier observations and to correct those that were in error. So far, all pigments that have been isolated are metabolic products of substances taken in with the food. The pigments can be separated into definite chemical groups.

Carotinoids. Carotinoids have been described as color-producing pigments in many insects and are always derived from food, either directly or indirectly from a plant source. The ingested pigments undergo minor alterations and occur in the insect either as an aqueous solution or as a protein complex.

When the carotene fraction of a plant is isolated, its principal component is an orange-yellow β-carotene, which is the most widely distributed of all the carotinoids. The protein complexes of β-carotene have a yellow component that makes up a major part of a pigment group to be described later under the general name *insectoverdins*. β-carotene has been isolated both in the free state and in protein complex from a number of insects. An isomeric α-carotene is said to occur in the red spots of the female of one of the walking stick insects, and in association with β-carotene in the elytra of some coccinellids, but the identification has not been confirmed by modern chromatographic methods. A monocyclic γ-carotene has also been described from *Pieris brassica*, but positive identification is lacking.

Several carotinoids that contain oxygen also have been detected. One of these is 1,3'-dihydroxy-α-carotene, which is sometimes called hypophasic xanthophyll or leutein. This carotinoid has been isolated in crystalline form from the cocoons of the silkworm where it is the principal pigment in some strains. It is also found in mulberry leaves, and in an esterified state it occurs in the propolis of some honeybees. This pigment is found in some beeswax, in a protein complex in some species of *Tettigonia* (Orthoptera), and in certain Lepidoptera. It is the only pigment of the general group of carotinoids that has been positively identified, although others of similar structure have been reported.

Xanthoquinones.   The second general group of insect pigments is known as the xanthoquinones. These pigments are dyestuffs that have commercial value, and they have been known for years. Cochineal is one of these dyes. Very little critical work has been done with this group although their presence in many insects, particularly among the coccids, has been known from antiquity.

Aphins.   The aphins are dyes found typically in the blood and integument of aphids. These dyes typically range from red to purple. If the insect is crushed, the pigment undergoes a series of color changes as it reacts with the air. The pigments are known to have a complex ring structure with approximately 30 carbons; they are soluble in water, and the color changes with pH change. Normally associated with the aphins is an enzyme that converts the pigment to a highly fluorescent pigment when it is exposed to air.

Anthoxanthins.   Anthoxanthins and possibly anthocyanins have been isolated from insects but appear to exist in fact as one pigment. Crystalline anthoxanthins have been prepared from Lepidoptera, and some attempts have been made to use the pigment as a taxonomic character. No real evidence exists for the occurrence of anthocyanins in insects although their presence has been suspected.

Pterins.   The pterins are by far the most common of the pigments in insects and in other animals. These pigments are derived from heterocyclic pteridine and make up the white purine-base compound observed in the wing scales of the pierid butterflies. Paper chromatography and UV (ultraviolet) spectrophotometry has demonstrated that pterin pigments exist in almost all forms of insects.

Insectoverdins.   The insectoverdins are usually green pigments. Early workers thought that they were chlorophyll, but further examination has demonstrated that the green colors arise from a mixture of yellow and blue chromoproteins. The prosthetic group of the yellow chromoprotein in each case is a carotinoid, and the blue chromoprotein is a bile pigment, mesobiliverdin. A number of other bile pigments and porphyrins have been reported from insects. *Rhodnius*, for example, converts hemoglobin into biliverdin, and the catabolism of chlorophyll in plant-feeding forms produces a similar pigment.

Omnichromes.   The omnichromes are a group of closely related brown, yellow, and red pigments, found particularly in the eyes of insects, although they are present in other parts of the body. The pigments are formed by the conversion of tryptophan to kynurenine and 3-hydroxykynurenine to give the immediate precursor of the chromagen. Various ommatins, or ommins, found in the eye pigments of insects belong in this group.

Melanins.   The melanins are responsible for some of the darker colors of the eyes and integument of insects. These pigments comprise a group of rather poorly defined, indefinite polymers that arise through the action of tyrosinase on tyrosine in the presence of atmospheric oxygen. The melanins may vary from yellow to black.

Color Variations Within Species

Colors of metabolic origin vary in intensity with any factor that alters the metabolic rate. It is, therefore, not surprising that changes in temperature alter the intensity, and as such, the actual color of some insects, which gives rise to the color series often used by taxonomists. Some of the green species of the family Pentatomidae (Hemiptera) are striking examples of this. Say's grain bug (*Chlorochroa sayii*) shows this color change response very distinctly; it varies in color from a dull olive drab to a bright green or even a straw yellow depending upon the ambient temperature. A complete transition in color is possible over a period of several days. This is a morphological color change brought about by the deposition of pigment or the metabolism of the pigment material.

A few species of insects are also capable of transient color changes of a physiological type. This is usually a protective mechanism controlled by neurosecretory hormones. An example of this is found in some of the walking-stick insects, which show rhythmic color change with a dark color predominating at night and a light color during the day. The change is produced by the migration of particulate orange and brown pigments in specialized areas of the integument. The darker pigments expand and spread over the lighter pigments, covering them; or the darker pigments are retracted, allowing the orange pigment to show through.

The Intrinsic Colors of Insects

Some insects have beautiful iridescent colors, often metallic or enamel-like, that are not the result of pigmentation. Watching the hues shift with changes in the angle of incident light has fascinated people for centuries and led to many artistic and decorative applications. Some insects are among the most beautiful of animals, and their brilliance rivals the colors in the feathers of some of the tropical birds.

Mason did a thorough study of the intrinsic color phenomena in insects and presented physical data to explain the origin.[12] In all cases, the physical color can be explained by one of the several variants of the thin-film hypothesis of color production.

The iridescence observed in the wing colors of the thin wing membranes of dragonflies and some of the dipterous flies is an example of the first type of thin-film color. Mason demonstrated that the colors arise as diffraction images brought about by the action of light striking superimposed layers of integument, each layer having a different refractive index. This work preceded our present knowledge of integumental structure, and it is interesting to observe that Mason postulated on the basis of physical measurement that insect integument is composed of superimposed layers, each with a different variety of chitin. These layers are in optical contact and form a nonpermeable tissue that constitutes the two lamellae of the wings. The wing iridescence is a true thin-film color.

The brilliant colors observed on some butterfly and moth wing scales and on the elytra of some beetles are not explained so easily, and the looseness of terminology used in some entomological literature has caused confu-

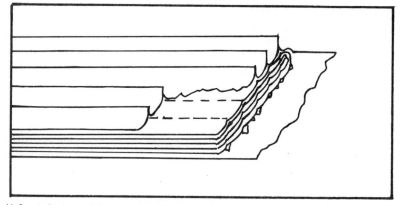

FIG. 11–2. A diagram of the multiple thin-film structure of the *Urania* type wing scale. Colors are produced by the light diffraction of the superimposed layers. The ridges on the scale do not contribute to the color. (Redrawn after Mason.)

sion. In summarizing the observations made by Mason, there are several significant conclusions.

This last type of iridescence can be explained most satisfactorily, as before, by a thin-film hypothesis. The scales of the Lepidoptera are of two types, but each owes its color to multiple thin films separated by air. In the *Urania* type (Fig. 11–2), the scales consist of color-producing lamellae, lying parallel to the plane of the scale. These lamellae may be overlaid with a rib or mesh structure, but this structure does not contribute directly to the production of color. In the second or *Morpho* type (Fig. 11–3), the lamellae lie in the veins on the surface and are inclined toward the proximal part of the scale. This type of wing scale shows color only when the incident light is directed across the lamellae; the color disappears when the beam is parallel to the lamellae. A third type of wing scale is characterized by some species of Coleoptera that have colored scales. The lamellae are enclosed by the cuticle and are tilted in different directions in sharply defined areas. This

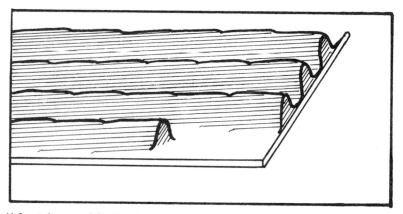

FIG. 11–3. A diagram of the *Morpho* type wing scale. The color is produced by the light diffraction from the inclined layers of the ridges on the scale. This factor accounts for the striking changes in color observed when the insect is rotated in a beam of incident light. (Redrawn after Mason.)

causes different shades or different colors in each area. The fine striations on insect scales are not related to the colors produced, and the reflection of surface color is not a property of the iridescent scales.

Metallic iridescence and the enamel-like sheen seen in the elytra of the Meloidae and Buprestidae (Coleoptera) and on the abdomens of some of the blowflies are other examples of optical or physical coloration explained on the basis of the thin-film hypothesis. Color variations may be great and shadings are distinct.

Metallic iridescence results from the presence at or near the surface of the wing scale of a thin laminated layer that acts as a multiple thin film. The color-producing structure may be somewhat thicker and may have laminae where the surface is sculptured.

Enameled integument owes its color to a thick multiple-film layer with properties modified by a very closely arranged group of fine rods that are either perpendicular to the surface or slightly tilted. These rods are uniformly distributed but not systematically arranged. The surface of the cuticle shows a thin outer layer divided into polygonal areas, but this outer layer may be removed without impairing the color. The colors probably are produced by the thin films and derive their enamel-like sheen from the physical structure of the rods.

The physiological importance of the various colors, particularly those due to physical phenomena, may be somewhat nebulous; however, the colors have a definite esthetic interest.

SECRETIONS OF THE INTEGUMENT

Secretion of the wax and grease layers as protective substances on the integument was discussed earlier in this chapter. Another aspect of secretory activity, which has practical importance but which has received very little attention, is the production of sticky secretions by the integumental glands on the pulvillar structures of the last tarsal segments of some insects. These secretions make it possible for insects to adhere to smooth vertical surfaces or to hang suspended from a ceiling.

The mechanism that enables the insect to defy gravity presumably is a secretion that is liberated through hollow hairs on the pulvilli. These *tenent hairs* are not universally distributed among insect species, but they do occur on the last tarsal segments of rather widely divergent species.[18]

Study of these pulvillar secretions occupied the interest of investigators during the latter part of the Nineteenth Century, and Power observed and mentioned them as early as 1644. The best descriptive works are those of Dewitz[5] and of Lowne.[11]

Lowne collected minute quantities of the secretions from the fly, *Musca corvina*, by milking the pulvilli, and he provided a rough description of the substance. From the pulvilli were obtained minute droplets, which had a sticky consistency and a milky white color. The substance solidified in air and formed a coagulum that was insoluble in water; the coagulum was highly resistant to cold sulfuric acid and to fat solvents. From such scanty data one might speculate that these secretions belong to the general category of mucins. The importance of these secretions is apparent when it is considered that they must play a role in the solubilization of dry or crystalline chemicals that are used as residual insecticides. It is logical to deduce that the residual insecticides go into solution, combine, or enter into a soluble complex with the secretions in order to penetrate the integument. Crystalline solids cannot cross unbroken integumental membranes. A study of these pulvillar secretions, which appears to have been overlooked for many years, could give a slightly new approach to some of the problems of toxicity, specificity, and effectiveness of insecticides.

SUMMARY

The exoskeleton of insects is a physically and chemically complicated structure with three general layers. The outer layer, which may be subdivided, is responsible for most of the physical properties of permeability, wettability, and resistance to adverse environmental factors.

It is important to recognize that the integument of insects is not chitin as has been stated in general textbooks for many years, but that chitin is part of a complex association with protein. There is little or no chitin in the epicuticle, but it is present in the procuticle, which forms the middle layer of the integument and gives the integument its bulk and physical strength.

The innermost layer of the integument is cellular and is responsible for the production of new integument and for the continuous renewal of the protective materials on the epicuticle.

The permeability of the integument to water is controlled primarily by epicuticular wax and grease. If these substances are removed by abrasion, or if they are disrupted by high temperatures, the permeability of the integument to water is markedly increased. The permeability to nonaqueous molecular substances depends both on the solubility of the epicuticular materials in the substance and on the degree of hydration of the procuticle. Asymmetry in regards to the permeability to water may also be a function of the procuticle. Electrolytes (which are ionized) always penetrate slowly.

The brilliant colors characteristic of many insects may arise from pigments that are metabolic products of the food, or they may have a purely physical origin. In the latter case, all colors and the various color phenomena can be explained by the thin-film hypothesis.

LITERATURE CITED

1. Beament, J. W. L. 1955. Wax secretion in the cockroach. J. exp. Biol., 32:514–538.
2. Beament, J. W. L. 1961. The water relations of insect cuticle. Biol. Rev., 36:281–320.
3. Bergmann, W. 1938. The composition of ether extractives of B. mori. Ann. ent. Soc. Amer., 31:315–321.
4. Chromartie, R. I. T. 1959. Insect pigments. Ann. Rev. Ent., 4:59–76.
5. Dewitz, H. 1885. Studies of the ability of insects to climb smooth vertical walls. Zool. Anz., 8: 157–158.
6. Eisner, T., Meinwald, J., Monro, A., and Ghent, R. 1961. Defense mechanisms of arthropods. J. ins. Physiol., 6:272–298.

7. Fraenkel, G., and Rudall, K. M. 1940. The physical and chemical properties and structure of insect cuticles. Proc. roy. Soc. Lond. (B), *129*:1–35. 1947, *134*:111–143.
8. Holdgate, M. W., and Seal, M. 1956. The epicuticular wax layers in the pupae of *T. molitor*. J. exp. Biol., *33*:82–106.
9. Kuhnelt, W. 1929. Composition of insect cuticle. Zool. Jahr. Anat., *50*:219–278.
10. Lower, H. F. 1959. Insect epicuticle and its terminology. Ann. ent. Soc. Amer., *52*:381–385.
11. Lowne, B. T. 1890–92. Exoskeletal structures of the thorax. *In* The Anatomy, Physiology, Morphology, and Development of the Blowfly. R. H. Porter, London, Vol. I, Ch. V, pt. 4, pp. 194–198.
12. Mason, C. W. 1927. Structural colors in insects. J. phys. Chem., *31*:321–354, 1856–1872.
13. Passonneau, J. V., and Williams, C. M. 1953. The molting fluid of insects. J. exp. Biol., *30*:545–560.
14. Ramsay, J. A. 1935. The evaporation of water from the cockroach. J. exp. Biol., *12*:373–383.
15. Richards, A. G. 1952. The Integument of Arthropods. Univ. Minn. Press, Minneapolis.
16. Richards, A. G., and Anderson, T. F. 1942. Electron microscope studies of insect cuticle. J. Morph., *71*:135–183.
17. Richards, A. G., and Fan, H. Y. 1949. Studies on arthropod cuticle. J. cell. comp. Physiol., *33*: 177–198.
18. Sarkaria, D. S., and Patton, R. L. 1949. Factors in the penetration of DDT through the pulvilli of several species of insects. Trans. Amer. ent. Soc., *75*:71–82.
19. Treherne, J. E. 1957. The diffusion of electrolytes through the isolated cuticle of *Schistocerca*. J. ins. Physiol., *1*:178–186.
20. Way, M. J. 1950. The structure and development of the larval cuticle. Quart. J. micr. Sci., *91*: 145–182.
21. Wigglesworth, V. B. 1933. The physiology of the cuticle and of ecdysis in *Rhodnius*. Quart. J. micr. Sci., *76*:270–318.
22. Wigglesworth, V. B. 1939. Principles of Insect Physiology. Methuen, London.
23. Wigglesworth, V. B. 1957. The physiology of insect cuticle. Ann. Rev. Ent., *2*:37–52.

THE PHYSIOLOGICAL
EFFECTS OF BIOLOGICALLY
ACTIVE CHEMICALS

Very few entomologists who study insect physiology do so with the intention of becoming physiologists. Instead, they are interested in the subject because insect physiology offers a logical approach to solution of economic problems that relate directly to the control of agricultural pests.

Before the introduction of DDT, relatively few poisons were used for insect control, and most research was directed toward finding more effective methods of application. Following the DDT era of the 1940's, the chemical industry has produced compounds of many types, and with the flood of new materials has come the problems of resistance, specificity, mammalian toxicity, and residual activity.

The introduction of new materials created a new discipline in the general field of entomology, variously described as insect pharmacology or the study of "mode of action." The use of the term *pharmacology* in this context is unfortunate because it connotes the biological activity of drugs, and drugs are defined as medicinal compounds. The phrase "mode of action" has appeared in the titles of many journal articles, but a very small percentage of these articles actually have definitive data on the biological activity of the compounds.

As nearly as it can be defined, "mode of action" means the description of the sum of changes in the physical and chemical processes caused by the action of the chemical. In this term of reference, "mode of action" means cause of death from the activity of a chemical upon vital systems. A mode-of-action study must include definitive information on the chemistry and mechanics of the processes that lead to the death of the insect. These are highly complicated processes in most cases, usually involving a long chain of events. In order to define the processes, many variables must be considered as they exist simultaneously in the intact insect; and the primary, secondary, tertiary, etc. effects must be evaluated. Owing to the magnitude of the problems presented, no insecticide exists for which clearly defined data are available.

THE IMPORTANCE OF THE INSECT CONTROL PROBLEM

The necessity for the solution of insect control problems becomes fairly obvious when it is realized that insects are one of man's greatest competitors for food. In addition to having inhabited the earth about 5 million years longer, insects have a higher biotic potential and a shorter life cycle, which factors combine to produce much more rapidly new strains that are adapted to specific adversities. Insects are even more resistant than man to the radiation produced by atomic energy. According to the World Health Organization, malaria has been eradicated successfully from an area inhabited by 280 million people, and proposed programs include eradication of malaria in an area occupied by an additional 697 million. The progress in alleviating human disease and increasing life expectancy, coupled with the prediction that the population of the world can easily double by the end of the century, makes food production of equal importance to putting a man on the moon or exploring outer space. In the foreseeable future, the necessity for protecting food crops or stored food from insects will not diminish.[30]

THE NEEDS OF THE FUTURE

The insect control problem is sufficiently acute that it may not be possible to depend upon the development of group-specific toxicants; however, the need for these toxicants is great. Compounds such as DDT, the cyclodiene insecticides, and many of the organophosphates are almost universally toxic to animals. Their use leads to the destruction of useful insects, upon which food production may depend (through pollination, for example), to the destruction of wild life, domestic animals, or even man himself if adequate protective measures are not observed.

According to Winteringham, use of the apparently safe universal poisons is favorable to larger animals as compared to insects because of two factors—the high surface-volume ratio of insects due to their small size and the relatively higher permeability rate of the insect integument.[30]

The development of highly selective toxicants has been a goal of long standing and has met with limited success. Nature has provided examples in pyrethrum and rotenone, which are relatively nontoxic to man because of fundamental differences in the physiological make-up between man and insects. Other laboratory synthetics have been developed that are also specific. Examples of these are shown in Figure 12–1.

THE PROBLEM OF RESISTANCE

The resistance to toxicants that develops in insect populations placed under pressure is not a new phenomenon, nor is it one peculiar to insect control. Most surprising, considering the experience of the medical profession with resistance to antibiotics, the residual nature of the insecticides

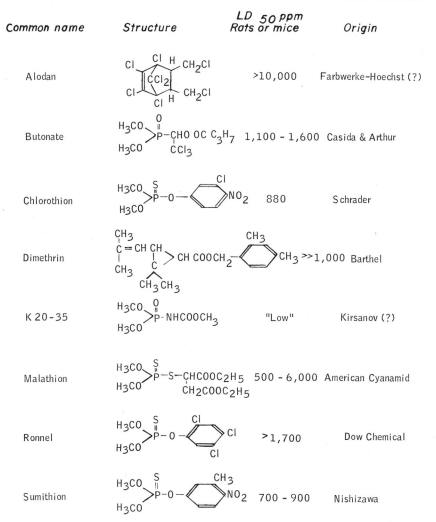

Common name	Structure	LD 50 ppm Rats or mice	Origin
Alodan		>10,000	Farbwerke-Hoechst (?)
Butonate		1,100 - 1,600	Casida & Arthur
Chlorothion		880	Schrader
Dimethrin		>>1,000	Barthel
K 20-35		"Low"	Kirsanov (?)
Malathion		500 - 6,000	American Cyanamid
Ronnel		>1,700	Dow Chemical
Sumithion		700 - 900	Nishizawa

FIG. 12-1. Examples of synthetic insecticides that are selective in that they have mammalian toxicity. The reasons for the selective toxicity are not entirely clear. (After Winteringham.)

used, and the evolutionary capabilities of insects, is that the problem was not anticipated.

Several factors control the susceptibility of insects to various toxicants. These factors can be lumped into two categories—behavioristic and physiological.[30] Both categories are important. The behavioristic factor is primarily an avoidance reaction, which causes the insect to avoid contact with the material. This appears to be a part of the natural resistance of some insects to DDT. The milkweed bug (*Oncopeltus fasciatus*), although resistant to DDT for physiological reasons, tends to walk on tarsal claws. It has padlike structures that can be pressed against a smooth surface to improve traction, but these pulvillar pads are normally retracted. The housefly, on the other hand, has a pulvillar pad that is in contact with the substrate at all times.[25] A repellent reaction to the insecticide is another behavioristic escape mechanism.

The physiological factors that control the suceptibility of insects to toxicants are intrinsic variations in the chemical processes peculiar to the species. These may vary appreciably with individuals within a species, with sex, with stage of development, or with factors that are of random origin. By far the most common type of resistance is found in the selection exerted by the residual action of many insecticides in regard to the concentration of resistant mutants that are normally present in low frequencies in the original population. That resistance has developed in almost every population where insecticide pressure has been applied is attested by the extensive compilation of Brown,[2] and by subsequent WHO reports.

Physiological Resistance

There are many examples of the inactivation of insecticides by insects, even though adequate contact has been made between the toxicant and the insect. Unfortunately, more is known about the factors that cause an insecticide to fail than those that make it effective.

The action of an insecticide in vivo is a specific property of the chemical structure, and it is possible to show that small alterations in a molecule change its toxicity. Examples of this are shown in Figure 12–2. Change in the chemical structure of the insecticide molecule offers a tantalizing, but very confusing, approach to the problems of synthesizing new materials, because it is only logical to assume that if the toxicity can be decreased by a minor change in the chemical structure, it can also be potentiated.

Most insecticides are subject to enzymatic modification after they enter the insect body, and the ability of insects to detoxify chemicals is not surprising. It would, in fact, be more surprising if they didn't.[30] This problem is complicated in experimental evaluation by the presence of many factors, some of which have been neglected, that contribute to the physiological well-being of the individual insects. This idea returns experimental proof of the toxicity factor (or even the practical application) to the fundamental study of nutrition, temperature, humidity, and all other factors that affect the well-being of test insects. Another factor of great importance is the ability of the insect to eliminate the poison by a rapid excretory process, either through normal channels or by way of specific adaptation.

Even the negative information showing how an insect circumvents a toxicant can have positive value. Suppose, for example, a strain is shown to possess a powerful dehydrohalogenase that renders the insect highly resistant to DDT. This indicates that a toxicant potentiated by the removal of halogen would reverse the resistance and make possible the temporary control of the population.[30]

Cross-tolerances

Cross-tolerance (or cross-resistance) is a phenomenon exibited by insects that have developed a resistance to one type of insecticide and show

Insecticide   *Structure*   *Inactive derivative*

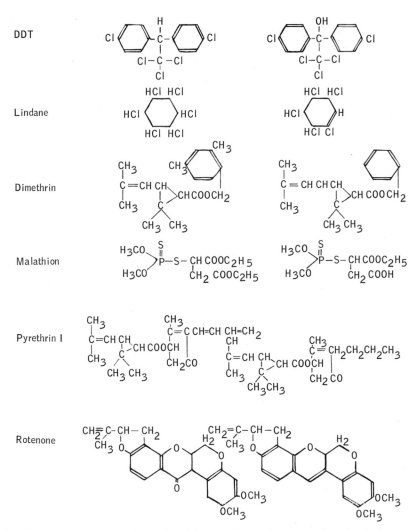

FIG. 12-2. Examples of minor chemical modifications that render insecticide molecules less active (after Winteringham).

resistance to a second insecticide to which it has not previously been exposed. Demonstration of this factor leads to significant conclusions regarding the mechanism of resistance. Either multiple mechanisms of resistance coexist in the same insect, or the same mechanism can protect against a broad spectrum of insecticide activity. The latter conclusion seems unlikely, and it is difficult to reason other than that insects have a range of physiological defensive mechanisms. This also leads to the conclusion that the intoxication (or detoxication) process involves more than one enzyme system.

HYPOTHESES FOR MODE OF ACTION OF BIOLOGICALLY ACTIVE CHEMICALS

The study of the effects of chemicals on physiological function is not new. Medicinal chemicals from one source or another have been used for centuries, and it is not surprising that a number of hypotheses have arisen to explain their activity. None of the existing schemes offers a complete explanation of observed phenomena, but it is certain that one or all of the hypotheses are involved.

The Physical Hypothesis

The physical hypothesis, which was proposed by Ferguson, Mullins, and others, has been reviewed by Kearns.[13] It relates the toxicity of a compound to its thermodynamic activity, which governs the penetration through, or the disruption of, the lipoprotein membranes. These membranes protect the organs and tissues of the animal. If the membranes are visualized as consisting of a micellar structure of protein molecules oriented in such a way that ions can penetrate the interstices between the molecules, ion permeability, which controls such phenomena as nerve stimulation and muscle contraction, would be a function of the size of the interstices, which in turn control the size of the ions that pass freely through the membranes. If the interstices are blocked, ions cannot penetrate resulting in narcosis. If, on the other hand, the particles are of such size and shape that they could become wedged into the interstices and cause distortion of the surrounding protein molecules, the interstices adjacent could become distorted to the extent that ions could leak one way or the other and cause abnormal effects.

The physical hypothesis is based principally on the penetration of the toxicant and the concentrations of the material (toxicant) at the site of activity. These factors are controlled by the physical disruption of the protective membranes, which alters the permeability of these membranes and causes further degenerative processes to take place. Changes in permeability are without doubt factors in the mode of action of insecticides, but it has never been proved that this is the only factor involved or that it is a principal factor in the ultimate toxicity.

The Toxophore Hypothesis

The toxophore hypothesis states that there is a definite link between a particular chemical group (the toxophoric group) and the configuration of the toxicant molecule, resulting in biological activity. Foregoing discussion has already indicated this possibility, and this approach has attracted almost every person who has worked either with medicinal drugs or insecticides. The many failures in attempts to tailor compounds to order compared to the few doubtful successes indicate that this approach is a gross oversimplification of fact. The obvious reason for lack of success is that there are still too many unknown variables in the physiology of the intoxication process, so that the end result—the alteration of a biological process selected in advance—is not sufficiently understood to provide the data necessary for correlation of biological activity and chemical structure. The toxophore hypothesis is as old as pharmacology, and it deserves to remain on the agenda for further investigation, pending the accumulation of fundamental physiological information that may make its application possible.

The Substitution or Antimetabolite Hypothesis

A corollary of the toxophore hypothesis suggests that chemical compounds can be constructed so that they have physical and chemical properties so nearly identical to essential components that they substitute for the essential component and disrupt a metabolic pathway. This approach has been used with limited success in many fields of study of biologically active chemicals. It has had particular effort in the development of anticarcinogenic drugs and in the detoxication by displacement and subsequent removal of various radioactive elements.

Selenium in an elemental form has been used to control insects on greenhouse ornamentals. The selenium is fed to the plant through the soil and becomes incorporated in the sap and tissue, so that when the insect feeds, the selenium is ingested. Selenium is not particularly toxic to plants, but it substitutes for sulfur in animals and brings about acute toxicity. What should have been a classic example of this was the postulation by Slade[27] that lindane had the same configuration as mesoinositol and therefore could act by substituting for this metabolite in an energy-producing pathway. Unfortunately, it was demonstrated that the γ-isomer, which has the greatest toxicity, does not, in fact, have the same spatial configuration; it was further demonstrated that insects appear to have no significant mesoinositol requirement.

This approach, in which a specific metabolite can be substituted or by which a relatively simple detoxification mechanism can be circumvented, offers some possibilities for limited success. Dauterman and Matsumo[3] found that changing the ethyl to a methyl group on the malathion molecule [S-(1,2-dicarbethoxyethyl)-O,O-dimethyldithiophosphate] would circumvent the activity of a detoxifying enzyme in resistant mosquitoes and render the compound effective. This approach involves the isolation of a system peculiar to a species or a strain and constructing compounds that can either substitute for a metabolite or not be affected by a specific enzyme. The limitations in this approach (or odds against success) are apparent when one considers that animals have almost unnumbered enzymes important in their metabolism, that these enzymes often act in complicated and interrelated pathways instead of singly, and that nature has been lavish in providing alternate pathways for metabolic processes.

The Enzyme Inhibition Hypothesis

The idea that the activity of a biologically active chemical, either beneficial or destructive, ultimately is defined by its effect on an enzyme or enzyme system seems so radical that it is a normal impulse to proclaim loudly that it is false. As soon as initial resentment has subsided so that it can be supplanted by serious thought, it is very difficult to find an example of known biological activity that does not fall into this category. Acceptance of the concept would seem to make the problems of mode of action somewhat simpler, and if the knowledge of the enzyme systems and metabolic pathways they control were not so nebulous, the problems would indeed be simpler.

METHODS OF APPROACH TO THE STUDY OF MODE OF ACTION

The approaches to the problems of mode of action have been almost as numerous as the investigators. There have been distinct trends with concentration on various aspects; these trends could well be called fads. Unfortunately, a large part of the work has been set up on a long-shot basis, starting with the end result and working backwards; however, the results show more negative information than positive progress. Most of the original problems remain to be solved, but fortunately a backlog of information on which to base future research is accumulating.

The Application of Radioactive Tracers

The world's first atomic pile reactor began production at Oak Ridge, Tennessee, in the Spring of 1944. This reactor was a prototype of later reactors and was limited to production of isotopes for military use, but its successful development led to tremendous opportunities for the use of radioactive tracers in biological research. The atomic pile made it possible to produce in quantity isotopes with long half-lives, and for the first time carbon-14 was economically practical to use. Many researchers, inspired by the novelty of the method began to trace labeled insecticides or analogues to find the final location (site of accumulation) of the radioactive atoms in the insect body. The assumption in this early work was that the site of deposition was also the site of activity. The fallacy of this assumption soon became apparent, and tracer techniques graduated from the fad stage, studies of the pathways of tagged molecules or a critical part of a molecule in metabolic processes began to take place. Many significant advances in physiological knowledge have come from tracer methods; with careful application and understanding of the limitations, there remain excellent opportunities for important research. Before embarking on this technique, it is of importance to recognize the limitations. These are real, and incorrect application will certainly lead to confusion.

The Metabolism of Biologically Active Compounds

This approach to the study of mode of action (see Chapter 6) became popular following the announcement by Ferguson and Kearns[5] that DDT was metabolized by the milkweed bug (*Oncopeltus fasciatus*) and the later report by Vinson and Kearns[29] that the American cockroach (*Periplaneta*) could convert DDT to the nontoxic DDE. It is unfortunate that haste and lack

of technical skill have caused most of this work to be done with brei prepared by grinding whole insects, rather than from carefully isolated organs
or tissues. However, the data derived from the results of this type of research
have pointed the way to other important discoveries and led to significant
advances, particularly in detoxication mechanisms.

Using this approach, it has now become possible to show how resistant
insects alter toxicants so that the toxicants become innocuous. This work has
provided important information upon which to base predictions of possible
detoxication of related compounds and the development of cross-tolerances.

Unfortunately, these data do not provide a clear solution to the problems
of insecticidal resistance. Instead, they offer some explanation of what happens. Somewhat the same conclusion can be reached regarding much of the
extensive investigation of the genetics of resistance.

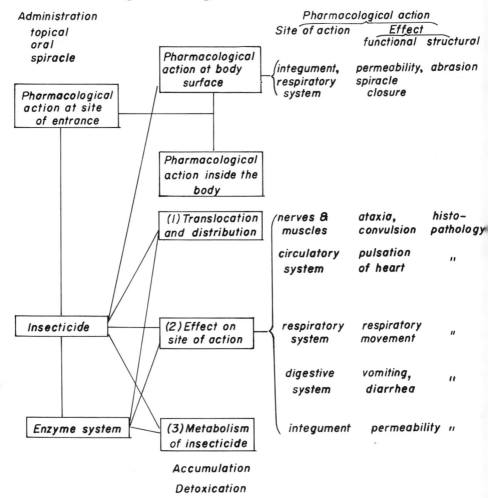

FIG. 12-3.   Diagnostic scheme proposed by Yamasaki and Ishii for determination of the pharmacologic action of an insecticide (adapted from Yamasaki and Ishii).

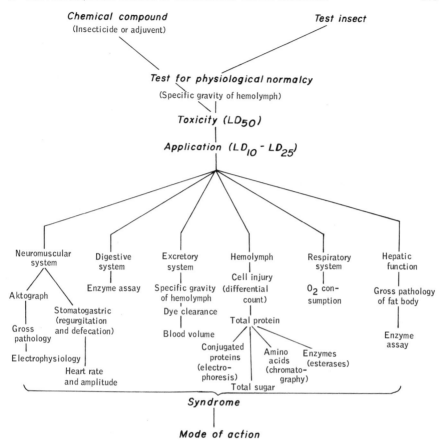

FIG. 12-4. Diagnostic scheme proposed by Patton for the study of chemical-biological activity.

The Study of Enzyme Inhibition

On the premise that the ultimate toxicity is exerted on an enzyme or system of enzymes, studies of the effects of various toxicants on isolated systems, either crude or partially purified, have been popular. Procedures have included both the assay of specific (more or less randomly chosen) enzymes, either from crude brei preparations or in partially purified form, in the presence of toxicants and the assay of brei prepared from insects treated with the same toxicants.

Some valuable data have been derived from these studies but relatively little information on the solution of mode-of-action problems. Many enzyme systems have been defined making it possible to postulate metabolic cycles as they exist in insects.

The Study of the Intoxication Syndromes

Another approach to the mode-of-action problem is the study of the

TABLE 12-1. The Effects of Organic Solvents on the American Cockroach

Compound	Volume Injected (µL.)	No. of Adults	Dead After (Hrs.) 24	48	72	Immediate Response	Mal. Tubes	Fat Body	Blood	Nerves
						ALCOHOLS				
Methyl	5	5	1	1	1	Hyperactivity for 1 to 2 hrs.	++++	+++	++	+++
	10	5	1	1	4	do.	++++	+++	++	+++
Ethyl	5	5	0	0	0	Irritable with locomotor instability				
	10	5	1	2	2	do			++ +++	
n-Propyl	5	5	5	5	5	Hyperactivity with locomotor instability. No recovery	+++	+++	++++	++
n-Butyl	5	5	3	4	5	Immediate and permanent loss of equilibrium	+++	++++	++++	+++
						GLYCOLS				
Ethylene	5	11ª	0	0	0	Normal	++++	+		
	10	11ª	0	0	2	Normal	++++	+		
di-Ethylene	5	5	0	0	0	Normal				
	10	5	0	0	0	Normal				
Propylene	5	5	0	0	0	Torpid	++++	+++		
	10	5	2	2	2	Torpid	++++	+++		
						CELLOSOLVES				
Methyl	5	5	1	2	2	Normal	+	+++		
	10	5	1	5	5	Normal	+	++++		
Ethyl	5	5	0	0	1	Normal		+++		
	10	10	3	8	10	Torpid		++++		
Butyl	5	5	3	5	5	Loss of equilibrium for 1 to 1½ hrs.	++++	++++	+++	+++
	10	5	5	5	5	do.	++++	++++	++++	++++
						CARBITOLS				
Methyl	5	5	0	3	3	Hyperactivity	+++	+++	++	
	10	5	1	3	3	Hyperactivity followed by loss of coordination	++++	++++	+++	
Ethyl	5	5	0	0	1	Normal	+++	+++	++	
	10	5	1	4	5	Normal	++++	++++	++	
Butyl	5	5	4	5	5	Hyperactivity with loss of coordination in 1 hr.	++++	++++	+++	
	10	5	5	5	5	Hyperactivity with loss of coordination in less than ½ hr.		All dead		
						PETROLEUM HYDROCARBONS				
2,2,4-trimethyl pentane	5	5	0	0	0	Normal	+			
	10	5	0	0	0	Normal	+			
Cyclohexane	5	6	1	1	1	Loss of equilibrium	+			+
	10	6	3	4	4	do. but more rapid	+			+
Hexane	5	6	3	3	3	Hyperactivity with loss of equilibrium				
	10	6	2	2	5	do. but more pronounced	+			++
n-Heptane	5	6	1	1	1	Hyperactivity with recovery				
	10	6	2	2	2	Hyperactivity with loss of equilibrium				+
n-Octane	10	6	1	1	1	Normal	+			
n-Decane	10	6	0	0	0	Hyperactivity with recovery				
Kerosene (deobase)	10	6	0	0	0	do.				
						AROMATIC HYDROCARBONS				
Benzene	5	5	1	3	5	Hyperactivity with loss of equilibrium	++	++++	+++	+++
Xylene	5	5	1	2	5	do.	++	+++	+++	+++

TABLE 12-1. (continued)

Compound	Volume Injected (μL.)	No. of Adults	Dead After (Hr.) 24	48	72	Immediate Response	Mal. Tubes	Fat Body	Blood	Nerves
						CHLORINATED COMPOUNDS				
Carbon tetrachloride	5	6	2	3	5	do.	++++	++++	++	+++
Chloroform	5	6	3	3	6	Hyperactivity with permanent loss of equilibrium	++++	++++	++	+++
Tetrachloroethane	5	6	2	4	6	do.	++++	++++	++	+++
						MISCELLANEOUS				
Dioxane	5	5	5	5	5	do.		All dead		
Tetrahydrofuran	5	5	3	4	4	Hyperactivity with some recovery	++++	++++	++++	+++
Acetone	10	5	0	0	0	Hyperactivity with recovery		++	+++	+

[a]Nymphs and adults.
(From Patton and Sarkaria.[21])

symptoms of intoxication, which when taken collectively are called a syndrome. This approach is advantageous in that the responses are observed with intact insects, so that the interaction of vital systems may be apparent. The principal disadvantage to this approach is that it requires instrumentation and technology that can measure the function of the vital systems without causing serious physiological disruption. This has been difficult to achieve, but with advances in instrumentation that enable accurate analysis of very small samples, it has become possible.

No single symptom is sufficient to warrant a diagnosis of the mode of action; conclusions must be drawn by considering the simultaneous effects of all symptoms—the syndrome of poisoning. That different toxicants have different syndromes is clearly evident by the fact that symptoms resulting from poisoning with DDT, lindane, and insecticides of the cyclodiene series are quite different for each toxicant, even though all these compounds are chlorinated hydrocarbons.

This approach to the study of the biological activity of insecticides has been used in at least two laboratories. While the data that have been accumulated are still far from conclusive, they indicate that clinical evaluation of syndromes offers distinct advantages. Yamasaki and Ishii studied this method and made some pertinent points in the description of their work.[31]

Regardless of how the toxicant enters the body (through the integument, digestive tract, spiracles, etc.), it must be distributed in the body. The only known means for this translocation is the blood, or hemolymph. Translocation can be studied effectively by using radioactive isotopes incorporated into the toxicant molecule, but it must be remembered that the original molecule does not necessarily keep its original chemical structure after it enters the body of the insect. Many examples support the idea that the active toxicant in insects is not the same as the chemical that was applied but is a derivative.

When the insecticide reaches the site of its primary action in a toxic form, it produces functional abnormalities that give rise to symptoms. It is convenient to classify the activity of insecticides according to the organ systems that are affected in a descending order based on the degree of the systems' functional abnormality. These data provide a guide for further physiological investigation to determine the intoxication on a quantitative basis; by comparative study these data pinpoint the sites of both activity and circumvention of activity (detoxication). In the latter instance, a backlog of data on the biological activity of various chemicals often points to an adjuvant that will potentiate the original toxicant. Two schemes have been developed for a clinical type of evaluation. These are shown in Figures 12–3 and 12–4. Both schemes are still in the developmental stage, and undoubtedly they will be altered as quantitative data are recorded.

An important by-product of the evalution of biological activity is to be found in the observations of Patton and Sarkaria[21] on the effects of organic solvents on the gross pathology of the organ systems of the American cockroach (Table 12–1). These data, which are based on the visible effects, have been corroborated by quantitative study. They indicate at least two things. First, these data point to a number of relatively simple compounds that may have potentiation abilities because of their activity on the normal function of specific organs; and second, they indicate that a certain amount of care must be exercised in selecting the solvent carrier for the insecticides to be studied. There are many examples in the literature in which the symptoms of intoxication reported could have been achieved by the solvent carrier alone and without the toxicant.

THE MODE OF ACTION OF INSECTICIDAL CHEMICALS

Conclusive data on the mode of action of even the most common of the insecticides are difficult to find, and searching the literature for finite information is a frustrating occupation. The best work has been done on reports of recently developed compounds. Some of these compounds are highly complicated, and there is a clear need for extensive examination of the activity of simpler compounds to provide a basis for further work.[28]

Arsenicals.   Arsenic is one of the oldest insecticides used in the United States. Its value as an insecticide is said to have been discovered when someone emptied a pail that had contained Paris green, a pigment once used in interior decorating, on a plot of potatoes infested with Colorado potato beetle. Arsenic has been little used as an insecticide since the introduction of DDT, but previously the arsenicals, principally in the form of pentavalent lead salts, were the mainstay in chemical control of insects.

The fact that arsenic in the trivalent state is toxic to animals has been known for many years. In acute dosages trivalent arsenic causes exfoliation of the digestive tract and fatty infiltration of the liver in mammals, and comparable effects have been observed from histological study of arsenic-poisoned insects. Arsenic in an organic complex was used prior to the introduction of antibiotics for the treatment of diseases caused by *Spirillum,* and some of the most critical evaluations of its physiological effects appeared in journals of syphilology. It wasn't until World War II, when Peters et al.[22] introduced a moderately effective antidote, that its mode of action was known.

Interest in the arsenicals and their mode of action by Peters came about through anticipation of the possible use of the arsenical war gas, Lewisite.

Peters found that arsenic acted to uncouple the oxidative decarboxylation of α-ketoglutaric acid in the citric acid glycolytic cycle and that compounds with mercapto groups would prevent this. The result was the introduction of a dimercaptopropanol called BAL (British Anti-Lewisite), which could be used with some effectiveness to relieve the vesicant action of Lewisite. That sulfhydryl groups could have an effect on arsenite intoxication has been known for many years; compounds, such as glutathione, methionine, and cysteine, have been investigated for their activity. When applied to houseflies poisoned with meta-arsenite, the results have been negative.[1] Some disparate opinions exist in this matter,[6] because arsenic trioxide used in some experiments forms a relatively insoluble compound with glutathion, while the sodium meta-arsenite–glutathione derivative is very soluble and penetrates animal membranes readily. Correlations between the glutathione content of insects and the susceptibility to arsenic intoxication are very poor. BAL detoxifies arsenic applied to insects, and there is some evidence that other sulfhydryl acceptors may exist, possibly oxidative enzymes, that detoxify arsenic.

Fluorides.   Fluorides have been used as insecticides for many years, principally in baits for chewing insects and as mothproofing agents. Like arsenicals, fluorides have been largely displaced by newer materials, and from an applied point of view they are principally of historical interest.

Aside from the observation that the fluorides are general protoplasmic poisons, there is very little information on their activity. It may be presumed that they exert their toxicity because of their affinity for calcium. This affinity would alter the permeability relationships within the animal and result in many possible physiological disturbances.

Nicotine.   Nicotine was the first of a group of plant derivatives called alkaloids that have been used as insecticides. Because of its wide use by humans, nicotine has been studied extensively, and its pharmacology is sufficiently well defined to provide an excellent standard for comparison with other materials.

Nicotine is an autonomic blocking agent.[10] Its action follows a pattern of initial stimulation followed by a persistent depression of all sympathetic and parasympathetic nerve ganglia. The typical response to nicotine is an initial period of hyperactivity followed by paralysis. In mammals, death from acute poisoning comes from a curare-like paralysis of the respiratory muscles, resulting in death from asphyxia. The hyperactivity phase of nicotine poisoning comes from an increased sensitivity of the ganglion cells to cholinergic stimulation, and the paralysis comes from the development of resistance to the same type of stimulus.

In insects, the symptoms of nicotine poisoning are comparable to those observed in mammals; but considering the type of respiratory mechanism in insects, it is not reasonable to attribute death to failure of the respiratory muscles. It is possible that the fatal effects may result from inactivation of an autonomic system, but to date such systems in insects have been very poorly defined.

Nicotine poisoning in both mammals and insects is a reversible reaction; if the animal can survive long enough to excrete the dose, recovery is possible. The Malpighian system excretes nicotine readily, but a large loss of water accompanies elimination. Under experimental conditions, nicotine can reverse the tremor phase of DDT poisoning,[19] which may indicate that these materials have opposite effects at a common site on the nervous system, presumably on the permeability of the nerve protoplasmic membranes to ions.[31]

It is of interest to observe that nicotine and curare are both classified as autonomic blocking agents. The difference between them appears to be that nicotine acts primarily upon the autonomic nerves, while curare acts primarily on the skeletal muscles. Curare is relatively nontoxic to insects. The explanation for this is unknown, but it might be related to the type of multiple innervation of the insect nerve-muscle mechanism.

Pyrethrum.   Pyrethrum is a plant derivative that was obtained from flowers of a chrysanthemum. For many years the dust made by grinding the flowers was marketed as "bug powder," and extracts of the flowers were used in household sprays. Acute shortages of the natural material as a result of World War II encouraged synthesis of a number of the active components, the pyrethrins. Several of these, either from natural or synthetic sources, are still used as a constituent of pressure-can insecticide formulations, primarily because of their rapid knockdown effect.

The pyrethrins are considered to be safe insecticides because of their low toxicity to mammals. They attack the nervous system, and in insects all parts of the nervous system appear to be subject to injury. This conclusion has been reached by histological study of the nerves of pyrethrum-poisoned insects, which show characteristic lesions in the nervous system.[11] Little more can be said about the mode of action of pyrethrins. It is obvious that these substances are metabolized, detoxified, or excreted by insects, because knocked-down individuals recover from sublethal doses. The suggested process is one of hydrolysis of the ester structure by enzymes. There are no data to support this suggestion. The toxicity of the pyrethrins can be potentiated from 2 to 12 times with synergists, but the reason for the potentiation is obscure.

Rotenone.   Rotenone is an alkaloid material used by the South American aborigines as a fish poison. It is derived from the root of derris or cubé. The active compound is dissociated rapidly in the acid digestive tracts of mammals so that it is considered to be nontoxic; but if it is inhaled in a solvent carrier, it causes a numbness of the oral mucous membranes. A part of this effect may be due to the activity of the solvent carrier. Rotenone is highly toxic to most species of insects.

In insects, rotenone alters the rate of heartbeat and ultimately causes muscle paralysis. A critical study of its action by Fukami[7] demonstrated that this compound affects the conduction of the nervous system, but primarily it causes a disruption of respiratory metabolism in the citric acid cycle. The oxidation of L-glutamate is inhibited, and the block apparently takes place in the respiratory chain of events between DPNH and cytochrome B. The inhibition of L-glutamic dehydrogenase is an important factor in the toxicity. The various factors involved in the toxic action and the effects of chemical structure have been reviewed by Fukami.

Ryanodine.   Ryanodine is an alkaloid extracted from a South American plant of the genus *Ryania*. It was introduced during World War II as a substitute material in insecticides, and because it came into use during a period of active research, it received more attention than some of the better established insecticides. Edwards et al.[4] found that ryanodine acts as a muscle depressant, which probably exerts its principal effect on the contractile process. Their work indicated that ryanodine interferes with the transfer of phosphate from the phosphogen in the ATP-ADP-actomyosin reaction. A perfusate of this material used a second time showed increased activity, indicating an alteration in the molecule because of contact with the muscle tissue.

Minor Organic Insecticides

A number of organic compounds have been used as insecticides, and relatively little is known of their mode of action.[15] Among these, are the thiocyanates, the dinitro compounds, and thiodiphenylamine, better known as phenothiazine.

The organic thiocyanates were suggested as potential insecticides in 1932, and thousands of derivatives have been evaluated as insecticides.[15] They were used widely as substitute materials during World War II, and they show the same characteristic of pyrethrum in that they bring about rapid knockdown. Poisoned insects show a typical vacuolization of the nerve cord, although not as severe as is produced by the pyrethrins.[12] It has been suggested that the action of the organic thiocyanates may be similar to that of HCN, which renders the tissues incapable of using oxygen. According to Fukami, the activity of the thiocyanates appears to be similar to that of rotenone.[7]

The dinitro compounds in various forms have been used as insecticides principally as acaricides, dormant ovicides, in poison baits, and as selective herbicides (blossom-thinning sprays). The dinitro compounds have been superseded by more effective materials in control practice, but their action in causing increased oxygen consumption without increased activity, probably through an uncoupling mechanism, makes these compounds important as an experimental tool. The effect on oxygen consumption is the most characteristic symptom of intoxication with dinitro compounds. Goble observed that honeybees fed as little as one-sixtieth of an LD_{50} dose of dinitro-o-cyclohexylphenol (Na salt) show an increase in oxygen consumption of 42 per cent.[9] From this, it was postulated that insects poisoned with the dinitro compounds die from the exhaustion of their energy reserves. Dinitro compounds also reportedly alter the rate of heartbeat and cause spontaneous nerve-potential discharges in cockroaches. In mammals, the dinitro compounds increase the rate of tissue metabolism, probably at the level of the cells. They selectively increase the oxidation of fat,[10] and at one time were used in the treatment of obesity. The selective oxidation of fat has not been conclusively demonstrated from insect study.

Thiodiphenylamine is a by-product of aniline dye manufacture and was used on a limited commercial basis as an alternate for lead arsenate to control codling moth and other fruit pests. Thiodiphenylamine is still used as a drench for the treatment of farm animals (sheep) for internal parasites. This compound is activated in the animal body by conversion to a leucothional that is toxic to undefined respiratory enzymes.[15] Fukami believes that the leucothional acts by depressing respiratory metabolism in muscles.[7]

The Organic Insecticides

Although most of the insecticidal compounds already discussed are organic in their chemical structure, the phrase *organic insecticides,* or *organics,* has a connotative meaning that limits the group to those synthetic compounds introduced since World War II. DDT was the first of this series, and with the stimulus caused by military necessity, many crash programs were instituted to study its activity. DDT was followed by a long series of chlorinated compounds that were synthesized and screened for insecticidal activity. In the early years, enthusiasm ran high that these compounds would be the panacea in insect control.

Chlorinated hydrocarbons as insecticides were made obsolescent with the introduction of the organophosphates, which were developed originally as chemical warfare agents. Organophosphates have been synthesized with many structural variations that have different degrees of chemical activity. The most striking (and most often studied) effect of organophosphates is their ability to inhibit acetylcholine esterase (AChE) in the cholinergic junctions of the nervous system. Another group of compounds acting at the same level are the carbamates. Carbamates are derivatives of carbamic acid and resemble eserine, an inhibitor of cholinergic transmission, which has a good background of pharmacologic understanding.

Much is known about the chemistry, toxicity, and nature of the ever-elusive toxophoric groups on these compounds; but when the results of research are sifted, they yield more information on how the toxophoric groups do not exert their toxicity than positive data on their biological activity. Much of this lack of information is due to the use of pre-war technology developed for the study of simpler toxicants, and the results are based largely on the number (or percentage) of an experimental population killed by the treatment. It is more important to study the processes that lead to the death of the insect than to count the number of dead insects.

The Chlorinated Hydrocarbons.   DDT was the first of the chlorinated hydrocarbons. From extensive study of its mode of action, it has been established that DDT brings about the production in the sensory nerves of spontaneous discharges that eventually reach an intensity of sufficient magnitude to cause a violent tremor. The tremor may last for several hours, during which time acetylcholine (ACh) accumulates at the synapses, either from a release mechanism or a synthesis, and overrides the action of the esterase, which normally would hydrolyze ACh as it is formed. That this is not the whole story is apparent, since the addition of ACh by injection does not potentiate the activity nor does AChE antidote it. Differences in membrane permeability appear to be indicated as an explanation, but the nature of the change and the membranes involved are both unknown. It has been suggested that DDT, which is a slow poison, may kill by causing the insect to exhaust its metabolic reserves through the energy expended by the tremor that DDT produces, but this explanation is not sufficiently definitive. DDT does not show any significant enzyme-activity inhibition in vitro,[15] nor does it inhibit excretory function.[20] One symptom of poisoning, observed both in laboratory study and in the field, is an acute flatulence that stretches intersegmental membranes of the abdomen and even causes rupture of the digestive tract. This response to DDT has been given almost no attention, because the tremor symptom has been assumed to indicate that the material is a nerve poison.

Resistance to DDT has developed in almost every insect species against which it has been used, and it has been demonstrated conclusively that the dehydrohalogenation of DDT to DDE (2,2-bis-(p-chlorphenyl)-1,1-dichloro-ethylene), which is nontoxic, is a principal pathway of escape. This alteration of structure is accomplished by a dehydrohalogenase that apparently exists in all insects, but the alteration is potentiated in resistant insects through a process of selective breeding. Many studies have been reported on the genetics of resistance, and the conclusions indicate the presence of both single-gene and multiple-gene mechanisms. It is probable that both mechanisms appear as specific differences in insects.

When it was introduced, lindane (also known as 666, benzene hexachloride, BHC, and gammexane) was considered to be much more promising than DDT. The killing action was faster, and for a brief period it seemed that lindane was the ideal insecticide. Early in the development of this chlorinated hydrocarbon it was shown that of the eight isomers the γ-isomer, now known by the common name of lindane, was the most toxic. However, lindane had not been used extensively before resistance to it appeared, and its use in soil treatment was found to impart a characteristic and disagreeable musty flavor to food plants.

By the time lindane had come into wide use, the impetus and the financial support expended on the investigation of DDT had diminished. It is known that lindane is metabolized in insect and in mammalian tissues, but the mechanism is obscure and most of the hypotheses proposed to describe its mode of action have proved inadequate. It is remarkable, but true, that relatively little is really known about the mode of action of lindane.

The successes of DDT and lindane demonstrated to the chemical industry that many possibilities existed for the development of synthetic insecticides. Many compounds were chlorinated, some more or less at random and some on a predetermined scheme, usually with rapid dehydrochlorination in mind. From this research came a series of materials with cyclodiene structure. Chlordane and its derivatives and toxophene belong to this group.[14]

According to Metcalf, very little is known of the mode of action of the cyclodiene insecticides. Superficially, they produce symptoms of poisoning that resemble those of DDT, but under more critical analysis they are found to be quite different. Some of the derivatives (isodrin and endrin) show a significant inhibitory action on insect excretory function,[20] an observation difficult to reconcile with the idea that these compounds are metabolized to dieldrin[8] in the insect body; dieldrin itself has little effect on rates of excretion.

Continuing developments in organic laboratories along with the development of resistance in insects have made the chlorinated hydrocarbons less interesting as insecticides, and much of the research effort on them has been abandoned. From the standpoint of the physiology of mode of action, they still offer many possibilities for important discoveries.

The Organophosphates.   Organophosphates were introduced with the publication of work by Schrader.[26] They are widely used, and at least two dozen members of the general group are marketed under trade labels. These differ quite widely in their structure and their toxicity. O'Brien presented a book-length review of these compounds in 1961.[17]

The best established toxic property of the organophosphates is their ability to inhibit AChE in cholinergic nerve transmission. The study of this factor in all stages and numerous species has become one of the fads in insect mode-of-action study. It has also been clearly demonstrated that the organophosphates inhibit nonspecific esterases (aliesterases)[15, 16, 18, 23] and that in this process they themselves are inactivated. This deactivation apparently takes place through a phosphorylation of the active enzyme centers, a reaction that appears to be irreversible.[15]

Uncertainties that exist in the knowledge of the nature of synaptic nerve transmission in insects and the nonspecificity of the organophosphates indicate that the problems of mode of action of these compounds are still unsolved.

The Carbamate Insecticides. A number of carbamic acid esters have been used in pharmacologic study because of their cholinergic activity. Among these the most common are physostigmine (eserine), which is a naturally occurring plant derivative, and a synthetic product with greater stability, prostigmine. From these two carbamates have come a series of carbamic esters that have insecticidal value. The ultimate use of these compounds appears to be as inhibitors of insect choline esterase (ChE). The toxic members of this group are all effective choline esterase inhibitors in vitro and show structural configurations that resemble acetylcholine. The carbamates differ from the organophosphates by their strong attraction to both the esteratic and the anionic sites of the enzyme molecule (the phosphates are attracted only to the esteratic site). The carbamates also show some activity against other animal esterases.[15]

PROBLEMS OF THE PHYSIOLOGY OF MODE OF ACTION

In foregoing paragraphs the author has pointed out a number of deficiencies that have caused confusion in the study of physiological aspects of the biological activity of chemicals. These discussions must not be construed as adverse criticism of the individuals who have worked in this field, nor do they indicate lack of either skill or knowledge. Instead the present lack of definitive information should be interpreted as a direct reflection of the high degree of complexity existing in the basic problems.

The greatest deficiency in the study of biological activity of chemicals is lack of detailed fundamental knowledge concerning the normal physiology of insects in general and test species in particular. The pressure of meeting emergencies in the field has, in many cases, caused the research to be guided into a head-on approach without the devotion of necessary time (and money) to the solution of fundamental physiological problems that control the outcome of the experiments. This approach is analogous to starting the construction of a masonry arch with the keystone. Successful understanding of the problems of chemical-biological activity, resistance, and the ultimate goal of tailoring compounds to order will be achieved only after much time and effort have been expended on study of the fundamentals of the physiology and biochemistry of insects. There is no apparent shortcut to solution of the basic problems.

During the years that have followed World War II, there have been a number of review articles prepared that summarize the accumulated knowledge; by fitting the fragments of information together it is possible to predict many potentially fruitful avenues of approach. One of the more recent reviews by Roan and Hopkins points out a number of factors that should be taken into consideration.[24]

First, it is indicated that symptomology has a distinct value as a means of studying the physiology of biological activity. Such an approach makes it possible to pinpoint the target and concentrate on important organ systems. Along with this, it is emphasized that secondary factors may be of great importance. One example is the effect of neurosecretory products on the detectable symptomatic responses. The implication here is that the toxicant may exert an effect on the chain of events, resulting in production of a syndrome characteristic of the toxicant activity, but that the real effect is secondary.

In studying problems of mode of action of biologically active chemicals, there are several rules that if followed will make the rational solution of the problems more likely. It must be recognized at the outset that the problems will be complex and that there will be many variables, some of which are unknown. It must also be understood that the process of intoxication is a transient factor so that timing the analyses is essential. Determination of end products of the reactions may be misleading.

The use of syndromes offers a good means of judging the timing for critical study, but the syndromes themselves may have no value except for pointing out the critical organ systems affected by the toxicant. If there were a sufficient backlog of information on the syndromes of organ system failure, the possibility of choosing adjuvants that could potentiate the activity of insecticidal chemicals would be greatly enhanced. Such a potentiation by multiple action could alleviate the problems of resistance, at least temporarily.

In mode-of-action studies it is highly desirable, if not essential, to consider the insect as a whole, intact animal. Methods that "simulate" or "approximate" the normal often lead to confusing if not erroneous results. This is a restatement of the general rule that the functional ability of the animal is not necessarily the simple sum of the functions of the individual parts.

SUMMARY

The study of mode of action of biologically active chemicals is of primary importance in the economic field of entomology, and physiology and biochemistry offer the most likely means of solving the many problems. It must be recognized that these problems are not simple. None of the toxicants in use at the present time are fully understood as regards their biological activity, and before many of the problems are resolved, there must be completed a great amount of fundamental work on the normal physiology of insects.

The use of intact insects for studies that have been carefully designed to isolate the physiological action through the observation of the intoxication syndromes is important. By this process, the over-all effects can be assayed, and the specific loci of biological activity can be pinpointed. Timing is very important in follow-up analysis of functional activity.

The study of the chemical-biological activity of toxicants is a challenging field worthy of the best efforts of the best trained personnel. The most promising solution for the specialized problems lies in a thorough understanding of the fundamental physiology of insects.

LITERATURE CITED

1. Anderson, A. D., and Patton, R. L. 1953. Sulfhydryl arsenite detoxication in insects. J. econ. Ent., 46:423–426.
2. Brown, A. W. A. 1958. Insecticide resistance in arthropods. World Health Organization, Geneva.
3. Dauterman, W., and Matumo, F. 1962. Toxicity of analogues of malathion (to mosquitoes). Science, 138:694–695.
4. Edwards, G. A., Weiant, E. A., Slocombe, A. G., and Roeder, K. D. 1948. Action of ryanodine on muscles of insects. Science, 108:330–332.
5. Ferguson, W., and Kearns, C. 1949. Metabolism of DDT in Oncopeltus. J. econ. Ent., 42: 810–817.
6. Forgash, A. J. 1951. The effects of insecticides and reducing substances on reduced glutathion of the American cockroach. J. econ. Ent., 44:870–878.
7. Fukami, J. 1962. Studies on respiratory metabolism of nerve and muscle of insects and the effects of rotenone. Misc. Publ. nat. Inst. agric. Sci., 7:1–15.
8. Glasser, R., Blenk, R. G., Dewey, J. E., Hilton, B. D., and Weiden, M. H. S. 1958. Non-aldrin residue on carrots in aldrin treated soil. J. econ. Ent., 51:337–341.
9. Goble, G. J., and Patton, R. L. 1946. The effects of dinitro compounds on honeybees. J. econ. Ent., 39:177–180.
10. Goodman, L., and Gilman, A. 1941. The Pharmacological Basis of Therapeutics. Macmillan, New York.
11. Hartzell, A. 1934. Histopathological effects of pyrethrum on insect nerve. Contr. Boyce Thompson Inst., 6:211–223.
12. Hartzell, A., and Wilcoxin, F. 1934. Histopathological effects of thiocyanate poisoning. Contr. Boyce Thompson Inst., 6:269–277.
13. Kearns, C. W. 1956. Mode of action of insecticides. Ann. Rev. Ent., 1:123–166.
14. Kearns, C. W., Ingle, L., and Metcalf, R. L. 1946. New cyclodiene insecticides. J. econ. Ent., 38:661–668.
15. Metcalf, R. L. 1955. Organic Insecticides. Interscience Press, New York.
16. Oppenoorth, F. J., and Asperen, K. van. 1960. Allelic genes in the housefly producing modified enzymes that cause organo-phosphate resistance. Science, 132:298–299.
17. O'Brien, R. D. 1960. Toxic Phosphorus Esters. Academic Press, New York.
18. Patton, R. L. 1961. Hemocytes in the detoxication of parathion. Ann. ent. Soc. Amer., 54: 696–698.
19. Patton, R. L., Unpublished classroom experiments.
20. Patton, R. L., Anderson, A., and Gardner, J. 1959. Excretory efficiency of the American cockroach. J. ins. Physiol., 3:256–261.
21. Patton, R. L., and Sarkaria, D. S. 1958. Gross pathology of insects caused by solvents. J. econ. Ent., 51:663–665.
22. Peters, R. A., Stocken, L. A., and Thompson, R. H. S. 1945. British anti-Lewisite. Nature (London), 156:616–619.
23. Plapp, F. W., and Bigley, W. S. 1961. Inhibition of fly esterase by parathion and malathion. J. econ. Ent., 54:103–108.
24. Roan, C. C., and Hopkins, T. L. 1961. Mode of action of insecticides. Ann. Rev. Ent., 6:333–346.
25. Sarkaria, D. S., and Patton, R. L., 1949. Factors in the penetration of DDT through the pulvilli of several species of insects. Trans. Amer. ent. Soc., 75:71–82.

26. Schrader, G. 1952. The development of new insecticides based on organic fluoride and phosphorus compounds. Monograph 62, Angew. Chem.
27. Slade, R. E. 1945. The mode of action of hexachlorocyclohexane. Chem. and Ind., 23:314–319.
28. Smith, J. N. 1962. Detoxication mechanisms in insects. Ann. Rev. Ent., 7:465–580.
29. Vinson, E., and Kearns, C. W. 1952. The detoxication of DDT by insects. J. econ. Ent., 45:484–505.
30. Winteringham, F. P. W. 1962. Action and inaction of insecticides. J. roy. Soc. Arts., 110:719–740.
31. Yamasaki, T., and Ishii (Narahashi) T. 1957. Mechanism of action of insecticides and how to study it. World Health Organization, Geneva.

Index

Italic page numbers indicate illustrations.
Page numbers preceded by a "t" indicate tables.